Battling Adult Philadelphia Positive Acute Lymphoblastic Leukemia

The *Real* Fight for Those with Ph+ALL

Battling Adult Philadelphia Positive Acute Lymphoblastic Leukemia

The *Real* Fight for Those with Ph+ALL

By Robin Clark, PhD

Copyright

ISBN 978-0-9990295-7-2
Written by Robin Clark, PhD

Published by Amber Light Publishing
www.AmberLightPublishing.com

Editing and Interior Design by Nita Robinson of *Nita Helping Hand?*
www.NitaHelpingHand.com

Cover by Kelly Martin, www.KAM.Design

Table of Contents

Introduction

I've always considered myself to be a strong woman. Strong in mind, body and spirit! Everything I do, I do with conviction and to the fullest. I am not a religious person, but I believe in God, and I trust in Her deeply to be with me in times of joy, pain and sorrow. I have experienced the emotional roller coaster ride of life during my first 50 years and I am thankful I'm still here and able to share the wonderful stories I have earned.

When I hit 50 years old, I felt like the queen of the mountain, raising my sword to the sky, roaring like a lioness. My children had made it to adulthood in one piece and were living on their own. I was retired, completely out of debt, and ready to begin my life with my new husband; just the two of us. We'd made it! It was our time to do whatever we wanted and we had big plans!

One day I woke up and the mountain came tumbling down on top of me, the boulders landing on me, trapping me. I had to beg and pray for strength from my mind, body and soul like I had never prayed before. The challenge that was put before me required every ounce of my being – from the darkest depths of my mind to the deepest parts of my soul, to the very fiber of every muscle in my body. My life as I knew it had unexpectedly changed drastically. Never in a million years would I have thought that at this age I would be faced with making life and death decisions and providing twenty-four hour care for my husband. I had suddenly, in one single moment, become a caregiver. For two years the emotions, stress, guilt, fatigue and isolation wore on me. At the end of two years, humility, acceptance, wisdom and knowing replaced these feelings. *We are never given more than we can handle.* I used to cringe at this phrase, but now I understand it. "God, grant me the serenity to accept the things I cannot change, the courage to change the things I can, and the wisdom to know the difference." The humility of this prayer now lives within me.

When I started writing this story, I was determined to explain to the world just what Philadelphia Positive Acute Lymphoblastic Leukemia (Ph+ALL) is and what it *really* means to participate in the clinical studies mandatory to survive. It's such a rare leukemia for adults over 50. With very little information to draw from except through sterile medical journals, I researched for hundreds of hours, trying to put together the million piece puzzle of this disease. All we have are my journals and the hundreds of pages of experience that transpired while I learned its true story. It's not very scientific, but brutally realistic. There are only a handful of adults over the age of 45-50 that get Philadelphia Positive Acute Lymphoblastic Leukemia each year, and it wasn't until just recently that a drug was discovered to treat it.

As my story was unfolding, I realized it wasn't just about my husband, it was about US. Together we lived through the most tumultuous time of our lives. I had been a nurse for over 35 years and I had seen it all! Or this is what I thought.

When I was asked, *So, what do you do? Tell me about you.* Like most women, I would say, "Oh, I'm a nurse, I'm a mom, and I am married. I have grandchildren. I just love them! When they visit, I love to cook for them" and so on.

1

But how often do you hear, "I'm a caregiver for my husband?" I bet never unless you have one of them in your family. Nobody wants to talk about *why* you're a caregiver. *You* don't want to talk about it; it's not a happy subject. So, you find yourself in a world all alone with only one person to talk to – your spouse. While my husband felt the excruciating *physical* pain during these two years, I experienced the tormenting mental pain. Together we leaned on each other for strength, hope, sanity and humor. I have been challenged in ways I never thought possible. I have had thoughts I never thought possible.

I am sharing our story through the unexpected diagnosis of Pre-B Philadelphia Positive Acute Lymphoblastic Leukemia (Ph+ALL). It is not intended to expound on the scientific genetic makeup of this disease or different blood cancers known today or as a tool to use for any research studies. It is our story, and an understanding of what life is *really* like after you are given this diagnosis. This is a story of a wife who loved her husband, who came to realize the important things in life, and who found the beauty in being a best friend, a fighter and a confidant for her husband. I have had many people say to me, "I couldn't do what you do. I just couldn't do it. I would have left a long time ago." These words were not an option for me and those that have said this to me are no longer a part of my family circle.

Because there was nothing to refer to for help when researching this disease, no personal stories or places to find tools, shared ideas or strength to draw from, I have decided to share what I have learned. I provide these necessary items throughout this story. I hope I can bring you, the reader, a tool guide and a *real* look at what it means to be diagnosed with Philadelphia Positive Acute Lymphoblastic Leukemia.

Preface

What is Pre B Philadelphia Positive Acute Lymphoblastic Leukemia?

I am going to dedicate this section to the definition of Pre B Philadelphia Positive Acute Lymphoblastic Leukemia (Ph+ALL). Acute Lymphoblastic Leukemia is defined as a sudden or rapid production of immature white blood cells in the bone marrow. These immature white blood cells, called "Blasts," are naturally formed and mature in the bone marrow, then venture out into the body to begin their journey of fighting infection. White blood cells protect us from foreign invaders such as germs and viruses that want to create illness within our body. Blasts make up about 5% of the bone marrow and share the space with red blood cells, which carry oxygen to all living cells in the body, platelets which help our blood clot so we don't bleed to death when the skin is cut, as well as mature white blood cells. Over 500 billion blood cells are formed in the bone marrow every day. In Ph+ALL, the immature baby "blasts" go into over-production prior to becoming mature white blood cells. So, baby white blood cells make babies, and their babies make babies, and their babies make babies, over and over again in a very short time period; hours to a few days. Quickly, they will make up 30-100% of the bone marrow. They will squeeze in together like an overstuffed elevator and consume the entire bone marrow space, preventing red blood cells, platelets and mature white blood cells from forming – literally suffocating them. This gross amount of baby blasts spill out into the bloodstream and lymph nodes, then cross the spinal cord barrier into the brain.

With the presence of severe flu-like symptoms, little red dots start showing up on the abdomen and legs. Bleeding of the gums in the mouth occurs, along with a pale, almost yellow tinge to the gums. If not stopped, death ensues within days. What you think is the flu, is not the flu.

Philadelphia Positive Acute Lymphoblastic Leukemia is caused by a genetic disorder found in chromosomes 9 and 22. Chromosome 9 and chromosome 22 decide to swap, or translocate, information. This abnormality creates a protein that is not normally found within our DNA. This protein positions itself on the leukemia cell and is the trigger that jump-starts the blasts in the bone marrow to go into mass production. This genetic disorder was discovered in 1960 and was given its name from the city it was discovered in – Philadelphia. It wasn't until the 1980s that the genetic abnormality was understood, and not until 2012 that the FDA approved a line of medications – for clinic trials only – that were geared to attack the protein that creates this leukemia. Just a few years prior there was no method of stopping the blasts from reproducing. This diagnosis was a death sentence. A team of researchers, one of which we were told is located at the Oregon Health and Science Hospital, developed one of the drugs that temporarily stops or inhibits this protein from functioning: Disatinib, the latest drug developed. There were two others developed prior to Disatinib – Ponatinib and Imatinib. These drugs have been proven to buy the patient about six months. Studies show that at about the six-month mark, the protein reinvents itself, or mutates, around the medication, and mass production starts all over. During this six months, the patient and family are counselled and advised to seek a bone marrow transplant which, to this date, we are told is the only true cure. The

3

medication Disatinib costs the patient $10,000 per month and this is only *one* of the many that are started with the treatment. But you can receive this medication for $25.00 a month if you agree to participate in the ongoing clinical study. This study, in its second phase at the time of this writing with the third phase to begin soon, allows the FDA to continue to follow and approve other drugs and treatments in the hopes of finding a cure for this disease.

There are approximately 320+ million people living in the United States, and there are four main types of leukemia.

1. Acute Myeloid Leukemia (AML)

2. Chronic Myeloid Leukemia (CML)

3. Chronic Lymphocytic-Blastic Leukemia (CLL)

4. Acute Lymphoblastic Leukemia (ALL)

Each year, approximately 6000 of those 320 million will be diagnosed with Acute Lymphoblastic Leukemia, (ALL). Of that 6000, adults make up 2500+ cases. Of the 2500 adult cases, 20-30% of those will be diagnosed with *Philadelphia Positive* Acute Lymphoblastic Leukemia (Ph+ALL), approximately 750 cases. 25% of those cases will be people over the age of 50, approximately 187 people a year.

My husband, Roger, was diagnosed with this disease at 58.7 years old. On December 21, 2013, we found out what Acute Lymphoblastic Leukemia was. It wasn't long after that, I found out what having Philadelphia Positive Acute Lymphoblastic Leukemia meant. These were moments of profound tears and extreme fear.

Book written in 2019
* is there still a trial?
* If not what was the statistics of the trial?
* Are they giving you this ~~chemo~~ Chemo?

PART ONE

1

A Love Story and a Diagnosis

In November of 2013, Roger and I bought our first house together, a 3.03-acre ranch fixer-upper in Oregon. We were about to celebrate our fifth year together as a married couple. We had both been married before; he for 23 years and me for 26 years.

When our youngests, my daughter and his son, started dating in high school, they had other plans for us and it wasn't to stay single. I finally gave in to their pressure and went on a date with Roger, and the two kids accompanied us. Roger was a retired Oregon State Trooper with decorated credentials, a Purple Heart, and a Medal of Valor. He ran a team of Troopers from this part of Oregon to the California border and was the deputy medical examiner in Coos, Douglas and Lane Counties. He had an impeccable reputation amongst the parents and the locals, and was considered a "good catch," as I was told many times!

I sat in that seat at the local diner next to Roger as he and the kids kept the conversation rolling. We laughed, and it felt good! When the dinner arrived, I took notice of Roger's hands. They were huge, causing the fork to disappear. I looked at him next to me and noticed that I was looking up at him as we talked. I asked him, "How tall are you?"

He replied, "6'7" then gave me an ever so slight grin out of the side of his mouth as our eyes met. He was about 12 inches taller than me. I was speechless, and my cheeks felt flush. His eyes were crystal blue and full of warmth. Soft and gentle, yet a little mischievous. I saw a look of pure awareness in his eyes as he was looking into me. He later told me it was at that moment that he fell in love with me and I knew it to be true. It was a look I have only seen in the movies, the look that all women want to experience, a knowing that you are the one, the only one. Your heart beats fast and your mind is praying that he doesn't ask you a question right now – school girl nervous! Through the evening I found myself noticing him more. Salt and pepper hair, fair skin and a strong jaw.

We fell in love. Life was changing for me. He let me be me. He didn't try to change me. If I needed space, he gave it to me – as long as it didn't last more than two days! We were married on December 8, 2008 in our backyard. Life was wonderful and exciting. We started traveling, but a few years in, 30 years of smoking cigarettes had caught up with him. His diagnosis was severe coronary heart disease. Roger had a three-graft cardiac bypass and three stents put in. Life became a little more quiet.

In November of 2013, we bought our first house together, a real fixer. We couldn't move right in because this was NOT a move-in ready place. I spent the next seven days explaining to Rog the many possibilities and the visions I saw for the place. Its pros were that it was nestled in a small canyon, had over three acres of beautiful gardens and fruit trees of every kind, two expansive greenhouses, two large banks of solar panels, water collection systems, a 2000 square foot garage, a chicken coup, and so much more. It was a dream spot, but the house had to be rebooted. Rog listened; he had his doubts, but with that mischievous grin looking down at me, he pulled me in and said, "What Robin wants, Robin gets." We spent the first month ripping out walls and carpets, replacing subflooring, laying hardwood floors, and painting every wall. Roger was feeling good, and we were so happy.

On the second day after finally moving into our house, winter hit hard and we were snowed and iced in. Roger was doing everything he could to help me with all the stress and commotion of moving and unpacking. The morning of December 18, Rog wasn't feeling well. He said, "I feel off, babe, tired."

I laughed and said, "No kidding, so do I," in a comical manner. We smiled at each other and went about the day, getting the tree up and trying to find the dishes. The next morning, Roger said he was sick and wanted to lie down for a while. I said, "Are you all right?" It was alarming to me since I had never seen him sick. I had never seen him go to bed because he felt bad. I thought, *It's the flu.* He *has* been working on the tracker in the snow and has worked nonstop for over six weeks.

He said, "I think I've just run myself down." He went to bed. I was able to get him to eat chicken noodle soup and drink fluids. He slept through the day and night.

Two days later, he was still not well, and his color started to change. He was looking pale and his energy was at an all-time low. Just getting up to go to the bathroom was an effort. He was slumped in his stature and shuffled to the toilet although his urine looked and smelled okay. I was relieved by this because I knew his kidneys were working and that's always a good sign. He wasn't running a temperature, so that too was a good sign. I said, "I'm going to give you an apple cider vinegar bath and see if we can get some of the toxins out of you." He agreed and I knew then it was bad. He NEVER takes a tub bath!

I washed him, kissed his eyes and just let him rest in the tub. After the bath, he couldn't eat and could barely get the fluids down. Nausea was overtaking him. I closed our bedroom door to the chaos outside and stayed with him. We both slept. The next morning, he called to me as I was trying to get breakfast. It was about 11:00 a.m., and he was sitting on the side of the bed. His color was pale yellow, and his eyes were bloodshot and muddy looking. He was slumped over and said, "My mouth is bleeding."

I looked in his mouth and his gums were yellow and all around his teeth, blood was seeping. I said, "This is not the flu, we are going to the ER now!" I stood right in front of Rog, dressing him carefully and keeping him focused on me. He was acting as if he was drunk and going in and out of consciousness. I was so scared! *What is going on?* We silently drove to the hospital in the pouring rain. Rog had laid his seat back and closed his eyes. My mind was swimming with various diagnoses, searching for a name for these symptoms, some I didn't even want to consider. I held onto the steering wheel as if it was my security blanket, saving me from the boogey man under the bed. Oncoming headlights were glaring at me, and the windshield wipers were on full speed. I couldn't feel the cold wrapped around me. The car did the driving – I was somewhere in my head, afraid for Roger.

The car stopped in front of the ER. I helped Rog out into one of the community wheelchairs sitting at the entrance of the front door. I left the car there. No sooner did I get him through the door, the nurses looked up and rushed to our side. They immediately took him to the back and got him onto a bed. The doctor was at our bedside within minutes, and blood was being drawn as the doctor got a quick history from us. I talked as fast as I could, ending with, "His mouth is bleeding." He looked in Roger's mouth and promptly left with the nurse and the full blood vials. My heart was pounding, I was feeling faint, and a lump was forming in my throat. A lump of sheer fear! I could hardly speak. I held Roger's hand, caressed his face, looked him in the eyes and said, "This too shall pass. It's going to be okay." I forced a smile, burrowing my fear deep inside.

Roger smiled back and said, "I know. I am sorry about Christmas." I wanted to cry, my mouth started watering, and my eyes started tearing up. He closed his eyes and just laid there, holding my hand. Within 20 minutes, the ER doctor came back into the room and said, "You are very lucky tonight. We happen to have a specialist in the ER right now seeing another patient and I had him look at your blood, Roger. He will be in in just a few minutes." I sat down and laid my head across Rog's chest, holding his hand and praying.

The specialist came in and startled me. I looked up at him. He looked at me and then at Roger. His face was emotionless, blank. He lowered his eyes then looked up at us and said very slowly and methodically, "Roger, I am Dr. Moros. I looked at your bloodwork and you have Leukemia."

I stared at him. It didn't compute. I said, "What?" He explained that Roger's white blood count was at 250,000 and growing fast. Normal is 4,000-11,000.

Roger looked at him and asked in a matter-of-fact manner, "So what do we do now?" I didn't move.

Dr. Moros continued, "You have about eight hours to live. A helicopter is on its way to take you the specialty hospital's intensive care unit. They have been notified and are prepared to connect you to a machine that will filter out the white blood cells. This will then give them time to figure out what's next. But first we have to get you there."

The ER doctor came back in, and the wheels of motion began to take charge. Nurses were starting IVs, hospital insurance agents were having me sign papers, and questions were being thrown at me. "How much does he weigh? How tall is he? Is he claustrophobic? Has he ever been in a helicopter?" A hospital social worker kept asking me if I knew where the specialty hospital was and if I had someone who could drive me there. I looked at her blankly and told her I could find it. The room was full of people and I couldn't think fast enough. All I kept hearing was, "Eight hours to live." Roger had hit a wall. He was not doing well. Roger's answers were not making sense anymore and the doctors explained that at this point, the white blood cells had filled his bloodstream and were making their way into the brain. This was a critical point, a possible point of no return.

The helicopter team was now present and transferring Roger to their gurney. After they got him onto the gurney, feet sticking out two feet past the end of it, they looked at me and said, "He is too tall and too big; we are going to have to remove some things in the bird." Roger's weight was at an all-time high of 316 pounds.

Roger said, "You better give me some Ativan or you're not going to stuff me in that helicopter." We all turned around and looked at him. He was alert at that moment and dead serious. His claustrophobia had set in and the adrenaline was flowing. The pilots, who reminded me of Goose and Maverick from the movie Top Gun said, "How much do ya want, big guy?" with big smiles. They gave Rog IV Ativan, his head fell back, he was out, and they all three left. It all happened in about two hours and he was gone.

I stood motionless, stunned, in the ER room all by myself, listening to the helicopter leave the roof over us. The ER gurney was shoved to one side of the room with the sheet hanging off it. IV trash was littering the floor, the bedside tray table, and the hospital bed. EKG cables were left hanging from the bed railing, and Roger's clothes were sitting in a rumpled pile in a chair. I stood there alone, as if the hospital had been evacuated and someone forgot to tell me. He was gone, and I didn't know if I would ever look into those crystal blue eyes that always smiled back at me with love again. I started crying. One of the nurses caught me in the hallway. She pulled me to her, held both of my arms, looked me in the eye, and told me to go home and pack a bag because it was going to be a long stay. She told me to find someone to drive me. I nodded and left.

I drove home as fast as I could, ran into our room, grabbed a duffle bag, and started throwing in underwear, toothbrush and toothpaste, the laptop and Kindle, my journal, pants, tops, some underclothing for Roger, all his toiletries, and his glasses. I was home for exactly 21 minutes.

That two hour drive was the longest drive of my life. Pouring rain followed me all the way there. With no moon, it was the darkest night ever. The only light was that of the oncoming cars' bright headlights that were distorted by the rain pouring down my windshield. The GPS took me to a massive hospital on the top of a mountain that overlooks the city. I quickly found out that after 9:00 p.m., all the doors into the hospital are locked, and the only way in is through the ER. I don't remember how I did it, but I found my way to the ICU where Roger was very much alive, connected to every kind of machine available inside that room. I ran sobbing to his bedside, embraced his smiling face, and kissed him. He said, "Hi – you made it."

I laughed and cried at the same time and said, "Yes, I did!"

The doctor came in and explained that they had given Roger medication as soon as he arrived, and he was already responding to the drug. He said, "It is an experimental drug that will stop the white blood cells from reproducing. His numbers are starting to *slowly* drop. It will be touch and go through the night. At this point, it's a waiting game." I put my chair as close to Rog's bed as I could get it, holding his hand and watching him sleep. The nurses worked throughout the night on him. He fell in and out of sleep as I prayed.

By morning, the white cell count had dropped considerably. The doctors were talking about Roger's future plans and what to expect if the numbers continued to fall. Roger was alert and speaking clearly again. His color was returning to a normal pinkish pale rather than a yellow pale, although his eyes were still bloodshot and his mouth was still bleeding. By the following day, that had stopped too. Roger spent the next three days in ICU, regaining his strength and sleeping a lot. The ICU didn't have beds for family members, so I sat in a small side chair and laid my head on Roger's bed to sleep each night. We held hands right through Christmas in ICU. No turkey or stuffing or present opening with mimosas, it was a day just like any other day. On this day, Roger was hooked up to several wires and constantly beeping machines. I cried as Roger slept through the days.

On the fourth day, Roger was moved to the leukemia floor. It is a 30-bed unit for all adult leukemia patients. I, being a nurse for many years, have never experienced the kind of compassion and love that I felt from the staff on this floor, every one of them, from nurses to janitors. It was incredible! Thankfully, they have beds or couches that convert into beds for one family member. There are also drawers under the couch beds for the family member's things. This couch and these drawers became my world in this small hospital room.

It wasn't long before we were introduced to the team of doctors that govern the floor. Being a teaching hospital, we found ourselves surrounded by a swarm of doctors specializing in every category; cancer, kidney, neurology, skin and liver, along with their interns. Every day we saw at least two of them and a handful of interns. I bombarded the doctors with questions; the biggest one was, "Will this experimental medication he is on cure the leukemia?" The cancer doctor skirted the questions. Instead, he went into this dissertation on the medication, Dasatinib. He explained that with the addition of large doses of Prednisone, Dasatinib would indeed kill the proteins that were causing the leukemia *for now*. He continued to explain to us that they didn't know what kind of leukemia Roger had, but with genetic testing and bloodwork, they should have the answer in a couple of weeks. Until then, everything was looking good.

And it was. Roger's appetite was returning, the bleeding had stopped, and his eyes and skin color were returning to normal. His jovial personality was back, and he was enjoying the rest. He had his remote control to the TV and his wife at his side. He was as content as he could be.

2

Reality, Caregiver Class

After a couple days on the leukemia floor, I awoke to a social worker asking me to step outside the room. I did, and was asked to join a caregiver class later that afternoon. I was informed it was mandatory that I attend. I was a little unnerved, not knowing what to expect. I didn't want to be away from Rog any longer than necessary.

I took my seat at a very long conference table with a large packet lying in front of each seat. Several family members of other patients on the same floor were there with me. There were donuts, bagels and coffee, with several types of juice to choose from sitting in the middle of the table. I was starving! During the past few days, Roger had ordered more food than a normal person would eat for each meal. He did this so I could eat too. This way we could save some money and I didn't have to leave the room to go to the cafeteria to fend for myself. I learned very quickly that a meal in the hospital cafeteria ran around $8.00-$9.00. I would have to learn how to live on one good meal a day. Financially, we were strapped. I knew that money for food at this price was going to really take its toll on the bank account, so I dove into the bagels and donuts on that conference table and enjoyed the first bottle of orange juice without even taking a breath. The second and third bottle I took my time with.

The class started about ten minutes late, which was fine with me – more time to graze. I asked why this class was mandatory and was told that it was "part of the process." The social worker introduced herself and gave us a brief outline of the class. The lights dimmed and a projector began showing slide after slide of what to expect in the upcoming months. It was a class geared just for the caregivers. Responsibilities outlined in the class included everything from preparing medications and meals to cleaning up their feces and vomit, and making sure the patient arrived at all the clinic appointments. I think I was in shock. Even though I had been sleeping on a couch in a hospital room with cancer patients walking past our room every day – no hair, pale, thin, weak, masks on, no smiles, just faces of pain and misery – I wasn't computing that Roger was going to be out there amongst them. I listened to the social worker explain the duties before us. "They are not going to be pleasant, on any level" she said with a stern face. I began to get a little scared again. A feeling of panic started to overcome me like a dark cloak. I looked at the faces around the table. They looked like mannequins. Blank stares, a few of the women were sobbing quietly, blowing their noses. I kept saying to myself, *This too shall pass, this too shall pass, right?*

Swallowing hard, I pushed it down deep and put my nurse hat on. I said to myself, *Okay, I'm a nurse. I am comfortable with these upcoming duties. I can do this, this is what I do!* Then she started talking about Prednisone. Prednisone is a steroid that is given for major inflammatory diseases and illness. Usually it's given for short periods of time at doses of 10 mg or less, and the patient is always tapered off as soon as possible. It was being explained that our family member would be on very high doses for a long period of time and their personality would change drastically while on these high doses. After she said this, she was silent and looked at each of our faces. It was an uncomfortable pause. I leaned forward, and I too looked around the table, following her eyes from person to person as she looked at us. I was wondering what I had missed. It was a pause that felt like doom and gloom. No one said anything. I said "Okay, so what does this mean, their personality is going to change drastically? My husband is taking 140 mg a day right now and I am told this will be for months."

A woman sitting a few chairs down said, "They become violent." She had been through this before. Her son, Shawn, was diagnosed with leukemia when he was 15 and he beat it. He was now 21 and it had returned. He was sitting at the table with us. He laughed out loud sarcastically, wherein his father told him to knock it off. His mother looked at me and explained that Shawn's diagnosis four years prior, had nearly broken the family apart. It was obvious that the first time around had left wounds that still hadn't healed and here they were sitting at this table doing it all over again. I got a bad feeling in my stomach as I watched and listened to Shawn's mom continue to describe the horror of watching their fun-loving son turn into a demon. We all listened without interruption to the stories of Shawn throwing things, arguing, fighting and causing all kinds of stress as the Prednisone dosages continued to creep higher.

It hit me all at once – Shawn's leukemia had *returned.* It was like everything was in slow motion in my head. This told me that the medication isn't a cure after all. But what was the cure? I thought for a minute and realized I hadn't been told there was a cure; I had placed that notion in my head! We were just waiting for the bloodwork to tell us what medications to take and all would be well again, right? My head was spinning. It was at that moment that I realized Roger and I hadn't even talked about the possibility of no cure. I thought I was going to be sick. The social worker took charge of the meeting by putting up another slide on the screen. It focused on the types of personality changes that we were to expect. They ranged from verbal outbursts to temper tantrums to even violent behaviors such as throwing things or physical contact that was out of character. Shawn continued to laugh sarcastically under his breath as she continued. She ignored him and spoke in a tone that allowed me to drown Shawn out and listen to her. She said, "Besides trying to get your family member to eat, this will be the hardest part of the process that you will be dealing with – the evils of Prednisone. During these times of personality outbursts, do not engage, just listen."

With this, Shawn's parents spoke up and said that this was the most important thing to remember – don't engage in conversation or try to calm them down. Just listen or walk away. Shawn chimed in and said in a defiant tone of voice, "Maybe you could do better this time around and not always argue with me!" It wasn't bad enough sitting there absorbing all this but the scene at the table was becoming uncomfortable. I sat back and watched the battle playing out with this family. No one else at the table said a word the whole time we were there. They just watched, and some cried softly. I just sat in disbelief. I was beginning to realize what was happening. This is not going to be a brief stay, or a few medications added to his heart medications. This was going to be a very scary and tumultuous journey, one that I didn't want to be a part of, but there I was. My best friend, my husband, has cancer, blood cancer. I know hearts – I was an end-stage cardiac nurse! That's what I know. I don't know cancer. What is cancer? What is leukemia?

It had been a very long week. By now I should know more, right? Well, it was not "part of the process" to tell you what was going on! No one was telling us anything except that Dasatinib was lowering the white blood cell count and test results were not in yet. Every day we watched patients walk the floors, exercising with drawn faces. The family member walking with them were looking just as tired. It was getting scary to think that this would be us walking the floors. We asked about the blood tests and what the results would mean to us. We were told the results would identify the type of leukemia Roger had, giving them a treatment protocol to follow. But all we kept hearing was, "They are not back yet, just let us know if you need anything." I wanted to shake the doctor until he said something that would give me hope that Roger would be okay. I felt like I was losing it, but I couldn't let Roger see me like that. I couldn't let him see the turmoil, the fear, and the panic that was engulfing my head and body more and more each day. I kept a smile on and tended to him just as I did at home; fluffing pillows, rubbing his feet and sitting in the bed with him watching countless hours of noise on the TV; all the while hiding from him. I had a feeling he was doing the same for me; being stoic, not asking questions, and treating this time together as a blessing. I knew he was scared, but he wasn't going to let me in on it. Roger had always been a man in his head, always quietly strategizing, an observer, a listener, not a conversationalist. His quiet was, for the first time, so loud it was killing me inside. There was nothing I could do to help him, to cure him. No chicken soup, no apple cider vinegar baths, and no aspirin or back rub would work this time!

3

Life Doesn't Stop at Home

Unfortunately, the life back home didn't stop and wait for our return. I had my friend pick up our cat Max and take him home with her. I didn't want to worry about him too, and he was used to her. We were living in the hospital, waiting for the blood test results. I didn't know how long that would be so off he went to safety.

Rog and I watched TV and answered the battery of phone calls and text messages from the family as the weeks passed.

There were five things the social worker went over in grave detail during the caregiver conference:

1. Prednisone is going to change your loved one into someone unrecognizable.
2. No animals can be around your loved one when you go home because they carry diseases on their feet from outside dirt and feces.
3. Make sure everything eaten is prepackaged from the store. No fresh vegetables or foods from delis or restaurants. The bacteria in and on these foods can kill the patient. All other vegetables, a list was given, must be washed thoroughly. No vegetables from family gardens due to soil contamination.
4. Wash your hands several times a day and stay away from the public and children. Germs!
5. Patient must wear a mask when in public.

At this point the one that stood out the most was No Animal Contact!

The 140 mg of Prednisone a day was beginning to affect Roger's moods. He was a kind man, a quiet man. Not much got to him, but stress was taking a toll on me, therefore, it was taking a toll on him. He started ordering me to give him the phone when someone negative called. I just kept telling him, "No worries, I will take care of it. Your job is to heal."

Roger was getting stronger by the day. The medications were working, and his body was responding to them perfectly. But the Prednisone was beginning to rear its nasty head more and more. I started taking the phone calls in the hallway so he couldn't hear the conversations. A lot of the time, I had to walk the halls a while to let my tears dry. I wasn't getting any help or compassion from the family.

Roger began verbally expressing his innermost thoughts. He now had no filter. If he was angry, I knew it and so did everyone else that came into the room. If he had a point of view, we heard it loud and clear! When the cell phone rang and he could see who it was, he threw the phone at the window. Once after he did this, he yelled at me to get the phone and give it back to him. I did, and he threw it harder at the window, hoping to break it.

I'd had enough. February had arrived and the doctors still weren't telling us anything. Roger was getting better and stronger by the day so I made plans to go home. With a very upset husband, I left on a Monday. My husband was lying in a hospital bed not knowing his fate, and his wife was at home dealing with the family issues and the issues of the new fixer-upper.

4

Lab Results

February was quickly passing us by and we were getting frustrated by the lack of any news on test results. I was trying to be patient and quiet, so as not to anger Roger with my concerns. I spent many hours looking at him while he slept. Roger was changing; not only in his behavior, but he himself was changing. His eyes were so blue, bluer each day. His strength was returning too, almost like he was climbing a mountain and reaching the top. It was a miracle! We both kept asking if they were sure he was still sick and that his leukemia wasn't gone. We were told countless times, "This is the calm before the storm. He will reach the top of the mountain and stand tall, feeling as though he has conquered this diagnosis, but the mountain has a down slope on the other side. Just enjoy these moments with him right now." The Dasatinib was erasing his age, making him look younger every day. It wasn't just targeting and killing bad leukemia cells, it was also targeting and removing his wrinkles and brown spots, even his nasty looking moles. It made me wonder what this drug was really doing inside his body.

I spent every waking hour on my little couch, studying every medical journal and clinical abstract available online to educate myself on this disease. The problem was, we still didn't know what type of leukemia he had. One weekend I finally got a doctor to explain to us what the hold-up was on the bloodwork. He stated that they were looking at a specific genetic anomaly in Roger's blood. This anomaly was a concern so they were doing the tests a second time. He sat down and explained Philadelphia Positive Acute Lymphoblastic Leukemia to us. He said there were precursors to this type of leukemia. One is caused by B cells and one is caused by T cells. B cells grow within the bone marrow and T cells grow within the thymus, and they were still looking into the origins and the genetic makeup of his leukemia. I asked about a cure. He said, "The only cure is a bone marrow transplant." He gave us a minute to let that soak in.

I then asked, "Okay, what's next?" Roger laid there listening and watching the conversation with no expression, just resting his hands on his abdomen with his head propped up on pillows.

This doctor wasn't Roger's usual doctor. This was the on-call doctor for the weekend. Thank goodness he was kind enough to sit and answer our questions. He said, "Well, with a bone marrow transplant, it is best to have a compatible donor, a sibling. We will test your brothers and see if either are a match and go from there. If not, we will enroll you in the registry, which is a donor bank made up of people all over the world

15

who donate organs for just this reason." He asked about Roger's descent and Roger replied with, "Just a simple Texan, Heinz 57."

The doctor replied, "Then you are probably of European descent, which is good. Most on the registry are, so your chances are pretty good in finding a match." I asked about the bone marrow transplant itself, and what it entailed. He explained, "Within the next few weeks, you will have time to sit down and talk to your doctor in the clinic and he will go over all the particulars after the bloodwork comes back. Just sit tight for now. All your lab numbers are back to normal and everything looks good." He shook our hands and left. Later, we were told this doctor had been at the hospital for over 20 years. He was becoming my best friend!

The next morning, we got a knock on the hospital room door. It was a representative from the hospital pharmacy. She introduced herself to us and said, "I am here to talk to you about the medication Dasatinib you are on." She got right to the point. "The medication costs $10,000.00 a month and that's just one of your medications. Are you able to pay that each month?"

I was in shock. I hadn't been awake for very long and there was no coffee in my system yet. I said, "What did you say?" She repeated herself. I looked at her and said, "Who can afford that? Just one of the meds cost $10,000? No, we can't afford that! What does this mean?" I was petrified. Roger just stared at her. I looked over at him to get a response. I saw his eyebrows rise up to his hairline and thought, *Oh God, here it comes*.

But she spoke first, saying, "You *can* get it for $25.00 a month if you sign up for the study. It is covered by the study."

I said "What? From $10,000 a month to $25.00 a month; are you kidding me?"

Roger said, "Where do I sign up?"

She handed him the piece of paper, along with a handy pen. Roger signed it and off she went. Roger and I talked about this for hours, both in shock. In the back of my mind, I had an uncomfortable feeling about the paper he'd signed without even reading it. This didn't make sense, and she didn't say anything else. It was either Sign or Pay!

I spent that day, as Roger rested, on the internet learning everything I could about Philadelphia Positive Acute Lymphoblastic Leukemia (Ph+ALL). There wasn't much. The articles I could find were all on children under the age of five. This search turned into days of research. I worked at night so my day could be spent visiting with Rog, holding hands, watching TV and dreaming about our future on the ranch.

Roger didn't talk much about his diagnosis or his prognosis. I think he was waiting for the bloodwork and a doctor to tell him exactly what he had before he started worrying. He was so in control like that. *Why worry 'til ya have to?* Me, I was already gone with worry. I had overheard conversations and really listened to the undertones of all that was being said to us. I knew this was much more serious than they were letting on.

One night, I hit the jackpot of information on this disease. It was the beginning of a very quiet death within my heart. No one at Roger's age had lived longer than five years after being diagnosed with Ph+ALL. Most died within the first two to three years due to infectious complications caused by weakened immune systems post-transplant. I kept this to myself and my journal, and kept reading and searching. There had to be something that increased the odds, and I was determined to find it!

Roger's lab work continued to get better, his appetite was good, and his weight was still sitting at just over 300 pounds, but he began taking a turn for the worse. The storm had begun. He was becoming weak again and getting weaker. Walking was an effort and doing small tasks like showering and dressing were exhausting. I began taking showers with him so I could do all his washing. His breathing was labored with any activity. Reaching his feet or bending over made him dizzy to the point of almost passing out. We were told it was the Prednisone. "It's going make him feel like a million bucks then it will turn on him and steal all his energy." We were told getting up and walking several times a day would help with the weakness. It was going to be a battle but we needed to push through it. This they preached a lot.

One morning when the doctors and their entourage of interns were making their rounds, I cornered them in our room and asked, "How many types of leukemia are you testing for?" I was told two. I said, "Okay, I know about the B cell and T cell precursor, but what else is there?" They explained to me that Roger had a genetic component to his leukemia that they were verifying in a second test. I asked what genetic component. They all looked at us, and I said, "You are not leaving this room until one of you tells us what's going on!" The interns all left, leaving one doctor to deal with the request.

The doctor sat down, crossed his legs, looked at us then stood up and started to pace back and forth as he began the explanation. I finally said, "I am a nurse so just tell us what's going on."

He started talking to us as if we were doctors ourselves, and he didn't hold anything back, using all the big words and proper names. He explained, "Roger could have Acute Lymphoblastic Leukemia (ALL) or he could have Philadelphia Positive ALL. Philadelphia Positive ALL is caused by the translocation of chromosome 9 and chromosome 22. They switch places, which then creates a protein foreign to the body. Proteins are the recipients and carriers of information from the outside environment we live in to the environment inside the body. This new protein that has been formed from this translocation signals the white blood cells to reproduce at an alarming rate, a rate that doesn't let them mature, only reproduce as fast as they form. Roger's leukemia had a B precursor which told us that his leukemia was formed in the bone marrow and in all the long bones of his body."

As he continued, I listened carefully. When he was finished I asked, "Which type, if you had it, would you want to be diagnosed with?"

He hesitated, looked at the floor and said, "Philadelphia positive."

I looked at him and said, "He has PH+ALL, doesn't he?"

He looked at us and said, "I don't know. Your regular doctor will talk to you about it more later when the test results come back."

I asked, "Is there a cure?"

He said, "The only possible cure is a bone marrow transplant. Again, your doctor will talk to you about it." I shook his hand and he left. I knew he had just lied to me. Roger had Ph+ALL.

As the days passed by, Roger looked younger and younger but his stamina was waning fast. We walked the halls with our masks on, used the exercise equipment with our masks on, did everything with our masks on. I began to realize that my health was just as crucial as Roger's was at this point. If I got sick, he got sick from me. I began wearing a mask everywhere and washing my hands every chance I got. I was in a hospital and people are sick in here! It was a bed of germs. I think the leukemia floor is the cleanest floor in the hospital for this reason. Every one of those cancer patients have no immune system so germs are not invited to this floor!

Another side effect of large doses of Prednisone is diabetes. It wasn't long before Roger was learning how to poke his finger and test his blood for sugar levels. He was also having to get over his needle phobia, although that didn't take long. He was poking his fingers three times a day, and poking himself an additional three times a day with a needle full of insulin, but he didn't complain. He never complained about anything! Never, unless it was about the family's bad behavior – then it was, *Watch Out!*

Roger's test results were finally in, and we were given the news by the touring team of interns and our clinic doctor, Dr. Perses. Finally, we met this illusive doctor from the clinic. He never sat down, he just started talking. "Hi, I'm Dr. Perses. How are you doing?"

Roger stared at him as he lay in bed with his hands in his usual doctor meeting position, resting on his abdomen with his head propped up on pillows. Roger said, "I could be better."

Dr. Perses nodded and said, "Your test results are complete, and you have Philadelphia Positive Acute Lymphoblastic Leukemia. I am aware that you have been given information regarding this diagnosis. We will go over it in more detail during your upcoming clinic visits, but at this time, it is important to get your family members tested for compatibility. My office will be getting ahold of you in the next few days to get their information. Also, my nurse practitioner will be here soon with your clinic schedule for the next few months. She will go over what to expect during these visits. All your questions will be answered during the clinic appointments. Your bloodwork looks good and stable. You can go home day after tomorrow. Do you have any questions for me right now?"

All eyes were on us. We were frozen. I didn't understand, my mind was in chaos, everything was all jumbled up, and I went blank. He has Ph+ALL, he can go home, all our questions will be answered at the clinic, not now. *Oh No! I should have some questions, where are the questions, Robin?* Roger said nothing. He stared at the doctor, blank. I asked, "Where is the clinic?" Yep, that's all I had.

Dr. Perses said, "Across the street." He stood there staring at us, kind of like he was trying to figure us out. He didn't add any more to the conversation, just stood staring. I looked at the interns, who were actually looking at me, waiting for me to say something. Instead, I just sank into the chair and put my head in my hands. He shook Roger's hand and left. I started crying. I had a huge lump in my throat, and it felt like my throat and head were being compressed in a vice. For the first time, I really realized Roger was going to die. My heart began to ache, my back started to ache, and I couldn't breathe. I felt like I was in a room with no air and there wasn't anyone to open the door. I just started to moan and felt dizzy. I was going to pass out. Roger got out of bed and just held me. I'm not sure he knew it, but he was trembling, and I could feel he was crying as he held me. He held me tight, so I couldn't look up at him. We didn't talk for a long time. Roger had Philadelphia Positive Acute Lymphoblastic Leukemia.

I was so nervous. *Now* I didn't want Roger to leave the hospital; he was safe here. He was being taken care of and had a team of doctors if anything went wrong. If we left, how was I going to take care of him? How was I going to keep him safe? Then it hit me, we were going home to the ranch. There was so much to do! *Is the house clean and free of germs? Are our bedsheets washed and ready for Roger to sleep in? There's no food, I need to shop!*

The nurse practitioner showed up a few minutes later with pages of appointments and discharge instructions. Every question we asked, we were told to write down and bring to the clinic appointment. It became very obvious that no questions were being answered by this woman. All I could think about was that I had one day to get home, clean, shop and get back to the love of my life. I explained to Roger what I needed to do and quickly left for home. That two hour drive home I spent rehearsing everything I was going to say to the family and praying that they really heard me.

5

Going Home: The Calm Before the Storm

When I arrived home it was a mess. The kids had been staying at the ranch and it looked like a post-apocalyptic frat house party had taken place, and I found myself sinking into a deep despair. I was so tired, so disappointed, so hurt, and for the first time I felt alone. How could this be happening? I started to sob. Tears just rolled down my face, my heart was hurting. I sank to the floor and just let it out of me. My son was explaining the mess, but I couldn't hear him. I had no ears. They had shut off all sounds except for my crying.

I just wanted to reset the clock, like resetting the computer back to factory mode. I wanted to pick the day we got married. We were so happy standing in our backyard, exchanging our vows with our friends and family. This happiness was gone! I just cried, sitting there on my deck slumped over, hugging my knees. After a while, my thoughts returned to what I needed to do.

I only had a few hours to get the house ready for Roger. He had called and asked how things were going and I lied to him. It had become a habit. If he didn't need to know, I stopped sharing. It wasn't worth him becoming upset. His energy was needed for healing. Knowing what I had walked into was knowledge his Prednisone didn't need. I was numb, literally numb.

After six hours, the smell of antibacterials and bleach filled the air. The house was ready for Roger's return. As I stood in the shower under the hot water, the memory of giving Roger an apple cider vinegar bath for the flu filled my mind. *How? Why Roger? He is such a great man! Why?* I cried until the water turned cold.

Back at the hospital, during discharge we were given a stack of paperwork that included doctor's appointments and clinic appointments that extended out two months. Some weeks there were appointments every day. All these appointments were at the clinic and hospital two hours away. How were we going to keep up with this schedule living so far away? Plus, Roger was going home with a permanent IV-line in. This was going to have to be taken care of too; flushed twice a week so it didn't clot off. Why hadn't we been given this information a long time ago? We thought about staying with Roger's mom who was about 30 minutes from the clinic until we could figure out the logistics of living and traveling back and forth. On one hand, this would be the perfect solution, but on the other hand, this would be a disaster! Roger's brothers lived with his mom, and I was concerned because of Roger's Prednisone buddy. Due to these concerns, Dr. Perses notified Dr. Moros, who agreed to follow Roger at our local hospital during the waiting period prior to transplant. Dr. Moros was the oncologist from the ER who gave us the initial diagnosis. There were several appointments that were mandatory in the clinic but it freed us up from about 75% of the long travel and from the Prednisone killing his brothers.

I was so happy to be in my own bed, and really happy that the beeping machines and nurses in and out of the room all night long didn't follow us home.

Roger was doing pretty well. Over the weeks we had been home, he found ways to keep busy and his mind off the leukemia and the transplant. We were still working on the house. Together we completed project after project, creating together, working together, and laughing together. His days were shorter and his stamina was weaker, but he gave it his all for a few hours each day then spent the remainder of it resting in his chair. Roger's favorite pastime was his TV. We had one in every room; the bigger the better. I don't like TV and before the cancer, I spent most of my time outside and utilized every ounce of daylight playing in the flowers and garden beds, creating all kinds of things. It was my meditation space. A place where thoughts and worries disappeared and I didn't come in until I had to.

After the cancer, I took up beading; making purses with beaded fronts. I had to come up with something that would give me the strength to sit there while the love of my life watched that TV screen for hours. This new hobby kept me next to him while he enjoyed all kinds of silly shows. I had to adapt quickly and I did, stringing one bead at a time. Roger was so happy with my hobby. He would rest his hand on my shoulder or thigh as I sat next to him. I swear he just wanted to make sure I was there.

Roger continued to get stronger. Being home, he was able to get more exercise, and after a while we were both questioning if he was really sick. Each time we went in for blood draws and IV dressings, we asked the same question, "Are you sure?"

They always came back with the same answer, "This is the calm before the storm."

When March arrived, Roger took a turn. He was in trouble.

PART TWO

1

The Clinical Study

That $10,000 a month Dasatinib reached toxic levels in Roger's system. He was feeling awful and it came on fast and furious; headaches, diarrhea, pain, and his blood levels were dropping fast. They stopped the drug for ten days then started it back up at a lower dose.

On March 14th, Roger's brothers were tested for a possible blood match, but neither matched. A huge sigh of relief washed over his face, but it was also bittersweet since a sibling's match predicts a better outcome. The hospital registered Roger into a program called Match, an organization made up of people around the world willing to become a blood donor for cases just like this. It wasn't long before a match was found. When we got the news, we laughed, cried and hugged each other. We were not told who the donor was or where he came from, all they would tell us was that he was as big as Roger and was in his 20s. I was jumping for joy! Nice young blood, this is really good. Blood is our life force, the younger the better!

Remember that piece of paper Roger signed so quickly when we found out the $10,000 Disatinib medication bill could be reduced to $25.00 a month if Roger agreed to be in a clinical study? This was a preliminary signature. We were notified to be at the clinic on April 23 to sign the final paperwork for the study. To receive the bone marrow transplant, Roger had to be fully signed into the study. No study meant no medications, no transplant. Death was the only option. It was a surreal moment to realize this. No one had talked to us about it, no one had explained this. If he decided not to be in the study, they would drop everything, refer him back to our primary doctor, and say goodbye. You're done, good luck!

Roger had to complete a series of tests prior to the bone marrow transplant. These tests were required by every participant in the study. They give the doctors a baseline of the patient's overall health prior to transplant. The list requirements are:

1. EKG
2. Echocardiogram
3. Heart catheterization
4. Chest x-rays

5. PET scan
6. Pulmonary function test
7. Lots of bloodwork
8. Bone marrow biopsy
9. Lumbar puncture with biopsy
10. Radiation consult
11. Dental consult, with any repairs completed
12. Signed consent to the study

We had three weeks to complete the tests, with the transplant scheduled for May 6 and the induction preparation beginning on April 29. We were then given the news that to receive a transplant, you must live within 20 minutes of the hospital. I asked why and was told that this was the only hospital that did transplants in the area so if anything were to go wrong, the patient must live close to care. I asked how often something went wrong, and I was told, "Every day." My head was swirling. How was I going to pull off this upcoming three-week schedule of tests and find a place to live? How? I bought a calendar, and along with my journals, they became my secretary. If I was asked a scheduling question, I referred to them before I gave an answer. The little squares soon became full, with little arrows pointing to the margins for additional appointments.

The testing began on April 10 and concluded on April 23 with the signing of the consent. I felt like we were running as fast as we could down a corridor with open doors. As we got to each open door, Rog ran in, did his testing, got up, and ran to the next door until there were no more doors. It was draining on both of us, but for the most part, the testing was pretty easy on Rog except for the dental workup. Within just a few months of 140 mgs of Prednisone a day, Roger's gums and jawbone had atrophied quite a bit; his mouth was taking a big hit. The dentist had worked with many transplant patients so when we walked in, he was ready to take care of everything in one day. Rog needed three crowns and one extraction. We were told that if the gums continued to deteriorate at this rate, most likely Roger would have to undergo more extractions in the near future. The Prednisone was not going anywhere so we put that procedure on the back burner until told to revisit it. Poor baby couldn't talk for hours because he was in so much pain!

The study consent was 15 pages long and addressed the induction period and transplant but nothing about the future or the statistics. I wanted to know what to *expect*. I understood what they were going to do *to* him, but I wanted to know how this would *affect* him. The consent read like a TV commercial, listing the drugs and their side effects. I knew that side effects happened to a very small amount of people, but what are the side effects that happen most often? What are the side effects that will happen? These were the questions that I asked repeatedly and never got an answer to. The consent had to be signed to move forward, and it was intense. Even as a nurse, I had a lot of questions about everything. It was too much to take in all at once. But Roger, as he did before, quickly signed and considered it just another step.

There were two paragraphs in the consent that I wish I would have read closer. If I had absorbed those words to the point of understanding, I might not have been so confused for so many months. Then again, I am not sure I *could* have absorbed them. I just wish I had. These are the paragraphs and how they read:

1. **Are there benefits to taking part in the study?** If you agree to take part in this study, there may or may not be direct medical benefits to *you*. We hope the information learned from this study will benefit *other* patients having a stem cell transplant in the *future* (italics by me).
2. **What other options are there?** You may choose not to participate in this study. Instead of being in the study, you have the following options: You may enroll in any other transplant trials *if* they are available and *if you are eligible*, or you may have treatment with other chemotherapy. If you decide that you do not want any further active treatment for your cancer, one of your options is "comfort care." Comfort care means that your doctor will offer you medication to control any pain you have, along with any other treatment, and support your need to help you maintain your overall comfort and dignity. It is often possible for this comfort care to be provided at home. Please talk to your regular doctor about these and other options (again, italics by me).

During each clinic visit we were given a follow sheet to take home. I had noticed that on the take home sheet there was a survivor box that said "Survivor Goal Five Years: NONE." When I asked about it, I was never given a clear-cut answer. I *now* realize that these studies, especially when the future goal at five years is NONE, are designed to experiment until they get it right. In other words, sign and participate, and feel good that you're helping people like you in the *future* to have a better future. If you choose not to help others, that's okay, we will provide you with comfort care. So you sign, hoping they are very close to getting it right so you can be the one who changes the "None" in the Future Survivor Goal box to "ONE." Why be upset when you realize your loved one is being experimented on like a lab rat? You're helping future people, right?

I came to realize my job was to fight for Roger every step of the way. Read, know, and ask our doctors and nurses questions over and over again. Talk to other patients around us and ask them questions. It's all we can do. If all we get is an understanding friend, it's worth it.

In the INTRODUCTION portion of this same document, on the first page it says: "You have been invited to be in this research study because your doctors have found that you have a cancer that is not curable with standard chemotherapy." Faith, hope and pray!

After days of searching for a place to live, I finally found our temporary home. I looked into Air B&Bs and rentals, but for some reason, the time of year was against me. Every option was booked. I ended up finding an extended stay hotel. It was perfect and approximately 15 minutes from the hospital. It had a private master bedroom with a bathroom, a family room, a small kitchenette with a stove and refrigerator, and a second bathroom. The move in date was April 29. Our housing instructions were to find a room on the bottom floor, with no stairs and easy access to the toilet. Food was to be pre-packaged, nothing fresh due to germs that might have landed on it from dirty hands or airborne contaminants, and no restaurant food. The "goal" was to get through the first 100 days after transplant without complications. If Roger lived to that 100-day mark, then we were given permission to go out to eat. At this point, I was confused about the pre-packaged food requirement that I was instructed to feed him. Why do I feed him heavily salted, toxic, preservative-filled food after his body just killed off everything, getting ready for someone else's blood to take over? It seemed like an oxymoron. Take a body fighting to live and give it junk to fuel it as it rebuilds. I began my studies into the world of food and its benefits; books, videos, magazines, anything I could get my hands on. Boy, was that an awakening! No wonder so many people have cancer! Our food supply is poisoned in more ways than one, but that's a whole other book in itself.

2

Induction

Induction is a huge process in itself. It is a countdown that reads like this: -5, -4, -3, -2, -1, 0, +1, +2, +3, and so on. Then it jumps to day 28, day 56 and day 180. The minus days, -5 through -1, represent the days preparing the body for transplant. During these minus days, very strong chemotherapy was given via IV to kill off as much of Roger's existing bone marrow as possible. After the chemotherapy, his whole body was radiated to kill off cells that might have escaped the poison. Unfortunately, radiation kills more than just the bone marrow. It's like a slow microwave treatment. The cells die slowly over time, up to a few years after. Plus days represent each day following the transplant.

The later days are goal markers: day 28, day 56 and day 180. Day 28 is a day of celebration if the patient hasn't experienced donor transplant rejection. Day 56 is a celebration if there's no donor rejection or infection. Day 180 is a celebration if there's no rejection or infection, and/or death hasn't happened. Once you hit day 180 and all is well, medications and visits to the clinic are reduced. Then the countdown begins again. Each day following transplant, no matter where you are on the calendar, is a day of celebration. We were told that if something was going to happen, it usually happened in the first 28 days after bone marrow transplant. Statistics of complications increase every day thereafter.

The clinical study is based on a pre-planned protocol. All medications, chemotherapy and radiation induction are outlined to a T. Roger would receive chemotherapy for four days; days -5, -4, -3, -2. Day -1 is a day of rest. Day zero is whole body radiation and transplant day. In this clinical study, Busulfan and Fludarabine are the chemotherapy drugs used and given via IV. Both are drugs given specifically for blood cancers like leukemia. The side effects include but are not limited to:

1. Irritation to entire mucosa lining from mouth to rectum
2. Damage to lungs, liver, heart and/or kidneys
3. Scarring in the lungs
4. Seizures
5. Increased pigmentation of the skin
6. Hair loss from scalp, underarms, beard, eyelashes and pubic area
7. Cataracts
8. Nerve damage

9. Immunosuppression, causing increased likelihood of debilitating infections

If there is a chance that the patient's original cells might have escaped into the spinal fluid, which it did in Roger's case, the drug Methotrexate is injected into the spinal fluid via a lumbar puncture. Side effects include:

1. Change in bowel habits, severe diarrhea
2. Nausea and vomiting
3. Mouth sores
4. Kidney damage and failure
5. Changes in skin color and itchiness
6. Loss of sex drive, libido and impotency
7. Fertility problems
8. Blurred vision
9. Headaches
10. Foggy mental cognition, difficulty understanding and comprehension
11. Miscarriages
12. Partial paralysis
13. Convulsions
14. Mood swings
15. Allergic reactions, shock
16. Pain in muscles and joints
17. Brittle bones

If any of these signs or symptoms occurred, Roger would be treated quickly with additional pharmaceuticals. If these additional drugs caused debilitating side effects, more pharmaceuticals would be given.

On day -3, Rog began a medication called Cyclosporine. This medication helps prevent his body from rejecting the new donor cells. Chemotherapy and radiation are designed to kill off as much of the original existing blood without killing the baby blast, the immature white blood cells hidden deep in the bone marrow. Mature blood cells that escaped the destruction process would detect the foreign blood cells, the new donor cells that have entered the body. The new donor cells would detect those original, escaped cells as foreign invaders now that they claimed this body as theirs. They would see each other as a virus, such as the flu or pheumonia, and set out to kill each other.

This began a process called Graft vs. Host Disease (GVHD). This was not likely to happen if you were given your own cells during transplant, called an autologous donor. As the new blood cells from the donor enters the body during the transplant process, they see the body as their new home and begin to find their way to the bone marrow where they will reside and take up shop, creating more new and improved cells not infected with leukemia. But if opposing cells see each other, a war will break out in whatever organ the battle commenced. This battle is, literally, destruction to the death! If it is in the liver, which statistics have shown is usually the first organ to be hit by GVHD other than the skin, the liver will begin showing signs of failure; jaundice, abdominal pain, nausea, vomiting and loss of appetite. If it is the skin, severe dryness of the mouth and throat occurs, leading to ulcers. The skin becomes scaly and starts shedding itself. Burning blisters occur from the palms of the hands to the souls of the feet, and all mucosal areas become dry. Statistics show that this will happen in 60-80% of all patients who undergo an allogenic stem cell transplant, cells not from self but from a donor. If you receive cells from a sibling, the statistic drops to 20-30%, and this can happen in the first 100 days after transplant. If this occurs in the first 100 days, it's called Acute GVHD. If it happens after 100 days or up to a year after transplant, it's called chronic GVHD. If the patient has an acute graft vs. host episode, chronic graft vs. host is inevitable.

The statistics of graph vs. host disease is so high, a medication called CellCept is automatically given, which helps prevent the battle from occurring in the first place, but it is not a sure fix, just a hopeful one. GVHD is an inflammatory process, so the Prednisone will be adjusted up and down as needed for as long as it is needed.

When the day arrived, I was so nervous. On this day, the final clinical study documents were signed, giving the doctors all rights over Roger's body and care from that day forward. We were seen by the nurse practitioner first. She talked about the new medication regime that was to begin in a few days, medications that would help prevent Roger's body from rejecting the donor's blood and help boost his immune system. She confirmed that we were living within 20 minutes and asked if we had read the Study papers. We said we had, and I expressed all my concerns, mostly asking, "What effects will this have on Roger?" She just looked at me as if she didn't understand. I said, "The Prednisone makes him irritable and weak. What effects will he experience going through the induction and radiation? What am I to expect in regards to symptoms? What should he be watching for?"

The nurse replied, "Every-*body* is different. Many of the patients get sore mouths so watch for that, but the doctor will go over your questions." She left. We waited for 20 minutes, sitting silent, taking in the room around us and listening to the conversations outside in the hallway.

The doctor arrived, asked Rog how he had been and if we had any questions. Roger asked the same questions we had asked the nurse practitioner. The doctor said the same thing, "Every-*body* is different." He explained that being seen in the clinic three to four times a week would help the staff stay on top of any unusual symptoms Roger might experience. He said, "We will be testing your blood so often that you will get tired of us real fast."

Roger joked back saying, "With this IV in, I don't care how much blood you want." They both laughed and that seemed to conclude the session. He handed Roger the document, with the signing page exposed on top, and a pen. It was done. I walked out, mind swirling with questions. So many questions, but so afraid to ask. The biggest lingering one, the one I had buried deep inside, the one I didn't want to mention in front of Rog, the one I couldn't find an answer to anywhere on the internet, the one I quietly searched for but never spoke of; what's the mortality rate? It ate at me like acid! I couldn't get away from it. It became my biggest fear. But maybe I didn't really want to know.

Roger began feeling more tired the closer we got, and his irritability was still present and in full force. He had gained weight despite the lack of appetite, and normally he was never without an appetite. Rog had reached a point that even pastries and candy bars did nothing for him. His desire for food was slowly diminishing as the poison of the chemotherapy transfused through his system. Even with the lack of food, he was still gaining weight, weight he couldn't afford to gain. The doctors said the Prednisone was playing havoc on his kidneys, and edema was expected throughout this process. He was instructed to reduce salt and rest with feet up, the usual protocol for water retention.

Roger was anxious! He just wanted to get it all over with. He was jumping in with two feet, boots still on. We would lie in bed in our new home, the hotel, and talk about the "what ifs." Actually, I talked about the what ifs and Roger listened. After I exhausted myself, he pulled me close and said, "I'm going to be fine. This too shall pass." It was frustrating, but I figured he had enough on his mind, so I got his stoic side. I just wanted to know what he thought about all this. How was he really feeling? Mostly, why wasn't he talking to me about all those feelings? I didn't push him.

The first day of chemotherapy was uneventful. The clinic was quiet that day. From the waiting room, you walk down a long corridor into the infusion room. Along the corridor are patient exam rooms where patients are seen by the doctors, nurse practitioners and phlebotomist prior to receiving IV therapy. Usually 30 people were seated, lined up in rows, all connected to IV poles with bags of chemicals dangling, slowly dripping poison into their bodies. The square footage of this room is just big enough for 30 recliners with a small, hard plastic chair next to each for the caretaker and a small walkway for the nurses to move about. There were no windows.

Today, many of the chairs were empty. They sat Roger next to a sleeping giant, a huge man who was slumbering away, entertaining everyone with his snoring. The caregivers sitting next to their loved ones giggled. Roger looked at me and said, "Don't ever let me do that!" I cracked up and agreed to poke him if he ever snored in his chemo chair. Another man was having a tiff with his wife. She had moved his IV pole which sent him into a tither and a few harsh words. Her cheeks flushed with embarrassment as she glanced around the room to see who was watching. I kept my head down and thought, *That's the Prednisone talking*!

Roger wore shorts to his first chemo session. As I sat next to him in my hard, tiny, plastic caregiver chair, I noticed the hair on his legs was missing. I asked him about it, and he said it had started falling out about a month prior. He was beginning to have problems with hot flashes as well.

It was a long day at the clinic. It started at 7:00 a.m. in the small patient exam room with a blood draw then we waited. After the blood levels were evaluated, the nurse practitioners came in and went over all the medications and what to expect in the next few days of chemotherapy. She explained that Rog could experience nothing or he could experience flu-like symptoms. The most important thing to monitor was his temperature and to make sure he got two to three liters of fluids in each day. When she was done, she sent us to the infusion room to take any seat we wanted as long as it didn't have a reserved sign on it. For the next five hours, Rog received his chemotherapy infusion. The patients around us read books, watched movies on their laptops or slept.

Today the cable was out to the building so Roger just slept through the first round of chemotherapy and most of the evening. His only complaint was discomfort in his back, I assumed from being in a chair all day with no back support.

On day two, or day -4, we arrived a little early. Roger had his blood draw and we were told to sit and wait. There had been an element of denial up to this point. This would not be us! He would not be like the people surrounding us with no hair, pale skin, blisters, and red bloated bodies to the point of not knowing if it was a man or a woman.

Most people kept to themselves. They were just tired. We had seen them and they us, all a part of the same family now who, by the way, didn't talk to each other much. With a family comes an understanding that some subjects are just not desirable to talk about. So each clinic visit we smiled, nodded, and sat and waited. I found myself on many occasions sneaking a peek at the really sick patients and praying, *Please don't let that happen to Roger!* Interestingly, down deep I wanted to ask them questions; *What's your diagnosis? How far into the treatment are you? What medications are you taking? Tell me what happens at each stage. What should we expect with each medication change? Do you have any advice? What happened to you? How did you get like this?* etc. They had all the answers, but my fear kept me from asking. Like the rest of the caregivers, after a while I just stared at the carpet as we waited our turn.

That morning we went on a short walk around the hospital. The day was warm and it was nice just smelling the fresh air. When we returned to the clinic, it was Roger's turn in the infusion room. The heavy double doors opened and the corridor awaited us. At that moment, I thought of the movie, The Green Mile. Tears came to my eyes and I immediately cleared my thoughts. We found a chair next to a woman knitting a beautiful pink scarf. Her husband sat next to her as she received her chemo. I admired her scarf and after a few minutes, all four of us were sharing our stories. Karen and George had been married forever, and he was a police officer in Oregon. The men talked shop, and Karen and I exchanged stories and diagnosis, and our artwork. After Karen and George left, Rog soon fell asleep.

I watched Roger sleep. I wasn't sure what to expect tonight, after the second infusion. I was told by Karen that during the third and fourth days was when the symptoms of the chemo usually set in. I was as ready as I could ever be. He was the love of my life, and we were in this together! I had seen the post effects of chemotherapy after sitting in the waiting room each day we were in the clinic. My fear was when and how it was going to affect Roger. The Prednisone and the Dasatinib had changed him. He looked younger, all his moles, age spots and wrinkles were gone, and his temperament was sketchy – like a box of chocolates, you never knew what you were going to get. How was the next phase going to change him?

The second and third transfusions were uneventful, just another two long days at the clinic. Roger was restless at night and complained of back pain each day, but for the most part he was handling it well. The fourth day was the start date of the Cyclosporine. Just a few months ago, Roger's medication list consisted of:

1. Pravastatin, for cholesterol
2. Baby aspirin, as a blood thinner
3. Norvasc, for blood pressure
4. Ativan, to calm his nerves

At this point, his medication list looked like this:

1. Pravastatin
2. Norvasc

3. Ativan
4. Acyclovir, which treats herpes virus, chickenpox, shingles and inflammation in all mucosal areas
5. Baclofen for muscle spasms and cramping
6. Insulin via injection four times a day, for Prednisone-caused diabetes
7. Fluconazole, which prevents fungal infections and treats neutropenia, an abnormally low white blood cell count which occurs after chemotherapy and total body radiation
8. Gabapentin for muscle spasms in legs and hands
9. Levothyroxine for low thyroid hormone
10. Imodium for diarrhea
11. Magnesium
12. Lopressor for blood pressure
13. Prednisone
14. CellCept for anti-rejection
15. Oxycodone for pain
16. Compazine for nausea
17. Mylicon for bloating and gas
18. Bactrim, an antibiotic

Yesterday I was told to go to the pharmacy to pick up these medications while Roger was receiving his chemotherapy. When I went to the window to pick up the medications, I was handed two large plastic bags as if I was leaving a department store after Christmas shopping. I kid you not! Both were stuffed full of all these medications. My first thought was, *He won't have room for food*, and *How is his body going to accept all this in his system at once?* The pharmacist went over each drug with me, stopping at the Cyclosporine. She put her hand on mine and said, "I have NEVER seen this dose of Cyclosporine prescribed before. It is a huge dose. What does your husband weigh?"

I said, "310 pounds." She just stared at me and repeated herself. I worried about this for a while after I left, but the thought was soon consumed with, *How am I going to dole these out each day?*

When the transfusion was complete, we headed back to the hotel to rest and start the new medications. Rog got comfortable on the couch with his remote in hand and I soon followed with a cup full of medications and a glass of juice. He looked at the cup and said, "You're joking, right?"

I looked at him and sadly said, "No, get used to it, babe. I am so sorry." After a while Roger started coughing as if something was stuck in his throat. He stood up and coughed for a while. His face was red as a beet and his skin was shiny all of a sudden. I didn't say anything, I just let him catch his breath. He sat back down, complaining that his chest felt tight as he continued to cough. I gave him an Ativan to help calm him down. I wasn't sure what had happened, it was like he had choked on his own saliva. After about 30 minutes, he settled down and I went back into the kitchen to prepare his dinner. His request was homemade tacos. At this point I made him whatever he wanted.

As I cooked, the room started to smell like spray paint. The hotel workers were remodeling the unit right behind us. Unfortunately, the air duct system to that room was connected to the vent in our bathroom. Before we knew it, the room was so heavy with paint fumes we had to move outside. I called and complained to management, and soon the fumes dissipated and we were able to return to the room. Roger was not doing so well. His breathing seemed more labored and his face was still deep red and shiny. I asked him if he was okay and he began to cry. He just sobbed, and through his tears he kept apologizing for everything – his cancer, the small room, the crazy early/late schedules, taking me away from the ranch, and on and on. He caressed my face, pulled me in tight to his chest, and just held me and cried. I felt a wave of emotions consume me. I too began to sob quietly with him as we held each other tight. I had been pushing this feeling down deep every day for so long. We cried together in each other's arms for what seemed like forever. After he let go, I reached up and kissed his cheeks and his eyes until he stopped crying and his breathing returned to normal. I reminded him that this too shall pass and before we knew it, we would be back at the ranch living out our dream.

We were only a couple days in and there was still such a long way to go. I began to pray for strength. He had finally broken down and I could see the fear and worry in his eyes. As I watched him rest, I realized that it would be up to me to keep this boat afloat. I was going to have to be stronger than I had ever been. I couldn't let him see me falter. I couldn't have him worrying about me. He had always been the rock in our lives – now it was my turn. This was going to be the hardest thing I had ever done. Being a nurse for so many years, I had learned to keep my emotions in check, but this was different – I loved him. He was my husband, not my patient. I didn't get to go home, rest and return to work the next day. This was my new life. I had to be alert 24/7, and pay attention to every detail. No more wine at night to relax with, no more medications that could alter my thinking or prevent me from being able to drive to the hospital at any hour of the night. These thoughts took me back to the time I had the babies; up all night, no rest because they needed me. I did it then, I could do it again – for the love of my life!

Roger couldn't eat the tacos, he could only keep down a couple of crackers, which helped his stomach handle the cup of medications that were dissolving inside of him. He spent most of the night on the toilet with the trash can in his lap. His stool was so pungent that it was more toxic smelling than the paint fumes. His nausea worked itself into dry heaves that continued all night. He said, "My stomach and intestines are on fire and it feels like I'm crapping acid!" He just moaned, all doubled over, sweating profusely. I gave him some Compazine and Imodium and prayed he kept it down. At one point he made it back to bed, but it didn't last long. Soon he was crawling back to the toilet. Stool was everywhere, all over him, the carpet, and the bedroom. He cried as I cleaned it up. I closed the bathroom door so he couldn't watch me. He was so humiliated and embarrassed, apologizing over and over again. I put him in the shower and washed him while he sobbed. I soaped up my hands and slowly caressed his body, washing away all the mess. I massaged his back and legs and loved him gently while he stood under the warm water and calmed down. I tucked him back in bed and was thankful the Compazine and Imodium were starting to work. His nausea subsided, and the yellow acid pungent stool had stopped flowing. I returned to the bathroom and washed it all down with bleach then took the pile of linens and put them outside our door in a garbage bag with a sign on it that said, "Really soiled linens, be careful." I was on autopilot. It was as if I had done this many times, or maybe it was the 30 years of nursing that slammed into gear and took over. I was outside my body, my mind blank, just going through the motions.

The calm before the storm. The calm before the storm? Was this what Karen was talking about? Between the third and fourth days, all hell breaks loose. Hell came out of his body and it stunk! My hands, even with the bleach and gloves, smelled like his stool. I couldn't get it off! I washed and washed, but it was still there. I laid in bed exhausted, but I couldn't sleep. Roger rested his hand on my stomach as he slept. I stared at the ceiling and the clock as it ticked on. I watched the sun rise, got up, made me a cup of coffee, drank it fast, and had a refill before Roger woke up.

I hated to wake him at 6:00 a.m. He was so weak he could hardly sit up. I used all my strength to pull him up to a sitting position and slowly dressed him for the day. He had one more day of chemo then tomorrow he had a day of rest. He slowly swallowed the pills. I slipped two pain pills in this time. After 45 minutes, we were in the car and headed to the hospital. When we arrived he said, "I am feeling a little better, and my stomach and bottom don't hurt."

I smiled at him, took his hand in mine, and kissed it. "I am so thankful, so thankful," was all I said.

The last chemo session at the clinic was uneventful. Roger slept through it all. His skin color was so ruddy and his body was bloated. His skin looked shiny and tight, like a stuffed sausage. He looked like he had gained ten pounds, all in his face. The nurses didn't seem to take notice, and when I asked questions they said, "This is part of the process, he's doing good." I explained last night's episode and was given a hug and told it was going to get worse before it got better. "It's the calm before the storm."

Roger was able to eat a cup of soup for dinner with some crackers, which helped with the medications burning up his stomach. Not long after, he was back in the bathroom, repeating the same story from last night. I repeated everything again as he rested. I kept the curtains drawn all the next day, keeping the room in darkness. It was his day of rest and I made sure it was all he did. I spent the day researching and reading up on all the medications and side effects. Between the chemo and the drugs, Roger's body was being eaten alive. Everything inside of it was dying – the good, the bad, and the ugly. It made me feel sick inside.

PART THREE

1

Transplant, the Storm

Day zero had arrived, May 6, 2014. First stop, total body radiation then donor cell transplant. It was hard to believe that we'd made it. This transplant was going to save his life, and from this day forward, it was all downhill. A part of me was scared but a part of me was relieved and so excited for him. Soon life would return to normal. We would go home and pick up where we left off, before the air was stripped from our lungs. He'd made it, and I was so proud of him! Not one complaint, not one *poor me.* Tears only shed for me. He was a remarkable man!

Rog was feeling a little better after sleeping 36 hours, and was able to make the long walk through the hospital to all the departments waiting for him. The radiation department was in another building, and when we walked through the inviting, pretty, double glass doors, we were greeted by the eyes of every kind of cancer, waiting their turn to be radiated. Some were laughing with family members and some were just staring out the windows at the beautiful river. No expressions, just staring. When it was Roger's turn, we looked at each other and said, "Here goes," and followed the tech who was talking nonstop about the weather, the new building, what to expect, instructions on changing his clothes, etc. We just followed him hand-in-hand, saying nothing in return, just walking The Green Mile.

The total body radiation room was huge! There was a gigantic machine suspended from the ceiling which traveled effortlessly along a track. The bigger the person, the farther away the machine was set. Against the wall, about 25 feet in front of the machine, was a wooden platform with an 8'x3' piece of 2" thick plexiglass standing erect on top of it. Attached to the edges were large screws that at some point I assumed would screw into another plate of plexiglass. Roger was asked to perform a trial run. They instructed him to stand with his back to the plate and face the machine. The techs walked him through the procedure and when there was a verbal understanding, I was asked to step out. Roger stood there and before I could get out of the room, he started to panic. His claustrophobia had set in so I turned around and reentered the room. I walked up to him, took his hand, and asked the technician to show Roger how the plates looked after they were screwed together, leaving the patient sandwiched in between. Both pieces of plexiglass were clear,

34

so Roger could see everything. They used a staff member to demonstrate. Roger walked around the contraption and said, "So I can get out pretty quick if I need to?" He was told yes, but was firmly told not to. During the radiation, he would be standing between the clear plexiglass for approximately 30 minutes. I had a bottle of Ativan with me so I put 2 mgs under his tongue and asked for a ten minute delay. They did as I asked and spent that ten minutes on paperwork and adjusting the huge machine. The radio was softly playing rock and roll, and the lights in the room were dim, kind of a very pleasing, yellow glow.

The pills started working and Roger began to relax. I was asked to leave the room for safety purposes so I walked into the dressing room and stood there. I put my head in my hands and began to cry. It came over me so fast and so hard, as if I had never cried before in my life. I couldn't stop! I was sick inside, knowing what was happening to him. It was so scary. Beams of radiation were penetrating his body; eyes, brain, heart, scrotum and every other part of his body.

This was the beginning of two paths. The first path, he gets the cells which take up shop in his bone marrow and rebuild his body. We go home and live happily ever after. The second path, he gets the cells, his body rejects them, and he spends the rest of his short life being eaten alive by his own immune system. I was going to be sick. Either way, there was no turning back. I dropped my bags and purse then dropped to all fours, crying so hard I had trouble catching my breath. After a few minutes, a woman peeked her head around the corner of the row of dressing lockers and asked if I was okay. She was in a hospital gown, waiting her turn. She knelt down and hugged me, then sat next to me and told me her story.

I told her my story and we hugged. From behind us we heard her name called; it was her turn and she left.

After a few minutes, Roger appeared in front of me, looking exhausted. I jumped up, wiped my eyes and grabbed him. I hugged him so hard and he hugged me right back. He pulled my chin up and said, "Let's go get some cells. And the Ativan is kicking my butt!" We both laughed and left the building. This was it – the moment we had been waiting for. We were told to go to admitting, sign in, and a bed was waiting for us up on the leukemia floor. Roger would have the rest of the day to just rest and enjoy the Ativan. We arrived at admitting to find that there were no beds. We were told that it was a waiting game now. When someone was discharged, we would get that bed. I said, "Oh no, he just had total body radiation. He went through four days of chemotherapy. He needs a bed now! He is having a bone marrow transplant, and has a bag of donor cells waiting for him. What do you mean there are no beds?" The man looked at me, made a phone call, and said a room was being cleaned so we should just sit and we would be called momentarily.

The admitting lobby was in an area of the hospital where the doors were opening and closing continuously, the public and staff making their way to the snack bar, coffee shops and gift shop all in the same area. It was so busy that many times one had to squeeze through the crowd to continue on their journey through the hospital. It also had a lounge with a huge fireplace large enough to be in a ski lodge at an upscale resort. There we were, sitting amongst society with them coughing, sneezing and breathing all over us! Roger with no immune system, smelling like burnt skin as if he'd just spent the day in a tanning booth, sat trying desperately to stay awake. So pale and slumped over in his chair with a mask on, he finally gave in to his weakened body. I was livid! I kept asking, "How much longer?" Finally, the admitting clerk told me that the person that was scheduled to leave was not leaving after all. Roger might need to go to another floor. In a low firm voice, I said, "I don't care what floor he is admitted to, just admit him and get him out of this lobby NOW!" He said okay and left his desk, never to return.

At one point our doctor, who we hadn't seen since he handed Roger a pen and the clinical study consent form to sign, walked past us. He looked at us and made eye contact but just kept walking. He never said, *Hi, how are you? Why are you sitting in the lobby hallway like this?* Nothing. He just turned his head and acted as if he never saw us. It was at this moment I realized we were just a number. Roger was just another number, a very large number that came in the form of dollar signs since cancer research brings in 160 billion dollars a year. Roger signed that paper, the clinical study document, and upon doing so, the government gave the hospital another installment of cash to continue the research. This was a research hospital. No patients, no money. His doctor got the signature so pleasantries were no longer necessary; now they were just an inconvenience. So, he walked faster down the hall to avoid simple human kindness and compassion. I wanted to cry. Actually, I wanted to stab him!

From that moment forward, he knew how I felt. I didn't care about what I said to him or how I said it. In the clinic the first day we met, I asked him why he chose this field. He hesitated for a moment, shifted in his chair then told me he chose the field of cancer because he was diagnosis with testicular cancer when he was younger and that had given him the drive to work in the field of cancer research. When he told me the story, it was as if he was searching for the right answer and this was it. Something didn't feel right. I asked, "Are you sure it wasn't for the money?"

The doctor shifted in his chair again, hesitated then said "No." We locked eyes for a brief moment before he changed the subject. There was something robotic about this man and it was just not right, but I couldn't put my finger on it until that moment. It all made sense to me now. What might have been a desire to learn about his type of cancer very well could have been why he chose this field at one point in his life, but now it was about the money. As time went on, this became more clear to me, or at least it was how he presented himself to me.

Finally, after four hours in that busy lobby, we heard our name called. A bed was available for Roger. It wasn't on the leukemia floor but one floor down on another cancer floor. I didn't care at this point, I was just glad to finally get a bed for Roger to lie down in. He was both excited and nervous. The adrenaline had kicked in and he was awake and alert. This was the day we had been waiting for, the day to receive the cure to his disease! We were being as positive as possible. We held hands and smiled and laughed, and all the memories of the past few nights were gone.

Then the nurse came in and said that the bed debacle had caused a backup. The transplant would be tomorrow instead of today. Roger went off! The Prednisone and the exhaustion were speaking, "Call the doctor now! I am getting this transplant today! It is not my fault I am on this floor. Bring the nurses down here that know what they're doing. If you don't, crap is going to hit the fan!" I sat quietly and let him go. She left the room and within minutes, a doctor was in our room apologizing. He agreed to proceed with the transfusion, and the tension in the room returned to normal. The nurse that had received Roger's verbal lashing returned with all kinds of equipment, IV poles, blood pressure machines, a portable computer station and a bag of beautiful, tiny donor cells.

She prepared everything then left the room for a minute. There were all kinds of writing on the bag of donor cells. I went over to see if I could find out anything about the donor, but all I could decipher was that the cells came from southern California. A nurse practitioner from the clinic came in so I asked about the donor. She said, "What I can tell you is that he is in his 20s, he is the same size as Roger, and has the same blood type. In one year, if you want, you can meet him if he wants to meet you. Also, he donated so many cells that you have a backup supply if you should ever need another transfusion. There are over 300,000 cells available to you if you need them. This is very unusual so you are very lucky! In this small bag are 846,000 cells and you get them all!"

We were like, "WOW!" She smiled.

Once again, we were left alone for a few minutes. I said, "Nice young blood you're gettin' there. I better watch out!"

Roger grinned, raised his eyebrows and said, "Darn straight!" We both chuckled.

The transfusion began, and for about 20 minutes the doctor stayed in the room as a precaution. He informed us that if anything was going to go wrong, it would be in the first 15 minutes. We didn't ask what "wrong" meant, we didn't want any bad juju or energy in the room. We made small talk, and Roger apologized for his behavior. All was perfect. Soon the doctor and nurse left the room and only popped in every so often to check on Roger and take his blood pressure. Roger slept and I watched him. After an hour, I noticed red blotches occurring on his face and neck. It was hives! I woke him and asked him how he felt. He said fine. I brought the bedside table over to him and raised the little mirror inside of it so Roger could see his face. He asked, "What is this?" I told him they were hives and that I needed to call the nurse. He grabbed my wrist and said, "No, they won't give me all my cells, they will stop the transfusion. I can deal with it, Robin, I don't feel anything, I'm fine!" I pulled my wrist back, said okay, and sat back down. After a few minutes, I checked his stomach. He was slowly being consumed by the hives. I called the nurse and he was mad! She came in and looked at him, told him it looked like he needed some Benadryl, and gave him 50 mg of Benadryl via IV. 15 minutes later the hives were disappearing and the transfusion was complete. We cried, we laughed, we kissed, we hugged and we laughed some more.

I asked the nurse what to expect now. She looked at Roger and said very matter-of-factly, "Roger, you will begin to feel the effects of everything you went through today, around the +6th day, and by the +8th day, you are going to be really sick. The type of radiation you just had will be what you suffer from most. Some people do better than others. Let's just wait and see, but it is better to be prepared and for you to know that the cells are going to do their thing no matter what. You will be seen every day in the clinic, and they will be watching you very closely." They monitored Roger for four more hours then sent him home.

That night I made Roger a nice lentil soup, rubbed his feet, and we talked and talked about the future, my mother, the kids, and Max, our cat. It was sad that the rule of "no pets" was in place. You would think that an animal would help the patient recover faster as they have shown they do in the nursing homes, but the germs they carry, Roger couldn't fight so Max would stay with Betty until we were cleared. We couldn't wait!

Once again, Roger was up all night in the bathroom. That night it wasn't about the diarrhea, it was about urinating. All night long. When we got up in the morning, he weighed himself and he was down six pounds. That's a lot of urine! He didn't complain but was grateful that it wasn't the acid stool that had kept him up the previous nights.

At 7:00 a.m. we headed to the hospital to begin the daily health checks. I had hoped the nurses would greet him with, "Congratulations, you did it! You got your cells! Yayyyyy!" Maybe even a cookie or cupcake, but no, it was business as usual. I was so disappointed.

That morning, Roger's magnesium levels were very low so he settled in for a four to five hour replacement infusion. As soon as Rog reclined in the chair, he was asleep. I had started to unpack my beads when the social worker approached me and said there was a caregiver meeting that she would like me to attend. I agreed, kissed Roger, and quietly told him I would be back. He mumbled I love you and was out again.

The meeting was on the opposite end of The Green Mile, adjacent to the waiting room. I took a seat and we waited to see if any other caregivers were going to join us. One lady did, which made just two of us in the meeting. We were asked to introduce ourselves to each other and give a quick synopsis of our journey to this date. She asked me to start so I explained Roger's diagnosis, where we were living, and that he had received his new cells yesterday. Cheers and a few claps made me feel a little better. I wished Roger could have heard the cheers. I thanked them and continued. I expressed my agitation at all the unknowns and the uneasiness I felt with each new symptom; hot flashes, nausea, acid diarrhea, no appetite, lack of fluid intake, extreme exhaustion, ruddy skin color, and sensitive skin. I explained that all I was being told was that it was part of the process, the calm before the storm. I expressed my anger toward Roger's doctor for passing us by in the lobby without any compassion or care while Roger suffered. After expressing this feeling, I looked at the social worker and ended with, "I keep asking you people what is happening to Roger's body and all I get is, *It's the calm before the storm.* There are over 30 patients a day sitting in those chairs out there. You are all quite aware of all these symptoms I am telling you about. Why couldn't you have prepared us better instead of creating all this worry? You don't seem surprised by any of this, but I am. I want to know what to expect next. He just had his transfusion, so what's next?"

It was flowing out of me big time, and it wasn't pretty. When I had gotten up that morning I was so happy, but they asked me to open up, and now I was mad again. When I finally finished, I realized I had their attention, jaws were dropped, faces were blank, and they were short on words. I went silent and so was the room for about 30 seconds. In that 30 seconds, my ranting slowly started to feel really bad and I wanted to run out of the room. I had just thrown both the doctor and his nurse under the bus. I knew darn well that this conversation was not going to be kept a secret. The social worker was not a lawyer or a priest, and this conversation was not confidential. *Oh no! What did I just do?* I collected my thoughts very quickly and slumped over and said, "I am so sorry, I think I have hit the anger stage and I needed to take it out on someone." I was feeling sick inside and the tears started.

They rushed over to me and said, "It's okay, this is normal. You will go through many more emotions, and anger is one of them." Part of me felt a little better.

The social worker looked at the other caretaker, and asked her to tell me her story. Kathy's partner of ten plus years had been diagnosed with cancer four years prior. She had gone through several rounds of chemotherapy over the years but continued to live life to its fullest. She swam in the public pool, the river and the nearby lake, all of which were no no's. She continued to go to parties with friends and socialized every chance she got. Many of these social events she didn't invite Kathy to join her because Kathy continuously reminded her of her cancer. After these escapades, it was Kathy that had to take her back and forth to the hospital to be treated for infections. She was watching her partner die just a little bit more each time.

Kathy's parents took ill about two years ago and eventually passed away. She was so fearful of leaving her partner alone that she didn't visit her parents or even attend the funerals due to fear that her partner might need her. She expressed her anger and guilt and how she was suppressing and hiding her feelings so her partner didn't feel bad. She wanted to run away but was in love, so she stayed and "take my partner's selfishness."

I thought about those words, "my partner's selfishness." I immediately thought, *Well, she doesn't have a long life ahead of her. She could die at any moment so she lives as if it is her last day. Hurray for her!* Then I looked at Kathy and saw the pain in her eyes. This was such a double-edged sword. Could I just leave Roger in the middle of all of this? Could I say, *Fine, have it your way, but I am not going to sit and watch you kill yourself faster?* No, I couldn't. My heart hurt for her.

The social worker looked at me and said, "Kathy has been in this room over a hundred times. It doesn't get easier," and with that, the meeting was over. I hugged Kathy and left. Again, my questions weren't answered, just evaded. I felt awful and told myself I would never do that again.

When I returned to the infusion room, I found Roger awake and alert. He asked me how the meeting went, and I told him it was great, really informative. He smiled and continued watching the soccer game on TV. I decided to call the kids and check on home. Two hours later, all the kids were informed of Roger's progress and a big "I love you" was sent back to Rog from each of them.

When we got back to the hotel, I prepared little snacks for Roger as he rested after his long day at the clinic. I put out five bowls of healthy tidbits for him to choose from so whatever mood he was in, he had something to eat; dark chocolate, fruit, crackers and nuts, all prepackaged from the health food store. A little sweet and a little salty, and several drink ideas as well. He nibbled a little and was able to get some broth down.

It wasn't long after we went to bed, the acid stools returned with a vengeance. He was in so much pain. I asked if I could draw him a bath to let his extremely sore rectal area soak. He said, "Oh, so I can crap in the tub? You want to clean that up too?" I gave him some pain pills and helped him back and forth to the toilet throughout the night.

The next two days were more of the same, and he was getting weaker and weaker. At the clinic, I was told to make him walk whether he wanted to or not. Walking was the key to building his strength back up. All we had was the hotel parking lot to use as a walking track, but the laps around the hotel were getting shorter and shorter. Rog had a hard time breathing during the walks so we walked in silence. During one painful trip around the parking lot, a squirrel ran up to Rog and stood right at his feet. It put its little paws on Roger's pant leg and looked up at him. The two looked at each other for a long time, as if it was giving Rog comfort.

Day +4

All hell broke loose. We had been at the clinic since 7:00 a.m. Roger was so weak, with a flat affect. No emotions. We were extremely exhausted from the restless nights up and down to the bathroom. I didn't bother him with questions, I just let him be. When we finally made it back to the hotel, Rog headed straight for bed, clothes on, and went to sleep. I had to wake him to drink watered-down broth, hoping to get some nourishment in. He wasn't eating or drinking. Today the nurse practitioner explained to me that Roger's intestines weren't absorbing much of anything right now, so I should do my best to get in at least two liters of fluids. From all the diarrhea, he was borderline dehydrated so they gave him extra IV fluids. I was so thankful!

Every movement was now a struggle. He walked bent over and shuffled tiny little steps back and forth to the bathroom. He was so pale and had started losing his hair. His mouth was sore and blistered, and his rectum was inflamed. Pain pills were now the most important pill.

Roger didn't look good at the clinic earlier, but no one seemed concerned. As he rested, I took his temperature, 98.2, so all was good. I finally snuggled up to him in bed and fell asleep fast and hard. At 4:30 p.m., the phone rang. If it hadn't woken us, I'm sure we would have slept right through the night. It was one of Roger's buddies, checking on him. I said my pleasantries and told him we would call back tomorrow. I turned to Roger, who was still asleep, and he was on fire! I woke him and took his temp, 101.7. We panicked! The protocol states, call the Bone Marrow Team (BMT) if:

1. Any temp is greater than 100.4
2. Nausea/vomiting are unresponsive to anti-nausea medications
3. Significant diarrhea despite Imodium
4. Inability to drink at least two liters of fluid a day
5. You develop a rash
6. Bleeding

Roger had experienced numbers 2, 3 and 4, but each time I voiced my concerns at the clinic and after his bloodwork was examined, the doctors didn't seem concerned. The one thing that did get their attention was a temperature. I called the clinic and they said get to the hospital ASAP. I got him up, dressed him and we rushed to the ER. I assumed they would have called and told the ER docs that one of their transplant patients was on his way, but that didn't happen. When we arrived, the ER was packed. I put Roger in a wheelchair, with his mask and gloves on, and I did the same. We had been wearing masks and gloves everywhere we went since his initial diagnosis. It was a necessary precaution. Yes, people stare, and a lot of the time I explained to them that we were protecting ourselves from them, not them from us. Most understood.

We sat for an hour in that full ER lobby before we were finally called back. I was so worried. Roger's temp had risen to 102.9, and he was so weak and slumped over in the chair. He didn't talk, he just sat there with his eyes closed. I could feel my throat tighten and my heart racing. I was panicking and felt like I was going to explode! People were everywhere, all around us, and he was being exposed to coughing, hacking and germs. I did all I could not to blow up with emotion!

Finally, the ball started rolling. Two doctors put Roger in a room and asked me a hundred questions. His permanent IV became the most popular thing in the room. Eleven vials of blood were being drawn from it, and his IV dressing was being checked thoroughly for infection. One doctor wanted to pull the IV, stating that nine times out of ten it was the IV that was causing the infection. Roger sat up, looking three feet taller, and in a very firm but haggard voice said, "NO, you perform all the other tests first. No one is taking this out of me before you get proof it's causing the problem." They rolled him over on his side, swabbed his rectal area, and gave him a Tylenol while the tests were being run, so his temp started falling. I was so happy, but still concerned. The hallway outside the room was bustling with people in wheelchairs, and a couple people were laying on gurneys in the overcrowded hallways. Sick patients were traveling in and out of ER rooms. Every person that came into our room, I kindly asked to put on mask and gloves. Each time I was told that he was not infectious, and I said, "Yes, but you are." Finally, a nursing assistant put a sign on the door that said **Droplet Precautions**, and shut the door to the outside world. I felt like I could breathe again. Roger slept; there was no energy for anything else. One of the doctors from the BMT clinic finally responded to the ER doctor's calls and told them to admit him. The cancer and leukemia floors were full so we were going somewhere else. I didn't care, I just wanted to get him out of that ER. Finally, he was admitted to another floor.

It was late when we arrived at the new room. The room was soaking wet – literally! The housekeeper must have just left. There was standing water on the floor, the bedside table, and the plastic that protected the mattress. Roger sat patiently, slumped in the wheelchair while the ER escort and I mopped up the room with a huge pile of washcloths we found on a cart in the hallway. Near midnight, the floor was dark and deserted. I assumed it was just protocol to lower the lights at night just as they do on all the floors, but I didn't see any staff, which was a strange feeling. We found the linen room and made the bed as Roger watched patiently. Every so often he put in his requests, "Don't tuck the covers in at the end of the bed, and can you get me a bed extender please?" At 6'7", Roger's poor feet stuck out a foot beyond the beds without an extender.

The escort didn't know what he was talking about, so I chimed in and said, "I will find you one as soon as I can, no worries." We got Rog to bed and all settled in then we waited.

After about 45 minutes, a tiny spitfire of a nurse came into the room, all smiles. She introduced herself and I asked her kindly if she could please wear a mask. She leaned over and looked me in the eye, and said slowly and sarcastically, "While I wait for the doctor's orders, I am going to get your vital signs."

Wow! *Okay*, I thought. *Roger comes first, don't cause any ruckus, Robin.* I asked, "What type of patients are treated on this floor?"

She said, "Neuroscience," and turned her back to me as she started booting up the bedside computer. I asked if there were patients with active infections on the floor. She turned and looked at me with a look that surprised me. She leaned in my direction again without moving her feet and said, "Yes, we have infectious patients on this floor. We have traumas, head injuries, brain cancers. We are a step down from your *BMT* floors." I contemplated that for a split second when she continued, "On *THIS* floor we do vitals every four hours, and at 12:00 a.m. and 4:00 a.m. we do our blood draws. After we do that, we hang your IV bags full of medications that the *DOCTORS* order."

Roger must have sensed my jets starting to boil as this nurse tried to intimidate me with her mockery. He squeezed my hand, and when she turned around to face the computer again he looked at me and raised his eyebrows with a mischievous grin. I hadn't seen that grin in so long – it was priceless. It was a grin that meant, *Go for it, it's all yours to play with*. I had really messed up with the social worker; I was on a foreign floor, it was late, and Roger was sick so I kept my cool.

The nurse began taking Roger's vital signs, but I was only interested in his temperature. She took the thermometer out of the machine, placed a plastic cap on it, and within a split second she shot the plastic cap into the garbage and placed it back in the machine. If I wasn't mistaken or blind, I hadn't seen her put the thermometer in his mouth. She began diligently putting a number in the computer.

I said, "What was the temp?" Was I missing something?

She said, "It's good."

I looked at Roger who was looking at her. He said, "You didn't take it, what do you mean it's good?"

She said, "Yes I did, under your arm, its 97.1."

I said, "Can you please take it under his tongue? He had a Tylenol earlier and it's important to take it the same way please." She blew out air from between pursed lips, making a rumbling noise like babies do. She was making it clear that we were causing her grief. She did as we asked, and it was 100.1. In our world that is a trip to the ER! This changed her little protocol. Now his temp needed to be taken on the hour, every hour, for four hours. It was clear that this didn't make her happy. I didn't care. Within an hour it was back up to 102.7 and she was *really* not happy! I assumed she didn't feel like working that night.

Before she left the room again, I asked her about the blood cultures that were taken in the ER. She said, "They take five days for results."

I said very cautiously, "I thought that maybe being a huge research hospital, there might be a testing method that gives results quicker than five days."

She said, "Nope."

I said, "You're kidding, right?" How could they wait five days for results when every minute of a transplant patient's life is on the line?

She laughed at me, leaned in again, and said slowly and sarcastically in her native accent, "NOOOO, THEY GROW IT FOR ONE DAYYYY AND LOOK AT IT. THEN THEY GROW IT FOR TWO DAYYYYYYS AND LOOK AT IT, AND THEN THEY GROW IT FOR THREE DAYYYYYYYS AND LOOK AT IT. At five days they treat you if you need it. Get it?"

I about lost it! My control was now out of this world! I was on the edge of throwing her out the window and watching her splat on the ground below – with pleasure! What the heck was happening here? Where did she come from and what was her problem? I looked at her and said in a very calm, respectful voice, "Yes, I get it, I just thought maybe *this* hospital's laboratory was a little more advanced."

She looked at me, ignored the statement and said, "Only one person can stay in the room." She turned her back to me and addressed Roger only, "It's your choice who stays so if you don't want someone here, we will ask them to leave if you like."

Roger looked at me, I raised my eyebrows and then glared at the back of her head. He looked at her, chuckled and said, "I would like to see you try that."

The little monster fired back with, "I will just call security!" That was it! I stood up and busted out laughing as I looked down at her. I laughed so hard tears were forming. Roger busted out laughing too. I don't know where he got the energy, but he was laughing. She stood there shocked, glared at me, and walked out, leaving the door open just a bit. I knew she was out there.

I said, "What was that? We must have really upset her night, making her work for her money. That nurse, she's in it for the money, no bedside manner. She works night shift for a reason! She would never make it one day on day shift. They would chew her up and spit her out, and she knows it!" We didn't see her for hours. Instead, she sent the nurse's aide in to take his vital signs who, by the way, was a doll. But that nurse was the least of my worries. Another Tylenol and a pair of pajamas, and Roger was out.

In the ER, no chem panel was drawn and no chem panel was drawn at the clinic that morning either. This type of blood panel gives an overall picture of what's going on in the body; electrolytes, white blood cell count, kidney function, liver function, etc. Up to 25 different blood elements are checked. The on-call BMT doctor who was monitoring Roger via the phone through the ER doctors ordered one, and about an hour later, Roger had potassium, calcium and magnesium dripping into his veins. His levels were so low that if we hadn't gone to the ER, if we hadn't gotten that phone call to wake us up, Roger might have died in his sleep. I was so thankful to Roger's friend at that moment! With that possible disaster averted, it was now the temperature that was the huge problem. It was not staying down. Every four hours another Tylenol was administered. The temp would drop to 100.1 only to rise again as the Tylenol wore off.

The ER doctor came up to see Rog. He said, "The BMT doctor said there is nothing to worry about. All is okay. If anything bad is going to happen, it will around the +7, +8 day when Roger becomes neutropenic." Neutrophils are cells in your immune system that attack bacteria and other organisms when they invade your body. They are made in the bone marrow, and with the bone marrow being killed off with the radiation and chemotherapy, it is inevitable that neutropenia, a low count, is going to happen. At that time, it will show up on the blood panel at +7 - +8 days post-transplant. So, at only +4 days post-transplant, the doctor didn't seem concerned. But what if Roger was an exception to the rule? What if his body was different? As I saw it, something did go bad. He could have died! I hate it when doctors put patients all in the same box. Many patients get overlooked until they are in a crisis. I hoped this wouldn't happen to Rog. He was resting, and this made me happy.

I decided to rest too. It was going to be another long night. Fortunately, the hospital rooms come with a nice little couch that makes out into a bed. I found the linen cupboard and proceeded to make up my bed. I kissed Roger's forehead and snuggled into my little couch bed.

It didn't take long after I settled in for a nap for the door to open and in walked the little monster, just a ray of sunshine. She turned on all the lights and talked in a voice that could be heard down the hall. She proceeded to answer all her calls coming from her walky-talky phone that all the nurses now carry. She could care less what time it was or how exhausted we were. I pretended to sleep and tried my best to just ignore her until she said, "I need you to go get a CellCept from your car. Roger needs one and our pharmacy is closed."

I sat up and said "What? Your pharmacy is closed?"

She said, "Yep." To get to the car required leaving a locked building, walking about a block away to the parking garage, and returning through the ER which was in an entirely different area than where we were. I was livid, and she could tell I was not happy. She said, "Sorry about that, but we don't carry CellCept on this floor" and smiled at me sarcastically. I really wanted to throw her out the window! Boy, was I going to turn in a complaint in the morning! Like all transplant patients, having your meds with you at all times was necessary and she knew it. I dressed and left.

Upon my return, Roger said she started asking him all kinds of questions; where we lived, how many kids we had, what we did for a living. Roger told her I was an end-stage cardiac nurse. She never looked me in the eye again, but she was still as mean as a rabid raccoon. I just ignored her, knowing she would be gone soon.

Who Is In Charge?

It was day +5, and Mother's Day. I laid in my little bed and watched Roger sleep. It had been about an hour since the little spitfire finished her shift and I was grateful. I think it was the only hour the door hadn't opened since we arrived, but I knew the day shift nurse would be in shortly. Roger woke with a start and was shivering. His temp must be up again. He just moaned and said good morning. I crawled into bed with him and let my body warm him up. He was hot, but I didn't care. Before too long, he stopped shivering and fell back to sleep. The new nurse brought him his pills, took vital signs, and confirmed the temp was on the rise again, 102.9. Another Tylenol down the hatch.

Within the hour we got the news that we are being transferred up to the leukemia floor since a bed had opened up. Good riddance to this floor! I called the Moms and wished them a Happy Mother's Day and caught them up on Roger's condition. Roger's mom was warm, kind and caring, and sent Roger much love. I was glad I called her because she made me feel better. My children called to wish me Happy Mom's Day and told me how much they loved me. It made me happy and sad at the same time. I wished we were at home, enjoying a barbecue on Mom's Day.

We were transferred to room 23 on the leukemia floor. The nursing staff on this and the other cancer floor are angels, almost literally.

The first preliminary results on the blood cultures came back and at two days, no growth had occurred. No bacteria were showing up that might be causing the high temperatures. Once again, the doctors were contemplating removing the permanent PICC IV line in Rog's arm, and once again, Roger fought to keep it in. The rest of the bloodwork showed that Roger's own blood supply was dropping fast. His white blood cells were dying off at an alarming rate thanks to the chemotherapy and radiation. We were told protocol shows that his new donor cells should be taking over, but at this rate it might be sooner. I continued to pray that this transplant and Roger himself would be the new poster child for the clinical study he signed up for and that nothing bad would happen. He would be the one that turned *None* into *One*.

Even though the tests were not showing a reason for the infection, antibiotics were started anyway. Roger slept most of the day and he wasn't talking much anymore. He had no energy and when people came into the room, he counted on me to do his talking. I sat and watched him sleep for hours on end. I was getting more tired by the day and feeling lonelier than ever. I missed Max, my go-to friend when I was feeling down, so much. I would hold him and kiss him and squish him. For some reason, I always felt better. Now I had nothing to make me feel better.

Roger continued to sleep as the antibiotics transfused so I took a shower. Afterward, I walked a couple laps around the floor and found all the fresh brewed coffeepot spots for future reference. I had some food with me – nuts, a few breakfast bars and some fresh fruit, but I was going to need a new supply soon. I noticed that my pants were getting pretty loose and I'd had to put another hole in my belt that morning.

Roger no longer wanted food. His temp was up to 102 again, and another set of blood cultures were done. He was getting weaker and the soreness in his mouth was at an all-time high. The back of his throat was red and raw, and even drinking water was difficult. His eyes were slightly yellow but mostly bloodshot and glassy. He was taking pain pills every three hours because of stomach pain, so he was now taking 32 pills a day. How can anyone's stomach handle that? Skin cells were just falling off him, his facial color was ruddy, and the rest of his body was purple like a beet. Every hair follicle had a dark, purplish dot around it; he was covered in dots. His personality came in spurts. If he got angry about something he perked up, spoke his peace using up all his stored energy, then returned to sleep. When he woke up, he asked me what was going on then went back to sleep. When I asked him how he was feeling, he said okay most of the time, although occasionally he said, "Crappy." I wished we were back at the ranch on a big blanket with a picnic spread out before us, and a couple of cold drinks to finish it off perfectly. Just to feel the warm sun on my body would be the greatest gift.

While I was daydreaming, Roger woke with a start. He was having pain in his lower abdomen and he wanted to get up now! I repositioned the IV pole so he could get to the bathroom, and as he slowly got up, I could hear every bone in his body creak. He was sweaty, greasy and stunk. I asked if he would like a shower and he agreed. I asked the nurses if he could, and they were shocked but said, "Sure, just cover the IV with the plastic. You know the drill."

His rush to the bathroom was a disappointment. He stood over the toilet trying to pee for about ten minutes. I had gotten all the toiletries ready and the shower water warming as he stood there trying, but only a teaspoon came out, so after what seemed like a half hour, he gave up.

As I have done many times over this journey, I careful washed his body as he stood towering over me with his hands against the wall for support. He kept his eyes closed as the water flowed from his face to his toes. I was so happy! I was hoping it would make him feel better. His body was so hot to the touch but he said he felt ice cold. When we were done, I tucked him back in bed and that was all he had in him. He spent the night tossing and turning as the pain in his body was debilitating. As I have done every night unless I was exhausted, I studied. I asked all the nurses if anything new was available for research. I got the usual answer, "No, I'm sorry." But I won't give up!

Day +6

Roger's temperature was back up to 102. This was really getting scary! It had become obvious to me that the Tylenol was nothing but a bandage. I hoped the doctors would have some good news when they arrived that morning. I was just not feeling good about all this, and had a bad feeling in my gut. Overnight, Roger's face had swelled up and he was almost unrecognizable. His eyes were so yellow/gray and bloodshot that he said it was easier and less painful to just keep them closed. He still wasn't peeing, saying it was so painful and just a waste of his time to get up and try so he was now using the bedside urinal. The little urine that did come out was dark amber in color. As I stood there with his urinal in my hand, looking at the teaspoon of dark urine in it, my mind began to whirl. His kidneys were shutting down and his liver was in trouble. The symptoms were so obvious, but what didn't make sense was that his *whole* body was dark purple.

At 11:00 a.m., the doctors and the entourage of interns arrived. The first words out of their mouths were, "WOW, you are red. When did this happen?" Before I could answer, one of the BMT doctors threw Roger's covers off him and started looking at his body like a mama ape looking for fleas on her baby.

Another doctor chimed in and said, "Red Man syndrome from the Vancomycin?"

I said, "No, it was present before the Vanco, but it has gotten worse." I showed them the urine and the look of concern was present on all their faces.

The doctor checking his body looked at me and paused, then looked at Roger who was quiet with his eyes closed. She turned on all the lights above him, and pushed and poked his skin. She said, "Roger, we are going to scan your whole body if your temp is not relieved by the end of the antibiotic therapy."

They all sequestered into a little circle, talking while turning pages in his chart back and forth. Medications were being addressed and side effects were being contemplated. At the end of the circle meeting, it was decided to spread the 32 pills out into two-hour increments instead of big batches three times a day. Their diagnosis: CellCept was causing the kidneys to shut down. Instead of four giant CellCept pills all at once three times a day, they decided to spread them out on the hour, giving his kidneys a break.

They turned the lights off and asked Roger to open his eyes. One of the doctors gasped as I started to cry. I put my hands over my mouth and just watched. There was no iris, no pupil, just a pure blood red eyeball. Roger was slow to answer their questions. When asked how he felt, he answered in a slow, slurred voice, "My joints hurt very bad and my mouth is so sore I can't eat. The painful knot in my lower back is back." She asked about his skin, and he said, "My skin doesn't hurt, even though it's falling off. Urinating is like bleeding razor blades, so I would prefer not to pee any longer."

The doctors and interns listened as Roger slurred his words. They just stood there, almost blank, as if they were in shock. Before they left the room, a total body scan was ordered. I asked what was happening and was told, "We don't know yet."

While I had their attention I asked, "I have been a nurse for over 30 years, and I know kidney and liver failure when I see it. Is that what's happening?"

They just stared at me for about ten seconds, looked at each other, then the head doctor said, "We will get a scan and go from there. It's too early to jump the gun." They all promptly left. Was it possible that Roger was rejecting the cells or having an early episode of GVHD? Was that even possible this early? I was getting more scared by the day!

A few minutes later, Roger's nurse came in and explained the scan. It would require him to drink 32 ounces of a Gatorade-type drink and to remain very still throughout the scan. He asked for two Ativan and he was given one. When the nurse left to get the gurney, Roger pointed at me and said, "Get me another Ativan," which I got for him.

Roger had gained ten pounds in just two days, up to 310. He would literally be stuffed in the machine. His adrenaline was pumping now, and I was afraid that using up all his energy was going to be a bad thing. After about 20 minutes, the Ativan was doing its thing and the energy he used up worrying left him in an exhausted state. He went through the scan without a scene, returned to the room, and was out for the night.

Day +7

The preliminary scan report only showed an enlarged gallbladder. The final reading would come the next day. Rog slept most of the day, his temperature remaining between 101-102 degrees. Tylenol and antibiotics were continued around the clock. Every time I asked the nurses for information, they did the best they could, but they too were at a loss. I needed fresh clothes and some food so I kissed him on the forehead and with his eyes closed, he smiled and said, "See you in a bit." I smiled. I headed to the hotel to reload my bags. No sooner had I started down the elevator that bad thoughts raced through my head. *What if he crashes while I was gone? What if he needs me and I'm not there?* I tried very hard to block those worries, telling myself out loud as I drove, "He is going to be okay, Robin, stop this right now!" When I got to the hotel, I gathered everything as fast as I could and headed back.

While I was gone, Roger's blood pressure had dropped to 95/56. They stopped his heart medications and continued to monitor him. He was able to get half a milkshake down, two bottles of Gatorade and a V8, which he liked a lot. I was surprised the acid didn't hurt his mouth, but he said it tasted great! A couple weeks ago he couldn't taste anything. Tonight, V8 tasted "great!" With the help of a nurse, he had gotten to the bathroom and had two bowel movements with no diarrhea. I laid down next to him and listened to him tell me about his three hours without me. I caressed his hair softly and hid from him that it was falling out in my hand. He used to have enough hair for three people, now I could see his scalp. He looked me in the eyes and said, "I think I have hit rock bottom. I should be getting better soon." I smiled. Sadly, he hadn't hit rock bottom and wouldn't for another couple of days.

I watched him sleep while I laid on my little couch bed, reminiscing about my life. I had been nursing since the age of 17, starting out as a nurse's aide in high school. From the age of about six, I knew I wanted to be a nurse. It was in me. Now, here I lay on a little couch in a research hospital, praying for my husband to live. Nothing that I had done or accomplished meant anything to me. Researching and learning everything I could about this disease was all that mattered. Life was so complicated; sometimes I wondered if this wasn't hell.

Day +8

The doctors came in to find Roger full of fluids. His eyelids were so swollen and heavy he could barely see out of them. His hands and ankles were full, his bones weren't visible, and his entire body was full of pain. He was putting out only 15cc of urine, yet the IV fluids were still running. They said Roger's CT scan was normal except for a few benign-looking lumps that they weren't worried about. They explained that his kidneys were full of proteins and shutting down, and his liver was failing. They hesitantly said they *thought* it was the anti-rejection medications causing the kidney and liver failure and that a urologist would be in later to discuss possible scenarios with us. His antibiotic was changed to Meropenem, a wide spectrum drug, and they ordered irrigation to his nasal passages to see if the infection causing the temperature could be found there.

At 3:30 p.m., the urologist arrived, all business with no bedside manner. He explained that Roger had ATN, Acute Traumatic Necrosis of the kidney, most likely caused by the combination of the CT scan contrast he had to drink, the anti-rejection medications, and the IV antibiotic all at once. He said that 90% of the time, by stopping these culprits his kidneys would recover, but if the kidneys continued to slough off, spilling the proteins and potassium, and his creatinine continued to elevate, they would put Roger on dialysis until the medications were adjusted. I was in shock; I didn't know what to say. We both just stared at him. The urologist stared back then said, "This could happen by tomorrow so keep your fingers crossed," and he left. Roger looked at me, closed his eyes, and let out a big breath of air. The IV fluids were stopped. I left the room to take a walk.

I spent the next 30 minutes just walking and praying that the new treatment would work. At the same time, if his kidneys were that close to dialysis, how in the hell could less than one day make a difference? With each step, I prayed and asked for all kinds of help from the universe, from the angels, from the spirit guides, from God. I asked that they surround him in their light and heal his kidneys and keep the new cells safe. I loved him so much! There are only a few of these men – men who are truly everything a woman wants, needs and looks forward to every morning when she wakes up. This big guy protected me without even thinking; it was just instinct to him. I was safe, I was loved, and I loved loving him. "Please give him back to me whole and heal him! Please don't take him away from me!" How much more could he take? I was getting nervous, but mostly I was scared. How could I handle life without him? He must shake this! His body must recover! I needed him!

I stepped into the bathroom and washed my face with cold water, collected myself, and headed back to the room. I was surprised to see that the IV fluids were started again, and he was on the phone with his son. Rog said slowly and methodically, "I just can't catch a break. Every time I turn around, something happens. My neutrophils are so low that I am weak, weak as a kitten now." He was venting for the first time, which made me so happy since I knew he needed to. How could one go through all of this and not vent? I would be complaining all the time, but not Rog, He is a man's man, a true gentleman, never wanting to make me worry, so he hid it. I hate that about him. I understand, but I wish he vented to me more, especially now that his life hung in the balance, teetering between life and death.

At 11:00 p.m., the night nurse came in to take Roger's blood pressure. She asked me if Roger had a problem with his heart rhythm. I told her no, and she left the room. I immediately felt his pulse and realized he was in arterial fibrillation, a condition where the heart's two upper chambers beat chaotically, irregularly, and out of coordination with the lower two chambers of the heart. It causes heart palpitations, shortness of breath and generalized weakness. If not treated, it can cause a stroke. Roger's blood pressure was 90/56 and he was full of water. The nurse returned shortly and stopped all IV fluids for the night. His heart medication was given but at a lower dose. Around midnight, he was able to urinate 50cc, a lot better than 15cc, but still not good. His body was so hard and tight with fluid, I pictured him cutting himself and water squirting out of him everywhere.

He was up 14 pounds of pure water weight gain. All I kept thinking was, *This transplant better work; this is no quality of life for him.*

Roger slept through the night, and after about three hours of research with no luck, I fell asleep too.

Day +9

The nurse practitioner showed up with new orders. She said she was going to restart the antibiotic Meropenem and the IV fluids. Roger's B/P had dropped through the night to 89/54. She said she was hoping the fluids would increase his heart rate, dissolve the atrial fibrillation, and flush the kidneys. She explained that the fluid he was carrying was all interstitial, the contiguous fluid-filled space existing between the skin and body organs, and she wanted it in his bloodstream.

I looked at her and said, "He is not peeing, it will all become interstitial. How much more can he take?"

She smiled and said, "That does sound logical, but it's not how it works." She did a quick assessment on him and left.

Twenty minutes later, the nephrologist came in and started explaining the dialysis procedure and had Roger sign the consent form. He said, "You will be transferred into the ICU shortly." He looked over at the IV then looked at me as if waiting for an explanation. I told him the BMT nurse had restarted it. He said, "All this fluid is strictly collecting interstitially, do you understand? It is not intravenous. It is increasing Roger's cardiac pressures and lowering his B/P. All the toxins are staying in his system. If we don't get them out, it could become critical quickly. How is Roger's mental status?"

I was speechless! I looked at Roger and he said, "I'm crazy," and smiled.

I said, "So far, so good." The doctor said he was surprised and would see us in the unit shortly then stopped the IV fluids. Roger asked for Ativan, but I held back, and he was not happy. We talked about the dialysis and I asked how he felt. He said he would do what he had to do, but he wanted that Ativan. I told him not to worry, I would get him some in a bit.

Thirty minutes later, the BMT nurse returned with the Meropenem and said she was hanging more fluids, looked at the IV bag then looked at me. I said, "The nephrologist just came in and had Rog sign these papers," As I held them up. I told her what he had JUST told me.

She said, "Oh," and left the room. Twenty minutes later, the BMT nurse, along with the BMT doctor and an additional nurse from the floor, were standing in front of me with their arms crossed.

The doctor said, "We are here to restart the fluids and the antibiotic." I looked at them with a *What in the world* look, sat back in my chair, ran my fingers through my hair, and explained to them all that we had been told in the last hour. The doctor softened his stance, apologized and said, "We have not sit with the nephrologist yet, but they *are* the kidney doctors." The doctor looked at Roger and started asking him questions; how do you feel, are you dizzy, do you feel nauseated, do you have any pain, does it hurt to pee, do you feel like you are holding urine, do you itch anywhere, do have any new or worsening rashes, do you feel disoriented?

Roger said no to all the questions then looked at me as I was staring at him in disbelief. He picked up the signal then said, "Well, I am not peeing much."

She listened to his lungs then asked, "Are you short of breath, are you bringing up any mucus?" Roger again said no to all. She continued, "Your lungs sound good and they are not wet. We know your B/P is really low, you are not peeing enough, and your creatinine is going up fast. You have a lot of fluid in your abdomen and legs, but that is interstitial fluid." She looked at me and continued, "This interstitial fluid won't make urine and if he becomes short of breath or his lungs get wet and his blood pressure continues to fall, we will put him in the unit. All this fluid is not good for his cardiac status. The unit is the only place they can give him the kind of meds that will increase urinary output. Also, if his heart rate decides to *stay* in atrial fib, not bounce in and out like it's doing now, we will need to put him in the unit."

I was livid! I stood up and firmly said, "So when he stops urinating, his lungs fill up with water, he becomes short of breath, his heartrate becomes dangerous and his blood pressure tanks, THEN you will put him in the unit and consider dialysis?" I continued without letting her answer, "At some point there has to be a fine line between catching this snowball before he ends up in a total body crash. Where is that fine line? I think it is right here staring at us. Four doctors, four different doctors, and a slew of nurses have walked in here, all with different game plans. I want you all to have a real quick meeting and come up with one game plan right now!" She listened to me, lowered her arms to her side then lowered her head and walked out with her entourage in tow.

The floor nurse stayed behind and sat down. I looked at Roger and said, "Babe, when the doctors ask you how you are doing *today*, they are actually asking you, 'How have you been since the last time I saw you? Are there any changes?'"

He said, "She asked me how I am doing, and I thought that meant right now. Right now, I feel okay. Truthfully, I feel like someone split me in two. There is a good Roger in there from before, and now there is the Roger now. I feel weak, tired. I want to pee, but I can't. I just want to sleep, but no one lets me. It's hard to take all these pills every day, all day. I have no appetite, I don't even want to try to eat, but I know I have to. I just want to sleep. My skin is tight, and it's a little itchy now, and my hands and feet are so cold."

He stopped and I said, "These are the things you have to tell the doctor." He said okay. I looked at the nurse sitting next to me and told her to document this conversation for the doctor when she returns. She nodded and left the room. A few minutes later, a phlebotomist was taking several vials of blood. I called the nurse in and was told they were going to check all levels one more time before they sent him to the unit. So, we waited while Roger slept.

I didn't feel like checking in with the kids. What would I say? I didn't want to alarm them, yet I thought they should know what was going on. Dialysis? The unit? Roger's neutrophils were at rock bottom. Anyone entering the room must be fully gowned, masked and gloved, except for me. If I leave the room, I must do the same while I am out but not while I am in. So, I leave as little as possible. I knew we were going to the unit, but I didn't understand why no one wanted to make the decision. I was told that there were no family member beds in the unit, no staying overnight. What was I going to do? I couldn't go back and forth from the hotel each day. I couldn't leave Roger. I had a fear that if I wasn't there, things were going to be overlooked. I know that sounds like I am a control freak, but so be it. I was not leaving him. I would sleep in a chair in the hall if I must.

The blood results returned. His kidneys were not producing urine and he was full of toxins. His blood pressure was falling, now at 86/54. We were moved to the Intensive Care Unit. As soon as they got Roger settled in, his blood pressure elevated to 111/70 and stayed there. He slept while they got him hooked up to all the monitors in the unit. The nurse said, "Look, his pants match his skin color! Pretty!" Indeed, they did – purple like a beet. He talked in his sleep saying, "Cells, cells, cells." I hoped he was pow-wowing with them and giving them encouragement to get started in their new home in the bone marrow.

It was getting late and as I got settled into my chair, which I talked my way into getting and staying, I worried what tomorrow would bring. This couldn't go on much longer.

I had talked my way into a chair, but the problem was that there was no bathroom nearby for visitors. The bathroom was through the double doors at the end of the hall, roughly half a block away. So, I didn't drink anything. It was freezing in the room, and I was wearing a pair of flip flops. I had a pair of socks in my bag so I put them on, pushed the sock down between my toes, and wore the flip flops.

I noticed on the board behind the curtain was a chart that said GOAL on it:

1. Follow vital signs
2. Keep comfortable
3. Dialysis catheter

I assumed the catheter would go in that night or early the next day.

In the middle of the night, I had the opportunity to vent to Charly, Roger's nurse. She was shocked after reading the chart, and came into the room and asked me to explain what was going on. She said, "In a few hours, the rounding team will be here, and I encourage you to be present. We usually don't let family in on rounds, but I will make sure it's okay. If they are reading the chart as I am, they will need help in deciphering it." That didn't make me happy.

Day +10

Just as it is out on the floor every morning, in the ICU a group of doctors make rounds. There is one head doctor and the rest are interns. Each intern is assigned a patient to present. He or she takes the chart before rounds, studies it, and when rounding, presents the case to the head doctor. The intern also presents a game plan, or a plan of action, for their chosen patient while they are in the ICU. Roger slept through it all. The entourage entered the room and the intern stepped forward and started her verbal assessment of his status out loud. She started at the beginning with Roger's first ER visit with transport to the hospital on December 21 then his successful remission with Dasatinib followed with a successful bone marrow transplant on May 6. She continued on to the ER visit where he presented with a temperature, diarrhea, painful abdomen and a noticeable red rash to the body. She went through the IV antibiotic therapies that were started, stopped and restarted, but kidney failure was now the main concern. Her conclusion and plan of action was to remove and replace the IV because most likely it was the cause of the infection, and continue antibiotic therapy. The head doctor listened along with the rest of the group, and agreed with her. He took the chart, wrote the order, and gave it to Charly. They then started to move the team on to the next patient in the adjoining room. I stood up abruptly and said, "Please don't take this confrontationally but I am hearing a different plan of action by several different doctors."

Every evening I researched and studied. I had looked up all the medications Roger was taking and considered all the side effects. I had found something the previous day that made me think that the problem all started with the Cyclosporine. One of the very rare side effects of Cyclosporine is a deep red rash, not raised, but can present itself anywhere on the body. In a few cases, the entire body is affected. I had been stewing on this for hours and had asked Charly to let me look at all of Roger's labs. We were on day +10 and the Cyclosporine had been discontinued over a week ago, yet he still had a therapeutic level in his system. I looked at the levels from the first ER visit that landed Roger there, and his levels were three times higher than the recommend level of being therapeutic. This overdose, as I saw it, caused extreme abdominal pain, diarrhea, headaches, purple coloring to the skin, and a slew of other side effects. This knowledge brought me back to the moment the pharmacologist told me she had never seen this dosage given in all her years working with transplant patients. I hadn't told anyone about this until I met Charly and she let me verify it with the lab results.

The team stopped and gave me their attention. I said, "The idea that the temperature was instigated by the IV causing a blood infection has been thrown around for days now, yet two sets of blood cultures say no. I have heard a different plan of action now from everyone involved in Roger's care. This includes the BMT group, who plans to continue IV fluids to flush the kidneys, continue antibiotic therapy to combat the infection, and change the anti-rejection medications. The nephrology group wants to discontinue the IV infusions because Roger's heart cannot handle the additional fluid retention that is causing cardiac overload, atrial fibrillation and kidney failure. Their plan is dialysis to relieve all complications, giving them time to reevaluate the underlying cause of the temperature. A secondary nephrology team, Team 3 as I understood them to be, wants a whole different approach – to slam him with a diuretic and hope for the best. If he starts urinating, problem solved. Kidney function returns to normal, and fluid overload and its side effects are gone. If it doesn't work, dialysis. And now your plan is to pull the IV, period? May I add, all these plans have been explained to me in the past 36 hours. So, which is it? Which one is the best plan? And let me tell you that Roger walked into that ER with a toxic level of Cyclosporine in his system. His blood levels were three times over the therapeutic level. With that information, we can assume the symptoms of diarrhea, abdominal pain and a body covered in a red rash can be attributed to the overdose. No one told me that information, I had to find this out on my own and I am not happy about it. So, he lays there in that bed close to death, and you want to pull his IV and move on to the next patient?"

They all just stared at me, and Charly clutched the chart to her chest, hiding her giant smile. I was livid! I had all their attention, all were looking at me with a blank stare on their faces – even the head doctor, Dr. House as I began to think of him – suddenly all turned their attention to the intern presenter. She stared back at them then stepped forward and took the chart from Charly and started to rummage through it, hoping the answer would pop out at her. No one said a word. She then looked up at me and said, "We will consult with each of the teams that you have addressed and get back to you after we come up with a safe and proper game plan."

I thanked her, closed the curtain on the group, and sat down next to Roger. I heard them shuffling away, no one saying a word. I was shaking like a leaf inside, feeling as if I had just run a marathon. Roger, with his eyes swollen shut, took my hand and smiled.

Charly came back into the room and said, "Girl, I need a raise. Can you handle that for me?" I gave her a nervous smile. She said, "They left for the conference room. Most likely they are calling a meeting with Roger's entire team, so if you need to do anything, do it now."

I ran to the car to deposit dirty clothes and get clean ones. Roger wanted to wear his t-shirts, not the hospital gowns. I had about 20 of them with me since I was using them for night shirts too. The previous night, because I didn't want to walk half a block to the bathroom, I used Roger's bed pan to pee in. As I tried to move the pan, I dumped it down my legs and had to use my last pair of sweat pants to dry myself off. I also needed more food. I carried a backpack with me, but with no fridge to keep food in, the little bit I had was going bad. At this point, peanut butter and jelly sandwiches or crackers were my best "go to" foods. Roger hadn't eaten in days, so I was no longer able to share his meals with him.

We spent the day waiting for the team of doctors to return. Roger slept and tossed and turned on and off. When he wasn't sleeping, he was trying to urinate, but was getting very frustrated. His mental status started to decline by early afternoon; he wasn't making sense. Whatever he was trying to say was coming out different, like a stroke patient, and if I couldn't decipher it, he would try again harder then give up and say, "Never mind." By 5:00 p.m., he was in trouble. He was not waking up. No matter how hard we tried, he was not with us. His eyes were still completely blood-red and swollen shut. He was drooling from the sides of his mouth, and his B/P was back into the 80s. The ICU nurses were working on him and taking phone calls left and right, then started to dump emergency meds into him.

3

Watch and Wait

Finally, a decision was made. They slammed Roger with a strong diuretic and hoped for the best. It was a waiting game. I clutched a pillow and just rocked myself, praying for it to work. Everyone was on stand-by, watching him – doctors, interns, nurses and me. When the drooling started choking him, they rolled him onto his side, and shortly after, Roger started peeing. He peed all night long. After two hours of this, he woke up and asked for me. He said with his slow, slurred speech, "Get me up, get me up now." The team got him to the side of the bed and handed him the urinal he asked for. This went on all night long. As soon as he got comfortable in bed, he was up again.

At 4:00 a.m., I was so tired I couldn't keep my eyes open. I told the nurse I was running on empty. She said, "Go to sleep, I will take care of him." I did, in the recliner that Charly so kindly found for me.

By 6:00 a.m., Roger had peed off TEN POUNDS! His IV was restarted with electrolytes to replace the depleted ones being dumped in every bottle of urine. Roger was exhausted and said, "I don't wish to pee in this bottle any longer." I was shocked. It had worked – no dialysis, and a bed was being prepared for us back on the leukemia floor.

The usual rounding team of doctors were next door; Roger was next. The curtain was closed, and as the team approached our door I heard the biggest swear word loud and clear. I got up, went to the curtain, and before I reached for it, the curtain opened and there stood the head doctor I'd met yesterday. He was about 5" away from my face. I smiled and said, "It's okay, Dr. House."

They all busted up, even Dr. House. He said, "I take it you are pleased this morning?"

I said, "Ask Roger."

Roger slowly said, "I lost ten pounds overnight."

Dr. House smiled and said, "I see that, hence the word! Young man, this floor is full of germs and you have no immune system, so you are going back to the leukemia floor as soon as possible. No dialysis, and I hope to not see you again." He shifted his eyes to me and we smiled at each other. He shook my hand and left. Disaster was averted, and I hoped that was the last one!

The nurse walked in and said, "His atrial fib is gone so we will start him back on heart med BID, not TID." I guess everyone knew I was a nurse now. BID = twice a day, TID = three times a day.

I said, "Great" and she left.

Roger said, "She talks in parables. What she is saying is that if you don't get results, go to HR."

I said, "No, she is just explaining the medication update."

He asked, "Who is she? Is it because of your bra size?" I kind of smiled, looked at him, and was wondering where that came from. He stared at me. He was being serious. I shook it off and explained the medication changes from the beginning and said that the nurse was just letting us know the changes.

He said, "Okay," and looked at the lunch tray that had just been dropped off. He was hungry and was presented with a ham sandwich, fruit, pickles and a Gatorade. I just watched, my heart full of happiness as he started to eat. There was also a soggy granola bar in a small bowl on his plate. He handed it to me and said, "You eat this." He then said, "Here, eat a pickle." He ate the other one. He said, "It tastes kind of like a pickle, crunchy and a little salty and I can see it so I know it is a pickle but it doesn't really taste like much of one." He still seemed a little confused in his thought processes, but it didn't matter. He ate all his food and laid back down to rest. That lasted about 15 minutes before he was asking for the urinal again.

For the next four hours, Roger continued to get his exercise by sitting up on the side of the bed to urinate. Slowly, the puffiness in his face, abdomen and legs began to diminish, and the urine color was becoming clear, not that dark amber color. He started obsessing about things, complaining about grease coming out of his big toe every time he stood to urinate, and kept asking me to clean it up. After trying to get him to realize there wasn't anything there several times, I just wiped his toe each time. He also thought there was water dripping on my phone, but it was a shadow from the trees outside the window. Every time I moved my phone he said, "Move it again, I'm not paying for a water damaged phone." I put the phone away so he couldn't see it. His hands started shaking a bit and he began complaining about ringing in his ears. He said, "My right ear has water in it and I can't hear you." I moved closer and he was happy. I looked at him and started to wonder what was going on. Something was still not right.

We finally got the transfer orders. I was up and starting to move about when Roger decided he needed to have a bowel movement. They brought him a potty chair and he proceeded to have a bowel movement right then and there, with all of us present. At home, he closed and locked all the doors, turned on the fan, and if you even tried to talk to him through the door, he was mortified. Before I could get out of the room, he dropped his drawers, grunted, farted, and had a huge, smelly poop. He then said, "I don't want my wife to see me wipe my butt so leave!" I was a little shocked he'd said it like that. The nurse stayed in the room and helped him. I stood in the hallway, remembering what I had heard at the caregiver meeting, "This disease makes or breaks a marriage."

We made it to the leukemia floor, our new room was the corner room, and like a corner lot, it was BIG. Finally, we'd made it to the big leagues, although I wasn't sure if that was something to worry about or just good luck.

As the day progressed, Roger started getting weaker and seemed to be preoccupied. His eyes weren't focusing, just rolling from object to object. He continued to pee and sleep and pee. Before bed, the nurses asked Rog to do a lap around the halls. He was having balance issues, swaying whenever he tried to get up. As we left the room he said, "The floor is in my face and I feel like I'm falling. I'm going to fall, Robin!" I took him to the railing on the side of the hallway so he could hold on. He walked very slowly, every step had a purpose. One lap around was all he could handle. He needed an Ativan after and the nurses brought him one.

Even with the Ativan on board, the night was starting out rough. Because he was weak and unsteady on his feet, the nurses put the side rails up and turned on the bed alarm. If he had to get up, he had to wake me, have me turn off the alarm and help him to the bathroom. He was still getting the high dose of diuretics and the nurses wanted him to get up to use the bathroom, not use the urinal. He was restless, dreaming, tossing and turning. I checked his pulse and it was racing. I nudged him, and he moaned and turned over. I decided not to wake him and just let him sleep, but he had other ideas. It was a night to remember. Roger was so restless, every 20-45 minutes he started scratching or pulling on his telemetry box as if it were a foreign object. He would pick it up, look at it, and try to put it elsewhere on the bed only to turn over and have it follow him. After a bit of staring at it, he would figure out it was connected to him. He studied the situation, breathing heavily out of his mouth as if his nose was stuffy. He was like a child trying to figure out a new toy; mouth open, eyes engaged, scratching his head every couple of minutes yet never taking his eyes off the 'toy' while trying to understand its purpose. He fiddled with his covers, turned over and looked at me and said, "I love you." I said it back, but I wasn't sure he could even see me. His eyes and skin were still purple, but the color seemed to be diminishing.

I laid there watching him in the dark on the other side of the room. After a couple hours I was so tired I fell asleep. I woke to "**ROBIN!**" in a very stern voice.

I woke up in a daze, threw my covers off and said, "What?"

He said, "I need to pee!"

As the night went on, I started to realize that the high doses of diuretics were causing hallucinations. I'm not sure he was even awake when he sat up, got my attention and started talking as if he was in the cartoon The Flintstones. He was trying very hard to get me to understand that Fred and Barney were up to something, believing he was in the town of Bedrock. Very seriously, he explained everything the two characters were doing. Then all of a sudden he woke up, right in front of me. His face would go blank and his eyes began searching for answers as he realized what had just happened, what he was saying. He apologized, clearly confused, scratched his head all over with both hands, wondering why this was happening to him. It broke my heart to see him like that. He said he was going crazy then laid back down and went right back to sleep. At times, his dreams were violent; tossing and turning, yelling and throwing covers. I had to wake him just to let him fall back to sleep and start all over again. The nurses helped a few times, stating they had documented the behavior and encouraged me to keep the alarm on.

Day +11

We were informed the BMT team would be in later in the afternoon. I wanted answers as to what the heck happened the previous night. We were both exhausted because neither of us got any sleep. I needed to do laundry so I took advantage of his sleeping through the morning, asked the nurses to watch him then headed down to the laundry room. I sat and stared out the window into the misty rain. I relaxed, wrote in my journal and found a few wonderful moments of peace.

The BMT team cancelled their visit and all existing orders stayed the same. Roger slept most of the day while I researched, helped him to the bathroom, and just stayed quiet on my couch with a pen in my mouth, paper at my side, and my computer brightening up the room as the night set in.

The night was another long one. Rog was up eight times going to the bathroom, and that night he was a publisher who needed to get his book done. Each time he got up, he refused to go back to bed. I was patient saying, "It's okay, get in bed, it's alright," but he wasn't having it. He wasn't going to get in bed until the LAST paragraph was complete. Then all of a sudden, I saw the shift, he woke up, and the awareness returned to his face. Stunned, he got back in bed. He was getting slower, and his words were becoming an effort. Long sentences were difficult, and he tired easily from just talking. Fortunately, he had lost most of the water weight, but his skin was thin and beginning to tear easily. The doctors ordered an air bed for him to help with the circulation. I had another restless night, but when I did sleep, it was hard, deep, and dream-filled.

Day +12

Roger wasn't interested in breakfast. While he slept, I, like every morning, got out of bed before he woke up and headed to the coffee pot down the hall in my t-shirt, sweat pants and flip flops, hair in every direction. I filled up then headed back with two large cups of coffee, both for me. Everyone said good morning and I smiled, raised a cup for acknowledgement, and disappeared back into the room.

While Roger slept, I noticed his face was peeling and his lips were cracking. His color had almost returned to normal and his temperature just vanished as if it had hitched a ride then decided to get off. I put lip balm on his lips and lotion on his face, and as I did, I watched little hairs fall off his head onto his face and gown. He brushed them off saying it tickled. His t-shirt was full of tiny silver hairs. That morning his weight was down to 294. I noticed the weight loss mostly in his face. His face was now drawn, with no life as he just looked up at me as I fussed over him. His eyes were still bloodshot but not as grey as I looked into his eyes and smiled. I didn't show him my thoughts. He was not my Roger right now, although I knew my Rog was hiding in there somewhere. His voice was so low and his words so muffled I could barely understand him. I kissed his forehead and told him to rest while I went to get something to eat.

I decided to go buy him a little birthday present, and it was a short trip down to the gift shop. I found a large rainbow cup that could also be used as a bowl. Good for his soups and bright enough to see. I found *huge* pairs of socks so I bought two pairs. I had been cutting the hospital booties on the top so I could get them onto his size 14 feet without cutting off his circulation. These made *me* happy! I found some peppermint, sugar-free gum because he had asked for gum a couple times to make his mouth feel better. The best present of all was a memory foam neck pillow. It was perfect for the clinic; his neck and head would be more comfortable. I bought a newspaper with some colored comic pages and used that for wrapping paper. It was perfect!

When I returned, he was semi-sitting up in bed watching TV with his hands folded over his chest like nothing was wrong. He smiled and said, "I missed you!" Wow, from one extreme to the other! His mental changes happened so quickly that I was becoming immune to the constant ups and downs. He saw my big bag of goodies, asked me where I had been and if I had eaten. I told him yes and that what was in the bag was a surprise, reminding him tomorrow was his birthday. He had forgotten and didn't seem to be phased by the thought one way or another. He asked me to take him for a walk, and I was delighted. It took about 20 minutes just to help him get to the side of the bed and his feet on the floor. I really didn't want to take him; I had a gut feeling this wasn't a good idea, but it was what he wanted. And what Roger wanted, Roger got! He pushed himself in the hallway, shuffling along, holding tight to the handrails along the corridor walls. We were told that he had reached the "puny" stage. At this stage all his energy was zapped and gone. He looked and walked like he had aged 30 years. Roger was able to finish one lap around the hallway, which was a big accomplishment considering how long the lap was. He was exhausted and plopped into bed immediately upon our return. He had a little dinner, fell asleep, and slept most of the night without incidence.

I laid in bed thinking. I hoped I didn't lose myself in this process! I was afraid the young marriage and the plans we'd had for our new property were going to require *me* to keep it together and "Get 'er done" as they say.

Day +14

It was Roger's birthday, and the BMT doctors arrived bright and early, making their rounds down the hallway room by room. As soon as they walked in I said, "It's Roger's birthday!"

They wished him a happy birthday as they checked his DOB to calculate his age as fast as they could. "Well, this is a good day for you. All your numbers look good and your temperature is gone so you are being discharged today. Happy Birthday," and they clapped. I was ear to ear smiles for a split second then was immediately in shock. He was so unsteady on his feet and dizzy when he walked, his speech was still slurred, and his mental status was still rough. He wasn't eating or drinking enough, and to shower was an effort that put him in bed exhausted for hours. I turned my eyes to Roger, still smiling but my head was reeling.

We were all looking at him and were literally dumbfounded when he said, "NO! I want to stay another day. I don't feel ready. I don't want to leave until all this water weight is gone. My feet are still puffy." He pulled his covers up to his chin as if to say, I'm staying!

The team looked at him and said, "Okay, it's your birthday, you can stay until tomorrow. We'll write your discharge orders so when you're ready tomorrow, you can go."

They looked at me for a minute as I was blankly staring at them, my mind whirling. I finally said, "Wait – when we go home, what should I expect? What should I look for? I don't want this to happen again. After many nights of research, it almost seems as if

Roger had an episode of graft versus host. Did he? Or was it the Cyclosporine? I mean, what do I do to make sure this doesn't happen again?" I talked fast without letting them answer each question. I realized my tone was almost pleading and it was obvious I was scared to take him home. One of the doctors tucked the chart under his arm then clasped his hands together, holding it in place and said, "GVHD doesn't happen until the 38th or 100th day post-transplant. We don't feel this was a case of GVHD. We think it was a combo of radiation, which we can see in his dry skin and lips, loss of hair and puny affect, and too much Cyclosporine, Vancomycin – and the straw that broke the camel's back, the contrast he drank for the CT scan. This was too much for his body to take in such a short few days. These symptoms have resolved, and his color is good. His blood chemistry is stable for being day +14 so he can go home. It's much safer for him to be home than here. This is a hospital, people are sick here, lots of germs floating around." He then looked at Roger and said, "You still want to stay?" Roger just shook his head yes. The nurse practitioner looked at me with a *come here* look and tilted her head as if to say "join us outside." They left, and I walked out with them. The doctors went to the nurse's station to dictate discharge orders for tomorrow and I followed the nurse practitioner. She explained to me that this was very normal. Patients feel safe in the hospital and Roger had been through a lot. It was of no surprise he wanted to stay. She said just take one day at a time and call anytime day or night if I needed support or guidance. She said, "Robin, it is going to get worse before it gets better, but it will get better." I just stared at her. She reached over and hugged me and said, "You're doing a good job!"

I said, "Wait. I read that GVHD can happen in the first to third day after transplant and if that does happen, it is a death sentence. Are you sure this is not the case?"

She said very calmly as she took my hand, "This is not the case. It was just too much, too soon. But everything looks really good right now." She smiled and walked away. I watched her join the others. I heard, "Everything looks really good *right now.*" I walked away but listened to them talk to see if they would say anything else to each other. They didn't.

I walked back into the room and said, "Wow, happy birthday. Want to open your presents?"

He asked, "What did you talk with them about?" I told him they said his fears were normal, everyone had them at this stage, and not to worry, they are a phone call away. He was happy with that and said he was ready to open gifts. I kissed him and laid down with him and we snuggled for a while.

His breakfast tray arrived, and it was a normal breakfast with French toast, his favorite. I laughed and said, "Wow, if you don't eat that, I am!"

So many of the hospital meals he tried to eat caused indigestion, sometimes so bad it caused severe abdominal pain. The meals were full of gravies and cream sauces – rich foods packed with calories. I asked the doctor about Roger's indigestion and he said, "The Prednisone causes lactose intolerance and reduced absorption of the foods he eats so indigestion occurs; it's normal." He ordered a daily antacid for him so he didn't have to take so many Tums.

My thought was, *Why does the hospital prepare foods for transplant patients that they cannot digest? They are all on Prednisone!* It was so frustrating!

Roger decided to rest after breakfast and asked if he could open presents in a bit. I could see the apprehension in his face, wondering if this meal was going to make him feel sick. I said of course and decided to take my last shower before we left.

After showering, I crawled in bed with him and he opened his presents. He held each one up for me to take a picture to send to the kids. We laid together and enjoyed each other. He wanted to sleep for a while so I went out into the hallway to call my friend Betty and check up on Max then called Mom to see how she was doing on the ranch. All was good. While I was gone, the nurses brought Roger a cupcake and a milkshake for his birthday, and sang him the birthday song. So nice. I ate the cupcake and drank the shake!

As the night went on, I could tell Roger was getting anxious. He was complaining about the bed covers, then the lights, then the door being open. I asked him what was wrong. He said, "I'm concerned about the clinic. They didn't do a chemistry panel on me that night and failed to catch this by not following through. They were supposed to draw a simple chem panel. Even the ER failed to draw a chem panel. Please, Robin, make sure they always draw a chem panel." I could tell he was scared to death to leave the hospital. I rubbed his feet gently and reminded him we were only minutes away, and told him I would be more alert. He seemed to be okay with that but asked for an Ativan. The nurse brought one in and I took another from the bottle I carried. My head was reeling. How was I going to be able to catch the next thing when I didn't even know the next thing? I know hearts, I don't know leukemia. My nights of research were going to be long and tiring. I could see the writing on the wall. It didn't take long for the Ativan to take over, and we both slept. It was an uneventful night.

4

Climbing Back Up the Hill

Day +15 started at 6:30 a.m. We were told that before we could go home, Rog needed an IV bolus of Lasix, his diuretic, and a bag of magnesium. Truly a day doesn't go by that magnesium wasn't hanging from his IV pole. Knowing this, I knew I had at least five hours before we could leave so I decided to use this five hours to my advantage. Pharmacy first, which took an hour since the line at the pharmacy was always ten people deep. On a good day there were two or more check-out windows open; today, only one. Once again, I left with a shopping bag full of pharmaceuticals.

I rushed to the store to pick up some fresh organic vegetables, lentils and organic chicken. I planned on making Rog a nice broth and veggie soup. I was hoping it would be easy for him to digest, unlike the hospital food. Roger was still at least 40 pounds overweight, so I felt a nice healthy meal versus one high in calories would be better for him nutritionally and easier on his stomach. In my research on best foods for cancer patients, I read that vitamin B17 was a cancer killer. I looked up all foods that had a high amount in them. One was the yucca root, so into the soup pot it would go. I was flabbergasted to read that the U.S. had a ban on anything pertaining to vitamin B17. Apple seeds, raw almonds, fresh apricot seeds and peach seeds are also great for cancer patients. The small amount of arsenic in them, when consumed, kills cancer cells by breaking down the cell wall, causing it to die immediately, yet the FDA puts a warning on these seeds saying the arsenic in them will kill you, therefore, you shouldn't eat them. I did find a few websites that sell these seeds, but they're based in other countries. As I researched, I started noticing that many simple cures like this weren't allowed in the U.S. My research also led me to a doctor named Roy Rife who, in the 1920s, realized that different cells in the body react to different frequencies. If the frequency is unpleasant to the cell, it dies. He was able to find the unpleasant frequency to almost all disease-causing cells *and* he was able to destroy them. He was curing all clients who sought his help of fatal diseases. He had them sit in a room reading a book while he flooded the room with an invisible frequency sensitive only to the bad cell. The bad cell membranes would burst, killing the disease-causing organism and curing the client. The client was unaware of the frequency being passed through them. The U.S. government found out about this diagnostic tool, confiscated it along with ALL his work journals and equipment, and labeled Dr. Rife a quack. To this day, the frequency machine is banned in the U.S. Amazing!

I finished my shopping in record time and headed back to the hospital. Roger was ready to leave. Still unsteady on his feet, I wheeled him out in a wheelchair. On the drive home, it was if he gained days of energy. He opened the window and breathed in the fresh air. The sun rested on his body and he just kept saying, "I miss this. This feels so nice. I miss this."

The hotel room was a little messy. We had left so fast, not caring about anything other than getting Rog to the ER. Roger sat on the couch, found the remote, and started watching TV. I cleaned up, got the soup going on the stove and put the groceries away. At the caregiver's meeting, I had been told to only buy prepackaged foods from the stores to insure no contamination or germs were present. I looked in the cupboards at what I had brought. Mac and cheese microwave cups, canned soups, box foods and tons of crackers. I just wanted to throw it all away. I was not putting that in his weakened and sensitive body!

The soup turned out fantastic, and Roger was able to eat it and enjoyed two bowls. Knowing tomorrow was an early morning at the clinic, we headed to bed, curled up, shut the dark curtains, watched TV, and fell asleep. There were six trips to the bathroom with help, all within 30 minutes apart, and then we slept until the alarm woke us.

Day +16

Unfortunately, urinating all night made Rog even weaker. He sat at the side of the bed hunched over, breathing out of his mouth, eyes closed as I dressed him. When I tightened his belt, I noticed he was down two more notches. I made him some warm broth for breakfast and as he drank it slowly, he laid back down and watched me prepare for the day. I always made us a bag of goodies to eat and drink, along with pens, paper, journal and my bead board to take to the clinic. Roger usually slept at the clinic. So, while I sit and pass the time, I have something to keep me busy in this little bag. All the caregivers carry one.

Getting Roger to the car was a slow and cautious effort, to say the least. It wasn't long after we arrived and his blood was examined that we were told his electrolytes were all out of whack again. Immediately, we knew it was going to be a long day. I got out my journal and caught up on my writing while he slept the entire seven hours we were there. His head was snuggled in his birthday pillow, mouth open as he breathed softly. His face was so pale, drawn and flaky even though I had put lotion on him that morning, and his hands were freezing. I got a warm blanket out of the blanket warmer and covered him up. He didn't wake. I got my coffee and settled into the journal, spending the seven hours writing and reminiscing about the ranch.

After the transfusion, we headed back to the hotel. Roger ate a bowl of soup with some crackers and was able to keep it down without indigestion. I ate almonds and apples with cheese at the clinic, but wasn't interested in food, just sleep.

The next day there would be no clinic, and we were both so happy. I felt like I was running on empty, with no gasoline in the tank. I closed the dark brown drapes in the bedroom and put Roger to bed. I needed to refill his medication dispenser with all his new meds before I joined him. I had to use my bead container as a medication organizer now since his giant pills no longer fit in the one we brought with us. Two hours later, I was in bed snuggled up to him. I laid there and thought about all the research I had read, worrying about how long Roger would be in my life. I tried very hard every day to keep these thoughts from invading my mind, but some days I was better at it than others. I had a deep, dark feeling that every day I was with him was a blessing. When these thoughts occurred, I had to hide in the bathroom or take a walk to hide the tears that would flow like a swollen river. I couldn't let Roger see me cry. I wrapped my arm over his chest and we both slept through the night like babies with full bellies.

Day +17

With no appointments this morning and the room blacked out, I almost had a heart attack when I awoke with sore hips to realize it was 1:30 in the afternoon. I panicked, looking over at Roger. He was snuggled in bed with the covers tucked up under his chin, laying on his back fast asleep. I nudged him and said, "Roger, it is 1:30 in the afternoon. Did you take your morning medications?"

He didn't move or even open his eyes and said, "Yes, I took them at noon when I got up to pee."

I said, "Yes! Good job! Why didn't you wake me?"

He said, "Because you need to rest too." I thanked and kissed him, and snuggled back up to him. My next thought was, *Great, all his meds would be late today.* Why hadn't I set the alarm? How could I have let this happen?

When we finally got up, I made us a nice breakfast of scrambled eggs with a little tomato, onion and cilantro, and a couple pieces of dry toast. His taste buds didn't taste much so I'd added the cilantro for two reasons; stronger flavor and it helps clean out the kidneys and liver. With all that crap medication accumulating in him, a little cleaning was in order. He loved it! His portions were a lot smaller, but he had less problems with his stomach this way. He seemed to be feeling pretty good; no new complaints, just tired. I checked his body as I dressed him, and his skin looked pretty good. Part of the caregiver's job is to check the surface of the body every day to look for changes then report them to the doctor at the next visit. I didn't see any new rashes, only a lot of dry skin. His mouth, the palms of his hands and soles of his feet were red, inflamed and very sensitive. He didn't like the feel of me touching his skin for very long. If he had clothes on it was okay, but not direct touch. His face was drawn and his voice was still weak. He complained mostly of pain in his joints and feet. His joints were slightly swollen and would creak a lot.

There was a knock on the door, which surprised us both. From the window it looked like a maintenance guy from the hotel. When I went to answer it, Roger said, "NO!" and slowly made the three steps to the door. He opened the door about two inches and before the guy could get a word out, Roger said in a very stern voice, "No one is supposed to touch my door or come in here. I am a leukemia patient!"

The guy looked up at Roger and waved his hands and said, "Okay, okay" and left. I giggled as I watched Mr. Prednisone's fur lay back down. He sat back down, and I went to the door to see if the guy was still there. Why would he knock on the door?

On the door was taped two pieces of paper. One explained that maintenance was going to be changing the locks today, and the second I had to read twice to believe what I was reading. There was an E-coli outbreak in the water system, and all water must be boiled. This letter was dated YESTERDAY. I freaked out! Are you kidding me? Like he needed to deal with E-coli in a body with no immune system. I told Roger not to shower and to stay away from the water until I got back. I put a big pot of water on the stove to boil so I could give Roger a "spit bath" as my Navy father used to call it. A pot of water and a washcloth was all you needed. I set Roger's alarm and said, "When that alarm goes off, turn the stove off."

He asked, "Why do I need an alarm? I can see it boiling."

I said, "It's just in case you fall asleep. I'll be right back." I headed to the store on the corner to buy water. The place was packed and there wasn't a bottle or jug of water on any shelf; they were all empty. I hurried to the juice aisle and grabbed as much Gatorade as I could. Half a dozen other people were doing the same and when we were done, that shelf was empty too. As I headed to the check out, in came a water distributor with two full crates of 2-1/2 gallon jugs of water. There was a limit of two. Within a minute, the crates were empty. It was like a fire sale; everyone was reaching and grabbing for water jugs. With my limit of water and 20 bottles of Gatorade, we were set for a while, I hoped.

The day was beautiful, and he wanted to try to take a walk. His feet were so sore, and every step was painful so this surprised me. The doctor had told him walking was essential to keeping alert and healthy, and I was told my biggest jobs were getting him out of bed, keep him moving, keeping him hydrated, and getting the pills in him. Indeed, that was very true, and boy, that was a hard job. Sometimes I felt like all I was doing was nagging him. I hated it!

I told Roger I needed to go to the front office to talk to them about our bill and pick up some quarters for the laundry. I asked him if he wanted to go. He said, "That's about as far as I think I can go," which was equivalent to about half a block. We had been paying the hotel by the month and it was time to start paying by the week. I wasn't sure how much longer we would be in the area and if you made a monthly payment but ended up staying less, there were no refunds of unused money, and I was being very careful to not waste. The manager was off for the weekend, so I got the quarters and we headed back. As we walked past the rooms, we saw doors open, letting fresh air in, and patients lying in their beds, people we recognized from the clinic. It was so awful, especially the little children. I tried not to look but found myself unconsciously doing so. None looked back – they were either sleeping or watching TV.

The walk took all of Roger's energy so I tucked him in bed, turned out the lights and let him rest. I researched for a few hours but found nothing new. No new studies except the one we were in. No new research articles or personal stories of anyone Roger's age with his disease that were living. I was beginning to realize that two to three years after a transplant is about all you could get. The info I did find was based on men in their 40s, none that were close to 60. It just wasn't available, but I wasn't giving up. This was the second phase of the study, so hopefully something would happen and good news was just around the corner. I just hoped it was a short block! The next day was an early day at the clinic so I decided to hit the sack early.

Day +18

It was hard to wake Roger up, and nearly an hour to get him to the side of the bed. He wanted to sleep. Like all mornings, I helped him wash up and thanks to the E-Coli outbreak, a spit bath it was. I boiled the jug water so he would have nice, warm, clean water against his skin. He didn't want to eat. I made him some warm Gatorade and used a mouth swab to brush his teeth because his gums bled when he used his toothbrush. I was afraid they would become infected so I bought the little tooth sponges at the drugstore. I packed my bag, pulled the car close to our door so he wouldn't have to walk far, and off we went. Roger laid his head back and slept. I prayed all his blood numbers would be great so we could turn around and go back home. The transplant medications deplete the body of magnesium and other electrolytes, so if you have good blood numbers, you get to go home. Bad blood numbers meant five to seven hours in the chair.

After the usual eight vials of blood were drawn from his PICC line, we were told that he would need four grams of IV magnesium, which meant four hours in the recliner. I put the birthday pillow behind his head, got a warm blanket and wrapped him up. After an hour I was told that the nurse practitioner (NP) wanted to see Roger after his transfusion.

After the disaster in the hospital caused by the toxic levels of Cyclosporine, the doctors stopped the medication to allow his system to catch up. Today he was prescribed 75 mg twice a day, down from 550 mg twice a day with CellCept and 70 mg of Prednisone twice a day. I asked why the increase in Prednisone since this dose of Prednisone made for a not-so-pleasant Roger to be around. During the hospital debacle, his Prednisone had been decreased down to 40 mgs. The NP said, "To help prevent him from having a bout of GVHD *again.*"

I said, "What? *Again?*"

He explained, not knowing we had been told by the BMT team of doctors who adamantly denied early GVHD, that the symptoms Roger had were like GVHD, not GVHD itself. He went on to say these symptoms could have started in the skin or maybe the liver, so to prevent it from happening again, Prednisone would be increased to cover him. I felt like I had been kicked in the gut. I couldn't talk or swallow; I felt a big lump in my throat, and felt like I was going to pass out. I put my head between my knees to regain myself. Both men just looked at me for a second, brushed me off, and started talking again as if I was just being weird. Because I didn't share what I had read regarding GVHD in the first three days after transplant with Roger, I kept my mouth shut and just listened to the conversation. The NP assessed Roger's body, asked a bunch of, *How do you feel?* questions and said, "Walk as much as you can and drink as much as you can. See you in a couple of days." After seven hours in the clinic, we left.

The drive home was very quiet. When we got to the hotel, I fed him a light dinner of soup, steamed organic veggies and some dry toast then tucked him in bed. He asked for pain medication for his feet and mouth. His need for pain medications were increasing, up to four a day. Being in bed a lot caused body aches and made his joints hurt more. When he could handle it, I gently rubbed his joints and put the heating pad on them. I cuddled him for a bit and tried to kiss him, but he pushed me away. I just let him be. No massage that night, just sleep.

I headed to the living room and had my first glass of wine in a long time. I sat in the dark sobbing with my head in my hands. I wished I didn't know what I knew. I should stop reading and just look at each day as a great day to be with Roger. I wished I could shut off my mind. I didn't sleep much, and the little I did get was full of terrible nightmares. I needed to go home, just for a day. I needed to feel a normal life. I needed hope!

Day +19

I had set the alarm for 7:00 a.m., deciding the previous night that we were going home for a day. We needed it desperately. No clinic for two days so it was the perfect time. I packed a bag with surgical masks, gloves, all Roger's medications, and anything that was of value, just in case. There were cameras lining the hallways at the hotel but that also meant they knew when we were gone. I let Roger sleep until I had everything ready and his breakfast was made.

He was hesitant at first to leave, but I assured him we would be back that night and all would be fine. I dressed him and noticed that, once again, we were down a notch on the belt. I asked him to weigh himself and was a little shocked. He was at 278 pounds. In 18 days he had lost 34 pounds. He looked at me and said, "One hell of a diet. I have no thighs and my arms are so small now." When we arrived home, my kids were at the ranch, working on the new front deck. I was so happy to see them! I hadn't told them we were coming. My daughter and I ran to each other and hugged for a long time. The tears started flowing so I buried my head in her shoulder and she just held me until I collected myself. My son in law saw what was happening and immediately grabbed Roger's attention. Roger rested on the back deck overlooking the gardens and the canyon of old homes, the school house, rural fire department and the rolling hills of pole pines mixed with maple trees. The breeze was perfect, and he was so happy to be home. He slept and let the sun bathe him in warmth.

At the end of the day we all had a nice supper together and a glass of wine. I was so happy! Roger stayed quiet and just smiled every now and then. It was getting late, 10:30 p.m., and we needed to get back. I started to say my goodbyes when Roger belted out, "You're not driving!" I jumped, and my daughter grabbed her ears. It startled us all! He had my purse and my keys. He got up without saying a word and headed to the car. I was embarrassed and a little confused. Everyone stared at me like, *What the heck was that all about?* I explained the increase in Prednisone again and they all hugged me and gave me kisses.

I headed down to our house and found that it was all locked up, and as I glanced out at the driveway, I saw that the car was running and he was sitting in the driver's seat. I went to the window and asked if I could have the keys to open the house back up since I needed to get all of our stuff and a few things I packed to take back. Roger said, "I got it all. Get in now!" I asked for the keys again, as nicely as possible. He rolled the window up. I had a spare set of keys and let myself into the house. I got the duffle bag of belongings that needed to go back with us, then sat down and waited. After a while, Roger was in the house asking what I was doing. I took that opportunity to storm past him and got behind the wheel of the car. Roger got in the car and sulked all the way back.

Those two hours back to the hotel were hell. The further down the road we got, Roger's loud silence made it obvious that he was very angry, and I had no clue what the issue was. Why did he have to end a perfect day like that? I was trying so hard to keep things afloat and bring this family back together, and it was totally unnecessary to treat me like that. It was easy to blame his poor behavior on the Prednisone, but usually after a few minutes he realized he was being nasty and apologized. Not tonight.

My mind was laying it all out there. I was angry about everything – angry about feeling guilty, angry because I missed my home and hated living in the hotel, angry because my husband was sick, angry because the property was a mess and I had a lot of work to do when I got home, angry at the fact that the man sitting next to me was wearing a diaper because he couldn't hold his stool because of the medications. I was angry because he was wasting away in front of me, angry because from the moment we married he had been sick, angry because kissing him felt like I was kissing my dad. I was angry because he got cancer, angry because deep down I knew that the life I thought I was going to have was a thought of the past.

With no talking on the way home, I figured whatever was bothering him he would have to work out on his own. I tried not to engage with him when he got like that. I remembered the advice I got in the caregiver's class – don't argue with them when they are on high doses of Prednisone unless you want to see violence. I hadn't seen violence, but for some reason I felt like he wanted to throw me out the window. My love for Roger was so strong that I knew this too would pass. I knew I must be patient and strong, and try not to take things personally. He was going through a lot. I didn't know what was going on in his mind, but I assumed it was much more than he wanted to share with me.

When we arrived and I shut the hotel door, he blew up. I looked at him, smiled and got his medications. I gave him a glass of wine and a glass of water with his pills and said, "It's your choice. I would choose the wine; you need it," and headed to take a long, hot shower in my bathroom. When I was done, he was in bed, the water was gone, and the wine had a note next to it, "Drink" is all it said. I crawled into bed and slept as close to my edge as I could. I wasn't liking him much right then.

The next few days were very quiet. Roger managed to walk twice each day with great grief, but he did it. I kept his meals light, mostly broths and rice, and he was able to get them down without much discomfort. His pain medications were every two hours for joint and feet pain. He spent the afternoons watching TV in the dark in bed. He was unable to hold his loose stools, even with extra doses of Imodium. I found him men's peri pads to help with the fall out. To keep his rectal area from ulcerating, he had to shower every day. I spent my time in the living room with the front door open, watching the rabbits and squirrels outside scurrying around, collecting the nuts and raisins I was throwing them. When I got bored with that I worked on my bead projects. I left Rog alone. He didn't want anything to do with me either; I was there to take care of his needs, that was all.

Day +22

The clinic was full and there was only one seat left in the lobby, which Roger took. We waited for two hours. I drank coffee, sat on the floor at Roger's feet, and read a hospital magazine. Everyone else watched the morning news. Today's visit was supposed to be "the big medication reduction" day. We were told by the doctor that around the 28th day post-transplant, medications were decreased, and the positive signs of the transplant should be noticed in the bloodwork. We waited patiently to find out if Rog was on the right track.

Roger's bloodwork showed that his magnesium level was just shy of normal. Normal is 1.5-2.5 mEq/L, and Roger's was 1.3, so his magnesium was increased to two tablets twice a day. His Cyclosporine level was also low, 68, a big difference from a couple weeks ago. We were told his level needed to be between 100-150. Since it was the only anti-rejection medication he was taking, it was important to keep it at a therapeutic level. Roger was okay with increasing it from 75 mg twice a day to 100 mg twice a day, a big difference from the initial dose of 550 mg three times a day in the beginning. The nurse practitioner also started him on a drug called Gabapentin for the pins and needles and pain he had been experiencing in his feet and calves. His feet looked better as of that morning, not so angry but still red and painful to the touch. The rest of his bloodwork showed that his own blood cells had still not died off 100%, but it did show that the new cells had found their way to the bone marrow and were taking up shop. With so many of his own cells still active, there was always the potential for a raging acute war of GVHD. As the office visit came to an end, we were given our new schedule. We would need to be in the clinic only two days a week. But as I got up to leave, Roger blurted out, "We went home for a day."

I felt my heart sink. Why? Why? I felt my face flush. I felt like I had just got caught in a big lie and all hell was going to break loose. The NP raised his eyebrows, looked at me, only me, handed me the schedule and said, "Roger needs magnesium. You can go back to the transfusion room now." I swallowed hard and asked about the Prednisone. He said, "It will stay the same. It is covering him until the Cyclosporine is at a therapeutic level." He stood up in front of me, stared me down, giving *me* the Mom look, and he left.

I asked Roger why he needed to say that. Roger replied, "Just felt like telling him you took me home." I got up and walked in front of him to the transfusion room. Why was he doing this to me? I was his lifeline.

I felt like saying, "Screw you," and leaving for a week. That would teach him! I can be Mrs. Prednisone! This was so unbelievably taxing. I was walking on eggshells every day.

The boy I met at the caregiver meeting, Shawn, who was on his second bone marrow transplant, was sitting next to us. He recognized me and we chatted for a bit while Roger was getting set up for the magnesium. Shawn was on day +29. His transplant went well, but a few days after, he had severe heart problems, severe shortness of breath and sternum pain. He recounted his experience, and it was horrible! I told him about Roger's ordeal and we enjoyed the conversation. I asked Shawn about the Prednisone, wanting a perspective from someone other than Roger. He said, "I just don't have a filter and I really don't care about what people think. I'm the one that's sick. I need an outlet too, so you want to be in my face about everything, well I can give it back too."

I asked, "Is that how you feel with your parents?"

He responded, "They were going to split up until all this happened; now they stay together for me and it sucks. All I get is guilt and I'm tired of it. So when they get in my face, I give it back." I asked if the Prednisone made him feel different. He replied, "Yeah, I feel angry all the time and my girlfriend is mad because I won't have sex with her. She nauseates me now. Don't know why, just happened after I started the higher doses." I sat back and thought about that one for a while. Could I be nauseating Roger? I asked Shawn if I could have his number just in case I needed someone to talk to. He was happy I asked and asked for the same in return.

Shawn and Roger talked the entire four hours. Their prednisone potty mouth conversation was a hoot, making me laugh out loud a few times After we headed back to the hotel. I asked him what he thought about Shawn. He said, "He is a good kid, funny kid."

We had a nice supper. Roger had a big bowl of vegetables with broth and rice, some fresh fruit and a handful of his favorite gummy candies, watermelon slices. He asked for a glass of wine and together we sat on the couch holding hands, watching a silly show. I was so happy he was holding my hand and was so in my head about it that at the first big laugh scene, he laughed hard and I was silent. I re-adjusted my thoughts back to the program and let my brain go silent.

Day +23

Roger woke feeling really good. I hadn't seen him with that much energy in a while. He went into the bathroom and before I knew it, I heard the shower running. I peeked in and saw that he was bathing on his own. He shaved and groomed himself, put on his own lotion, dressed himself, and came out asking for eggs and toast with a cup of coffee. I acted as if this was all perfectly normal and did as he asked, but inside I was jumping up and down screaming, *Yay, he is alive, he has energy, he is motivated, he is going to make it!*

He opened all the curtains and said, "Today I need to walk, and we need to do laundry."

I said, "Sounds good!" He finished all his breakfast and coffee and started stripping the bathroom of all the dirty laundry and picking up any that was on the floor. I couldn't believe what I was seeing! He worked slowly but he was doing it.

There was too much laundry to carry to the other side of the complex, so Roger drove the car over without a traffic accident in the parking lot. I was flabbergasted, but so happy for him! To take his keys away was like taking a piece of his soul away. Not good for his ego, manhood or self-esteem. While the clothes were washing, he decided to climb the set of twenty cement stairs to the second floor. He went up and down twice very slowly, but with very little shortness of breath. I was so proud of him and I let him know it over and over again. He smiled at me and said, "Thank you. I love you very much and I am thankful every day for you. Don't you forget that!"

I started sobbing. I couldn't help it. The tears just rolled down my face. I blew my nose on my shirt, and he laughed and kissed me softly. I was so happy! He was happy and his face looked so young at that moment. We sat on the stairs waiting for the clothes and I asked him questions about how he felt. He opened up and said, "I'm not really worried. I know I'm going to get better and we'll get back to the ranch soon. I don't like the fact that everything is such an effort, but they warned me so I expected this. I'm glad I am losing this weight. I feel a lot better, my back feels better. I actually feel pretty normal right now – tired but normal. I don't have the pain in my feet right now and that makes me really happy."

I asked, "How do you feel about the disease? The prognosis?"

He responded, "I will beat this; others have and so will I." But he hadn't done the research, I had. He hadn't even begun to research. Roger was a research freak, just as I am, but he hadn't even looked up leukemia. He said he knew at the moment he called me in to look at his mouth and body that he was in trouble. I sat as he talked, and I listened to every pause, every intake and output of breath, and every syllable. I knew as the strength returned, he would start researching more. But for now, I was hearing his voice, his thoughts, out loud. It was wonderful!

We put the clothes in the dryer and went back to the step. Without looking at me he said, "I want to go home for a day, tomorrow." I looked at him as he continued, "I want to mow the yard."

I said, "Roger, no, you can't do that! All the dust that surrounds you when you mow is full of germs that could kill you. You can't use up that kind of energy right now either. I asked Todd to help out and mow every week for us and he was fine with that. No, you are not mowing three acres, no way!"

He turned and looked at me with anger in his eyes. He said, "I cannot believe you asked Todd to mow our yard! He is so busy trying to get his girlfriend's business up and running and he is working overtime at work. He is way too busy for that pressure! I can't believe you would call him like that and make him feel guilty. He doesn't need the stress!"

I said, "I really don't care if Todd is busy. He is our son. He wants to help us. Your health means more to me than Todd's schedule."

Roger got up, took my hand and yanked me up. He looked me in the eye and said, "You go and call him right now and tell him that he doesn't need to mow our lawn. I'll do it!" I pulled away from him and told him he was selfish and that he could call Todd himself.

Standing in the hotel corridor, I begged him not to mow when we go home. He said, "I will do what I want to do. It's going to get done and I'm going to do it. It's a riding lawn mower, Robin!"

I said, "Then I won't take you home and it doesn't matter if it's a riding lawn mower. It's still a lot of work and you are still in a dust cloud while you mow!"

He said, "Then I will go without you. Don't challenge my dignity, Robin. I'm still a man, and this is part of being a man, a human. I'm not just a sick person. I am going to mow the grass!" I started crying. He said, "Fine, I will just mow the upper yard and around the perimeter." He glared at me then headed to the laundry room. Where was all this energy coming from? In just a day he had vim, vigor and determination! It was like he had been given an energy pill. He still looked drawn and tired, but his words and manners weren't reflecting how he looked.

I texted Todd and told him to meet us at the house, mow today, or just call his dad and talk to him. I couldn't sleep all night. I tried to think of anything to stall this trip, but he wasn't having it. He slept like a baby, not even getting up to pee.

Day +24

Roger was in a hurry to get started when we arrived home. He told me to weed whack around all the trees in the apple orchard so he didn't have to worry about being stung by a bee or getting scratched. Since he must use an Epi Pen for bee allergies, I got right on that. It was a perfect day, without a cloud in the sky and no breeze.

My mom showed up with groceries so I stopped to help her, which enraged Roger. "Robin, get back here NOW!" he yelled. He was fully dressed in a hat, long sleeves, sunglasses and a mask. At least he was being smart about this dumb thing he was doing. He could barely maneuver the John Deere mower, but I didn't dare help him. I dug in and got all the trees done and the branches pruned back to make mowing around them easier. He mowed for almost two hours. I took him some juice and water and asked him to rest a bit and have some lunch. I was hoping the fatigue would set in during lunch and he would stop. He ate a little bit and said he just wanted to get back at it. During his ten-minute rest, he went on and on about the beautiful day and the beautiful property we had bought.

When the agreed upon part of the lawn was mowed, Roger didn't stop. When he finished, he was shy only about a quarter of the three acres. He was hot, sweaty and exhausted but so happy. His face was tired and drawn, and he walked very slowly away from the machine. I had a bad feeling his body was going to be hurting. I made him drink two bottles of Gatorade and glass after glass of water.

It was getting late and I knew we needed to get on the road. I asked Roger to get ready to leave and he said, "We're staying. There's no clinic tomorrow so we are staying. Did you bring the wine down?" I said I did and he proceeded to pour me a big glass and him a small one. I didn't challenge anything he was doing. He was in a good mood and I didn't feel like fighting. We drank more wine, watched a little TV and went to bed. Rog got up three times in the first hour to pee then after that he slept like a rock and so did I. We woke at 9:30 a.m., both sore and still tired.

PART FOUR

1

Graph Versus Host – Or Is It?

It was day +25, and the day didn't start out well. I knew it wouldn't and I was worried for morning to come. Roger's hands, calves and feet were killing him. He explained, "It feels like I ran a marathon and didn't drink anything through it." I knew that meant dehydration. I took his blood pressure and it was up too. He was feeling extremely weak and he said his head was foggy. I wanted to strangle him for being so determined to mow the yard. I figured we'd better get back to the city ASAP. I packed up everything as fast as I could while he drank a bottle of Gatorade and a bottle of water. He couldn't eat anything because he said he felt nauseated. He took his meds and that was about all he could get down with a few crackers. It was a long ride back, and he couldn't get comfortable no matter what he did.

We arrived back at the hotel at 2:00 p.m. I helped him with a shower and put him to bed. I prepared glasses of juices and water for the bedside. He said his legs felt like noodles and he had no strength. He asked me to bring his urinal to the bedside in case he had to go. I asked, "You don't feel like you can make it 10 feet to the bathroom?"

He said, "No, and I am really cold." His temperature was 94.7 so I put a pair of socks on his ice cold feet.

I could tell he was down more weight when I helped him shower, he was looking even thinner. I caressed his hair as he talked to me, and I noticed my hand was full of hair. It was falling out at exponential rate now.

His cramping continued throughout the evening so I gave him a pain pill and he was able to sleep. As soon as it wore off, I gave him another one.

I laid in bed next to him. I wanted to say, *I told you it wasn't a good idea to spend a day in the sun mowing the yard!* and I could feel he knew I wanted to say it.

He held my hand and said, "I'm sorry."

I said, "Yeah, I love you." He finally fell asleep, and I stayed in my head for hours, thinking about his symptoms, knowing it was most likely low potassium and magnesium, but it could be the increase in the Cyclosporine. The most likely candidate for these symptoms was dehydration. I prayed for morning so I could get him to the clinic. Roger had a long and painful night.

Day +26

I had to push Roger in the wheelchair into the clinic that morning since there was no way he had enough strength to walk from the parking garage, up the hill and into the clinic. At one point I thought he was asleep, but he said he was just resting his head on his chest. They took him right back to draw his blood when they saw us arrive. There was no waiting in the waiting room today. Sure enough, his potassium was low, his sodium was high, and his kidney function was decreasing again. His blood pressure was skyrocketing and the diagnosis was dehydration. Did Roger blurt out, "I mowed almost three acres of grass yesterday in the sun?" Nope, he didn't say anything, nor did I.

It was going to be a long day. Four bags of fluids hung from the IV pole above him. Five hours of transfusion. He slept for the first two hours then woke up feeling a lot better. I had texted the kids with an update and the dehydration diagnosis. I didn't want Todd to feel bad about the yard or tell him Roger did the mowing and was now paying for it, so I blamed it on the Cyclosporine.

Shockingly, while I was talking to Roger about his kids, his daughter texted me back. Her text read, "We just finished running a 13.5-mile marathon for leukemia research. My dad didn't raise a quitter, even though halfway through I wanted to sit down."

As I read this to Roger he started sobbing big fat tears. I went over to him and said, "What's the matter?"

He said, "I don't know what I did to deserve such wonderful children." At that moment, I was so thankful she had texted me. I do wish that she had called him though. It's as if this family didn't know how to deal with emotions so they just didn't deal at all.

With his electrolytes back in balance, we headed home. He still couldn't walk, he was way too weak and his body hurt all over, but he was hungry. He ate his staple of chicken, rice and veggies, and we watched TV in bed until we fell asleep. It wasn't long before he was in the bathroom with diarrhea which lasted all night. Not even the Imodium relieved it. Every time he crawled back in bed, I made him drink fluids, which he did without complaint. He couldn't talk, his voice was too weak. He just nodded at me.

Day +27

I got up early and let Rog rest. I needed to restock his medications in the bead container. He was now taking:

1. Acyclovir 800 mg twice a day
2. Amlodipine 2.5 mg once a day
3. Baclofen 10 mg three times a day
4. Cyclosporine 100 mg twice a day
5. Fluconazole 400 mg once a day
6. Gabapentin 300 mg three times a day

7. Glyburide 2.5 mg once a day
8. Levothyroxine 75 mg once a day
9. Imodium as needed
10. Lorazepam 1 mg three times a day
11. Magnesium 400 mg three times a day
12. Metoprolol 50 mg twice a day
13. CellCept 500 mg four tablets twice a day
14. Prednisone 25 mg twice a day
15. Compazine as needed
16. Simethicone 80 mg twice a day
17. Triamcinolone Acetonide 1% to feet twice a day
18. Oxycodone 5 mg as needed

When I finished, Roger was laying on his side in bed watching me. He said, "Every time I go to the clinic I feel terrible." I knew that the trip home was the real culprit, but after I started thinking about this for a minute, I wondered, *Could all this just be too much for his body? What can we do? Could we stop the Cyclosporine and just take the CellCept and Prednisone for a year?* I didn't know. I hated seeing him like that. He was so fragile, so tired, so weak. He couldn't eat or take his pills. He gagged with each one he tried then just gave up and said, "NO, it's not happening." He rolled over and fell back to sleep. I woke him in an hour and was able to get a G2 Gatorade, broth and some water down him, but it took almost an hour for him to swallow the liquids. He refused the medications except for the pain pill. He was very weak so I called the clinic for advice.

They went through the drill, "Does he have a temp? Is he drinking? Is he answering questions appropriately? His numbers were good in clinic. This is just part of the process. His body is going through a lot right now. Don't worry, just let him rest. Don't change anything, meds are exactly where we want and need them. Make sure he takes them as prescribed, even if it takes hours to get them down!" I was worried. During the night I continued to wake him to drink fluids and tried my hardest to get him to take medications. Each time he threw them up and just wanted to sleep. At 3:00 a.m. I finally fell asleep.

Day +28

At 8:30, I got up and made Roger a piece of toast, poured him a glass of Gatorade, and put some V8 on his tray. A couple people at the clinic said V8 was one thing the patients could taste and made for a nice meal if nothing else would go down. I needed to get the fluids down; his kidney numbers were once again going off the charts. We were told that once the kidneys take a hit like they did in the hospital ICU, kidney failure was always a future worry. Roger sat up in bed and started his morning task of getting all those giant pills down. He gagged with each one and some he refused to take. He said there was no way he could swallow them. If they were scored, I cut them in half for him. After two hours, with the help of the V8, which he loved, and the G2, he got them all down along with a piece of dry toast which he soaked in the V8.

Roger smelled kind of like dirty feet – musty, yeasty. He agreed to shower. I took the rolling chair from the hotel desk and turned it around so he could use it like a walker to balance himself as he shuffled slowly to the shower. He couldn't get his leg up over the bathtub to get in, so I showed him how to sit on the side of tub and use his arms to help raise his legs over the tub and into the shower. He did it perfectly and was happy. He moaned with pleasure; the shower felt good. I used the washcloth and scrubbed him from head to toe. He had been complaining about itching all over, so this was welcomed. I figured the itching was coming from the increase in pain medications and the toxins in the kidneys. Out of the shower I weighed him. His weight was at 274 pounds. When his shower was done, he went straight back to bed. It was just after 11:00 a.m. but he was out like a light.

I spent the early afternoon making a large pot of broth. I put in all the veggies and cooked them down until they were soft, close to mush. I strained out all the veggies and tossed them out for the rabbits and squirrels to eat. I woke Roger with his afternoon medications and two cups of broth. He enjoyed the broth, but as soon as a medication was swallowed, it came right back up with the broth he had just gotten down. He stood over the toilet, lid up, and salivated after each pill was swallowed, concentrating on keeping it down. His salivary glands were on overdrive, just dripping saliva into the bowl. It was a long, arduous ordeal. He finished with the second cup of broth, looked at me and said, "I can't believe I got them down!" He shuffled back to bed with his chair, a new pair of PJ bottoms, and a new pad to help with the leaking. The vomiting always caused a bit of stool leakage so the pads came in handy to help keep him clean. When I first brought them home he was mortified, but then he freaked out if there wasn't at least five available at all times and made me go to the store to buy more immediately.

At 9:00 p.m., I went in and woke him up for more fluid intake and medications. Back to the bathroom to stand over the toilet bowl again. He was able to get the warm broth and medications down, repeating everything as he'd done earlier. I asked him to sit up for a bit, but he said no then peed and headed back to bed. After he was in bed, he told me to go and look at his urine in the urinal. I asked why he used the urinal and he said it was because he wanted me to see it. It was dark amber like it was during his time in the ICU. I asked if he was in any pain in the mid back or abdominal area, or had any burning. He said no. This was not a good sign so I took his temp and it was 94.7, which seemed to be his normal now. I sat with him and as we talked, I scratched his back and head. He said, "Oh, that feels so good!" He was feeling a little better so I used this time to encourage him to drink more fluids. He said, "I'm doing the best I can, I promise. I need to sleep now." I tucked him in and shut the door so he could rest.

I felt pretty good since Roger got his meds down, plus two cups of broth and a liter of fluids so I finally headed to bed. Roger looked at me, said goodnight, and rolled over. No kiss, no hug or holding hands like we normally did, just put his back to me. I wondered if he knew how much I worried about him, how scared I was. I knew it was the bad thoughts going through my head that were causing my high blood pressure. I looked at the patients sitting in the chairs at the clinic, their caregivers sitting next to them. Usually there were no conversations, no laughter, no smiles, no holding hands. It was as if they too were consumed with their own fears of the disease that they took home every day, the disease that was hiding in their loved one's body, eating it alive. We, as caregivers, are there every day, all day and night, at every call, every appointment, every meal. We made every decision and kept most of them secret to keep the peace, tired and alone in our heads with these thoughts. Do they, our loved ones going through hell, have anything left for *us* or was I just being selfish thinking they should be more grateful and tell us more often how appreciative they were? I must realize that it is what it is. There was no changing the dynamics of the whole diagnosis and what came with it. I knew Roger had great comfort in knowing I was here taking care of him; getting him through hell. All he needed to worry about was getting better and getting through the next bag of IV fluids, whatever solution or poison was dripping into him, and keeping his food and drink down with a pile of poison pills three times a day.

At some point you would think the human psyche would wake up and say, "What are you doing to yourself? Get out of here, run as fast as you can!" But no, these patients sit there and they agree to be poisoned. It's an amazing and unbelievable act of sheer faith that being poisoned will help them, even though they are not seeing any progress. All they see is more wasting away, more throwing up and poop in their pants. They are tired, full of sores and have lost interest in life. How do they do it? What do they think when they look in the mirror? I hadn't asked Roger this question, only because I was afraid to. So, we caregivers sit there and stay quiet, keeping to ourselves. It was a wonder how we got through it all. I took Roger's Ativan sometimes just to quiet my head. Sometimes it worked, sometimes not so much.

Day +29

It was a clinic day. Roger was feeling a little better, but I think it was because he would be seeing the nurse practitioner. He was able to eat half of a banana and some Gatorade for breakfast. The CNA came in first to take Roger's vital signs. Roger started telling her everything that had transpired over the past few days as if she was the NP. I just let him talk. He painted a rosy picture, "I'm doing pretty good. I ate, I pooped, I have been resting and doing a little exercise when I can, mostly in the room right now. Just nervous about being outside amongst people with all this flu going around."

When the CNA finished, she looked at Rog and said, "Great, I will let your NP know."

He sat back, looked at me and smiled. I was in shock, staring at him. He had no clue! The NP showed up seconds after the CNA left. The CNA had not forwarded anything Roger had just told her. The NP said, "Hello, how have you been?"

Roger started in again with all the rosy pleasantries. "I'm doing good. I have been eating and pooping and getting a lot of rest. I have been exercising in my room. The flu is pretty bad, so I'm staying away from people."

I slowly and cautiously interjected reality, telling her that Roger hadn't eaten but a few pieces of dry toast and a half of banana, along with a few cups of broth, a few bottles of Gatorade, one V8, and about two liters of water since we were there last. I let her know he was throwing up a lot of this fluid with his medications, and he stood over the commode draining copious amounts of saliva while he concentrated on keeping his medications down.

Roger interrupted with more rosy words, "But I kept them down and did great the rest of the night." I proceeded to tell her his stomach was in so much pain that he was taking pain meds every two to three hours just to be able to rest, and that his exercise consisted of using a chair to get from the bed to the bathroom where he was still having bouts of diarrhea and was now wearing a pad to protect his skin.

Roger was livid! He started talking over the top of me. He said, "The last few days were pretty bad. I had a bad bout of diarrhea, but I am eating now and drinking good, and

I got up and sat on the couch and am doing better now. It was a little rough there for a while but not now."

I was in my head saying, *REALLY? And when did NOW begin? When we walked in the door a minute ago?*

The NP looked at me then at Roger then back to me as if she was trying to sift through the information just presented. She said, "I'll be right back" and left the room.

Roger sat back in his chair, ran his fingers through his hair, closed his eyes and let out a big sigh. I touched his arm gently and said, "I'm not trying to undermine you, but you can't say you are doing so good, eating and drinking and taking your meds when you're not. These past few days have been hell. You've had nibbles of food and I'm having to force fluids on you every hour, hoping you can keep them down. You can't even raise your leg up to get in the tub, and once again we used a wheelchair to get in the clinic."

He said, "You are bringing all this doom and gloom in when I am doing better today."

I said, "How are they going to figure out what is going on inside you, which has been horrible, if you're not honest? You can't leave out all that has happened over the past few days just because you feel better at this moment. You still can't eat without gagging and your stomach is on fire most of the time. You have to be honest. If something bad is happening inside of you, they need to jump on top of it so it doesn't progress into something really bad. They won't know how to treat your symptoms if you continue to paint a rosy picture over doom and gloom because you want to be a star patient. I have been watching you suffer and worrying about you day and night as you lay in that bed unable to move, eat or keep fluids down. Roger, tell them the truth, what is really going on! Do you want to be admitted again?"

He took my hand and said, "Okay, okay, okay... stop! I will tell them, fine!" We sat in silence for a few minutes. The doctor walked in. We were both surprised to see him. We never saw him, just the nurses. He asked Roger to tell him what was going on. He had a handful of lab results. I wished they were in my hands. When Roger was done telling the truth, the doctor looked at us, paused and said, "You have GVHD. We have now realized this is your body showing us that a battle is happening. Not to worry, but to be very careful with the symptoms. Roger, the next time you have a bout of diarrhea, I need you to call us so dehydration doesn't occur again. Your medications will stay the same. Take it easy. Your body is fighting your old cells that remained after the induction phase and it won't be pleasant for a while, so just be careful. If we need to up the Cyclosporine again, we will. I will check your labs again next clinic day."

Roger said, "I don't want to increase the Cyclosporine. If you need to do that, I want the medication Dr. Cooke told us about."

I said, "Tacrolimus." Tacrolimus is also an anti-rejection drug like Cyclosporine. Patients get put on one or the other.

The doctor replied with, "Okay, if or when we have to increase, we will change you over." Roger smiled, and the doctor shook his hand and said, "You're doing really good, but now we will need to follow you even closer because of the GVHD. You have dropped quite a bit of weight. It's a good thing you had some to lose!"

I told him about the research I did every night and asked about the implications of getting GVHD in the first 30 days post-transplant. He looked at both of us then glanced at the floor. I said, "Please be honest."

He said, "Well, it's not good, but Roger is still in the early stages. I will watch the labs closely. I really don't think we need to talk about this yet. It's all a part of the process." I asked where the GVHD was in his body. He said, "Maybe the skin is where it started. He had a pretty bad rash all over his body, and his liver is under attack right now, *but* the numbers look pretty good today. It changes a lot." I felt like he wasn't comfortable talking to us about this. He wasn't finishing thoughts or sentences and he seemed like he just wanted out of the room.

I asked, "What do I look for? I mean, is there anything that I should be aware of or be cautious about? You know, what should I assume is *not normal*? What should I watch for?"

He said, "You are doing all that already. Just keep doing what you're doing. And it is imperative that he not miss a dose of his medications. I will increase the Prednisone to help with the GVHD, but that's all." He stood up and started talking to the NP about Roger's next visit and what labs he wanted to add to the list. He looked at us, smiled, shook Roger's hand and left. If he only knew that Roger had mowed the lawn.

We went home, and Roger went to the couch and turned on the TV. I went out to the couch to talk with Rog about what his doctor said and the new diagnosis of GVHD of the skin and liver. He kept his eyes on the TV and said, "The doctor didn't seem worried about it so I will take the Prednisone like he said." I asked if he was worried or nervous. I didn't want to tell him that the studies showed that if GVHD occurred within the first three to 30 days post-transplant, the mortality rate went up exponentially within two years. In that two years, the patient goes through hell. He said, "No, I'm not worried or nervous. I won't be mowing the lawn again, that's for sure!" and he started channel surfing so I let him be. I was nervous and worried enough for both of us!

Roger was able to eat five big pieces of watermelon and a protein drink; Premier energy drink, which I'd found at the warehouse store. The hospital gave him Ensure, which he promptly handed back after he smelled it. The Premier drinks gave him 30 grams of protein and actually tasted like a really good milkshake. All three flavors – vanilla, chocolate and strawberry – tasted good. I made another pot of soup, bound and determined to keep his body alkaline since no cancer can live in an alkaline body. I was planning on seeing a whole lot more sunsets with my handsome man.

Day +30

We had gone to bed the previous night at 9:00 p.m. and set the alarm for 6:30 a.m. At 5:41, we were both awake and feeling like a million bucks. Neither of us woke up tired or exhausted and it was wonderful. I let Roger take his time getting up and using the bathroom while I strained the still warm broth off the veggies from the night before, and tossed the remnants into the ravine outside the door where the rabbits, birds and squirrels lived. Roger's mom had an appointment so we offered to take her and she agreed. I brought Rog his tray of juices, a piece of toast, and some fruit to take his medication with. I had already packed our travel bag with all his necessary goodies for the trip. Rog's mom lived about 20 minutes away so we were in no big rush. I told Rog to take his time getting the pills and food down. This morning he had no problem. No gagging, right down the hatch.

After the appointment we headed straight to bed when we got home and took a two-and-a-half-hour nap. I snuggled right up to Rog and fell asleep immediately. It was wonderful. We had an uneventful night. Roger was able to get a couple cups of broth down with his medications and that was about it. He was in his head most of the evening; I'm sure he was thinking about his mom and a comment the doctor made. It was awful, but to be honest, he did look like he could be my father. He had aged 30 years in such a short time. I kept quiet.

A couple of our friends from the Elks Club called, inviting us to the big 4th of July camping trip that we usually attended each year. I said we would try to make it. I missed life!

Day +31

Today was a shopping day. I needed some groceries and asked Roger if he wanted to go. He said yes but would stay in the car. I was glad he added that because he didn't have the stamina or strength to walk far. He had refused a cane, saying it made him look like an old man. No matter what twist I put on the cane idea, he said no. I did the shopping as fast as I could so he wouldn't have to sit long. His butt was so bony now that if he sat in one spot for too long he got very uncomfortable. For his birthday, his daughter sent him a $100.00 gift certificate. I had told the kids I was going through organic veggies by the pound to make Roger's broth and how much it was costing. The irony of it all was that all these veggies were lying in my garden right now wasting away, and here I was having to buying them. I used all but $2.04. It was going to be a great soup! The butcher had a very large knuckle bone full of marrow, the perfect protein for the soup.

When we got home, I prepared the soup and let it simmer while Roger went to bed. He wasn't talking much. I thought we could take a drive to get some fresh air, but he wasn't feeling up to it. He was lying in bed with the sheet on him, his hands folded across his chest and his eyes closed. I snuggled up to him, but he was so cold to the touch. There was a time when I couldn't even snuggle for a minute with him because he was like a furnace, and my hot flashes made it worse. I studied his face as he rested. The bags under his eyes were all puffy and raised, he was pale in color, and his lips were chapped. His hair was so thin now that I could see the freckles on his scalp. I asked the NP about his dry skin. He said it was a result of radiation called "a great shedding," but the skin underneath would be really nice. Roger's muscle mass was getting so thin it was hardly visible. His arms and thighs were so thin, and his belly was completely gone. His pants were two sizes too big and when he shuffled around in them all bent over, he looked 80 years old. I planned to go to the secondhand store to get him some smaller pants soon. I had a feeling he was going to lose more weight so that would save us some money while his weight fluctuated.

Roger slept the day and night away. I brought him soup, medications and fluids throughout the day and night, and let him rest. I spent the afternoon watching the little animals outside the door. I enjoyed feeding them nuts and raisins. Some of the other patients in the rooms next to us started their days watching, smiling and waving at me through the window. Seven squirrels and two bunnies became my friends, which helped me from missing Max. These little creatures entertained me when I was lonely.

Day +32

This was a clinic day. Roger was getting his usual transfusion of magnesium, but interestingly, his Cyclosporine level was too high. The NP decreased his Cyclosporine to 50 mg twice a day and increased his magnesium. He also decreased his Prednisone to 20 mg twice a day. I kind of freaked out. If he was experiencing GVHD, why the decreases? Wasn't that dangerous? Every time these two medications – Cyclosporine and Prednisone – were messed with, Roger had a couple bad days of exhaustion and just slept. The NP said, "This is part of the process. Medications will change often, that's why we test his blood every three days. Don't worry, it's routine." For the body to make such big changes constantly just seemed counterproductive. It never had a moment to rest; it was constantly in flux.

Roger's weight was holding at 274 pounds. The NP noticed Roger's shuffling gait and his puffy face. He asked a lot of questions about his stamina, walking and appetite. Roger replied, "It's all hit or miss. Some moments good, and some bad. But lately I just want to sleep." The NP reminded him to walk as much as possible and not to worry about diet, telling him to eat when he wanted but to make sure he got two liters of fluid in every day.

Roger slept the rest of the day and night. No food, just broth. Temperature was at his usual 94.7. I played with my beads and watched a little TV.

Day +33

Rog decided a drive home would be nice so we headed home for the day. My kids were at Mom's again, working on her house, and Mom was in the garden picking veggies for soup. Roger was slow and tired but enjoyed sitting on the deck in the fresh air with the sun shining on him while I tinkered around the place.

At the end of the day we had a nice meal together then headed back. It was a nice, peaceful day with no fighting or arguing. I tried to talk Rog into staying but he said he still feared being so far away from the hospital. At day +60, if Roger was doing well we would be released to go home so these little trips helped get him ready for what was to come.

Day +34

Roger slept through the morning. When he got up, we took a small walk around the complex and that was all he could handle. Every time the Prednisone dosage was changed, he went through a complete exhaustion period where everything was an extra effort. Whatever gains he had made were lost and he had to start all over again. I did the laundry and made a nice lentil soup. I had told Shawn at the clinic I would bring him some homemade soup. We had been on the same clinic schedule for a while now and all I ever saw him eat was fast food, which made me crazy. You would think his mother would make an effort to feed his body better, especially since this was his second transplant. Each day, sitting in my little plastic chair, I noticed patients eating fast food, junk food and sodas. No nutritional value at all. Do they not know their diet is a HUGE part of the reason the United States is in the cancer business in the first place? I just wanted to shake some intelligence, some common sense, into them!

I spent the day cooking, beading, researching and feeding my furry friends out the door. I got our goodie bag packed for the next day's clinic and headed to bed early. Roger slept peacefully throughout the night. When he did wake, he quickly went to the bathroom, drank one of the glasses of fluids I put by his bedside each night then back to sleep he went.

Day +35

I brought a nice big bowl of soup for both Shawn and Rog to eat at the clinic. I made sure the veggies in the soup were nice and soft for the boys, providing less work for their bodies to do. Shawn was in rare form, sitting right next to us and talking for four hours straight. Roger was so tired. It was another day of needing the wheelchair to get into the clinic. He just wanted to sleep through his transfusion, but Shawn wasn't having it. Every time Roger laid his head back, Shawn would bump his arm to make sure he was paying attention. Shawn loved the soup and was grateful that I had brought extra so his mom could have some too.

Roger seemed a little too tired. He had slept for the most part of two days. After the magnesium was complete, we were called in to see the NP. Sometimes it was Tammy and sometimes it was Soter, it just depended who was on call that day. During the last clinic visit, Roger appeared too lethargic so they ran a few extra blood tests. The labs showed "abnormal atypical cells and other premature cells" that shouldn't be there. I asked what that meant and Tammy said, "I should let Soter talk with you on this one, but he isn't here today. So what it means is that possibly the leukemia is back. If the leukemia is back today at +34, it's really bad."

I sat up and said, "Well, he has a butt-load of stored donor cells waiting for him, right? And you will put him back on Disatinib, right?"

Roger sat forward and put his head in his hands. We both heard him sniffle. The NP said, "Let's not jump the gun just yet. We need to change the Cyclosporine to 75 mg in the morning and 50 mg in the evening. Your blood level last time was sitting at around 99. Today it is 214, which is 75 points too high. Your kidney function is very poor right now which is most likely causing the increase in all your levels. You are at day +38 if we count the induction, which we do. If GVHD is going to rear its ugly head, it is now."

I said, "He had GVHD the week after transplant and we were told by the doctor, if you recall, he has it possibly in the skin and liver, so I'm confused." She explained that they really didn't know about the first diagnosis of GVHD, he just presented with the classic symptoms of it so they assumed it was GVHD. Today his bloodwork and lethargy, as well as his overall look, showed that this *was* the case. She told us she would be talking with the doctor later, and at the next clinic visit they would repeat all lab work for comparison. She seemed a little uncomfortable and it was obvious she wanted us to ask the doctor our questions at the next visit.

We drove home in a daze. Was the leukemia back? What did that mean? Was it the same kind of leukemia, the kind that almost killed him IN THREE DAYS? Why were we waiting for the doctor to do something maybe at the NEXT VISIT? All we were doing was increasing the Cyclosporine? It doesn't stop leukemia cells! That's not remotely what it does. I was screaming inside! Why are they not more concerned? What am I missing?

Roger wasn't talking, he just stared out the window on the way home. I asked him if he was alright and he said he was just tired. He had some juice, a bowl of soup and his meds, and went to bed when we got back to the hotel. At 7:30 p.m., he was in the bathroom with diarrhea and vomiting. He was in there a long time, and at one point I heard the bathtub water running. I went to the door, it was locked. At 8:15 he came out. I crawled in bed with him and asked him if he'd had an accident. He said, "Yes, from both ends. I needed to rinse my night pants out." I told him I would have done that so he didn't have to use up his energy. He just laid back and closed his eyes. I got him some Imodium and water.

At 2:00 a.m., he was up again with the same diarrhea and vomiting. He came back and sat on the side of the bed. I came around in front of him and he leaned forward, put his head on my chest, and just rested it there. I rubbed his shoulders and caressed his head. I gave him two more Imodium and took his temp which was 99.9. He said, "I had too many covers on me. I'm alright." He was asleep in seconds.

Day +36

Roger stayed in bed most of the day and his behavior was really off. I didn't know if he was confused because he was so tired or if it was something else. At one point he came into the living room, sat down, took the TV remote control, and started calling it a wrench. He was acting as if he was working on a car. He explained everything he needed and what he was doing to the imaginary car in front of him. At first I thought he was being silly but soon realized he was asleep. He was sleepwalking. I softly but firmly called his name out loud in a tone that got his attention and he looked at me and woke up, looking around as if saying, *Why am I here?* He stayed on the couch for a while, dozing in and out. I finally put him back to bed, and once again he sat on the side of the bed and rested his head on my chest. I loved those moments when I got to be so close to him and smell him.

At 3:45 p.m., I brought him some water, juice and broth, and gave him his afternoon meds. He got up to pee but headed into the living room where my bathroom was. He had never used my bathroom. I said, "Your bathroom is in here." He turned around and headed toward his bathroom. As he walked, his night pants fell to the floor, right off his hips. He didn't flinch, he just bent over, pulled them up and held them as he walked. I took his temp; it was 99.4. Since his temp usually ran 94.7 – 97.4, when it was 99 or above, that was a temperature for Roger. For some reason I couldn't get that point across to the NPs in the clinic. It was a fast and hard rule, 100.4 or higher was a high temp, period. He sat on the side of the bed again. I knelt in front of him and looked up at him. His face was warm to the touch and red and glossy. He was having trouble making eye contact with me, as if he was in a fog. His eyes were bloodshot again, and he wasn't talking much, his voice at a whisper. I started to get a bad feeling. I asked him if he remembered working on the car earlier. He looked at me funny and said no. He asked what was on TV, I answered, and he said, "Hmmm," then lay back down and fell asleep within seconds. I was worried.

I called Roger's mom who told me that in church, one of her friends confided that her son also had a bone marrow transplant for leukemia and was doing really bad. She said, "Boy, Robin, this is serious isn't it?"

I said, "Yes, it is, Mom."

Roger slept through the night with only one trip to the bathroom with diarrhea and was in there a long time. I got up to check on him and he was asleep on the commode. I woke him, helped him clean up, and put him back to bed. I set the alarm to check on him every two hours. When 9:30 a.m. arrived and the alarm sounded, I just wanted to throw it out the window. I was so exhausted.

Day +37

After rising, I got the pills and a small tray of crackers, fruit and an assortment of juices for Roger. He sat on the side of the bed and ate the crackers, drank most of the juice, and took all the medication. He was so oily and the sheets under him smelled bad. I asked him to shower, and let him know I needed to change the sheets. He said okay, laid down and went back to sleep. I opened the curtains, he told me to close them. The room was once again dark and quiet.

I sat and watched him sleep, snoring lightly. Just a few months ago he was on a tractor, moving a mountain and swinging a hammer, building shelves in his new 1200 square foot garage man cave. He was happy, fun, loving and so hopeful for our new future as ranchers. Now he laid there in that bed shaky, tired, sick and dying. All that change in just a few months. I wished I was at home. I sat in that dark room, scared, sick to my core, bored and so lonely. My best friend was so sick he couldn't be my friend, let alone my husband. He was just dwindling away in front of me. I felt like something wasn't right, that he was getting worse. I couldn't believe the transplant was the best idea. I was almost afraid that we weren't going back home together. What was I going to do if I ended up alone? How would I pick up the pieces? How would I save my house from being foreclosed on? How would I get out of the five-year balloon loan? I didn't like this feeling. Maybe I was just too tired. I let Roger rest as I went to the couch, found a movie, and just stared at the TV.

At 1:00 p.m., Roger got up and sat on the couch with me. I had to take this opportunity to change the bedding before he laid back down. He sat staring at the TV with a blank stare. I told him I would help him shower and change his clothes unless he would like to do it himself. All he said was, "I will," yet he did nothing, so I just left him in front of the TV and made him up a fresh bed, knowing he was going to feel so much better on clean sheets. In a very shaky voice he said he was hungry, which was a good sign. He was able to get five bites of soup in, about a half cup of noodles, some water, and the rest of his electrolyte juice. He kept to himself through dinner, like he did most days now. Whenever I could, I got as close to him as possible and hugged him. Sitting on the side of the bed was my favorite time because I could hold him while he sat. He could relax and just be held. He didn't pull away. My strong, handsome man was now at 266 pounds and looked at me as if I was an empty vase in the room.

At 11:00 p.m., I said, "I really need to look at your body to make sure no new rashes have occurred. I need to give you a shower now." He agreed. I really just wanted to wash him all over with the washcloth, caress his skin and stimulate it to get the blood flowing, and scrub off all that dead, sweaty skin. As I was washing his legs, loose diarrhea and bloody water trickled down the inside of his legs. I asked him if I could look at his bottom because he was bleeding, and he turned his back to me. His whole rectal area was raw and inflamed. I cringed with disbelief of what I saw. I said, "Oh, are you in pain down here?"

He said, "Sometimes."

I said, "If you're not feeling better tomorrow, maybe we should go to the clinic.

He said, "They don't say or do anything. It's part of the process. I will be okay."

Once at the clinic they had said, "Yeah, we know you feel crappy, it's part of the process." So, what do you do? At what point, if you *don't* have a temperature, aren't throwing up or unconscious yet and still able to drink fluids, do you decide that what's going on could possibly be something wrong? Call only if you fit the criteria below:

1. Any temperature is greater than 100.4
2. Nausea/vomiting is unresponsive to anti-nausea medications
3. Significant diarrhea despite Imodium
4. Inability to drink at least two liters of fluid daily
5. You develop a rash

I have come to realize that the answers go like this when you call, pertaining to each consecutive number above:

For #1: Take a Tylenol; if it doesn't lower the temp, call the clinic.

For #2: Take one Compazine, then two, if needed.

For #3: If you can't get off the toilet, it's just running out of you and you have tried two Imodium, wait then take another two.

For #4: At least get in one liter. Two is recommended. After a few days, we will see you in the clinic anyway.

For #5: Roger was purple as a beet and it didn't draw attention for days.

I really didn't know what constituted an emergency call anymore. I was tired of being told, "Don't worry, we will just see him at the next clinic appointment. Unfortunately, this is part of the process."

Calling the BMT clinic and describing your loved one as, "He's acting different, off, catatonic, saying things that don't make sense, not eating or participating in life, bleeding from an inflamed rectum," was going to most likely get an answer like this; *Don't worry it's part of the process, we will see him at the next clinic unless he gets worse.* To me, this was *all* very bad. *They* had seen it over and over again and were numb to the fact that we caregivers were babies. We don't know how to rate each symptom that pops up. To us, this was bad! To them, It's *part of the process.* I just wanted and wished someone would have told me, just pulled me aside and told me what to expect next. If they know the "Process Symptoms" then why don't they tell you? Why is it not openly talked about at each clinic visit?

I was so mentally tired, my hair was turning gray so fast, and my positive attitude was fading. Roger had said I was "doom and gloom" the other day. It was hard not to be doom and gloom when all that stood before me was doom and gloom. I had no one to talk to, to get these thoughts out of my head. I believe when we vent we release all the worry, so fresh new, positive ideas can come in. Every day was frustrating. If Roger wasn't doing better soon, I knew I needed to take him to the ER no matter what. Screw the process!

We went to bed after the shower. I laid there thinking about tomorrow being Father's Day. The last thing I wanted to do to Roger was to make him sit in the ER or sit all day at the clinic if he didn't have to on Father's Day.

Day +38

At 9:00 a.m., I woke Rog with his morning meds, a scrambled egg, and a protein drink. He ate the egg and finished the drink before he went back to sleep. At 1:00 p.m., I woke him again for a little lunch and his meds, and he decided to get up and sit on the couch for a bit. I let the kids know he was awake with a group text. One by one they called and wished him Happy Dad's Day. He talked to each one for about five minutes. It was so hard on him to talk. He was trying to sound strong, healthy and happy, but he didn't do so well. With each minute that passed, his voice got weaker and scratchier. He cut the calls as short as possible. I felt so bad for him. He was fading so fast as all five kids called. When the last one hung up, he looked at me and said, "I have nothing left, I need to go to bed." I tucked him in bed, closed the curtains, and kissed him gently on the forehead.

I sat in the living room the rest of the afternoon, looking out the window at the overgrown vegetation in the ravine and all the different kinds of birds jumping from branch to branch. I tried to study and research a bit, but nothing I read made me feel better, just more worried. I wrote in my journal, dumping all my thoughts onto those sheets of paper. I wondered what it would be like when I re-read those pages in the years to come. I thought about Max who I needed so much. Just touching his soft fur and snuggling my face into him made me feel so much better when I was feeling down. Betty was keeping him safe, and that was my only peace of mind.

I woke Roger with his evening meds. He sat on the side of the bed to take them, went potty then returned to bed. I rubbed his lower back for a bit then snuggled up to him. He laid still while I snuggled him. This was my happiness, even if I didn't get snuggled back.

Day +39

Roger woke up at 7:00 a.m. and shouted, "I'm late. I'm late." He bolted to the bathroom and turned on the shower so fast it was unbelievable! He didn't stumble, he ran. I looked at the clock, which was set to go off in another 30 minutes. I just laid in bed and rested. After a bit he poked his head out and said, "I'm sorry, we're not late. I got confused."

I said, "I know, it's okay." When he was done with his shower, I helped him dress. His energy surprised me. He took one sip of the coffee he had made us and that was it. We had a light breakfast of fruit, a protein drink, toast and a handful of meds.

I was so thankful clinic day was finally here! I was really worried about all this sleeping, and the bleeding and rash on his rectal area. We hadn't been on a walk in days. The NP wanted to see Roger ASAP. I wheeled him in and Soter said, "Wow, how much weight have you lost, Roger?"

He started to shuffle the paperwork, looking for his recent weight and Roger said, "50 pounds in five weeks," and he was right. He surprised me again. He tried to tell Soter how awful the past four days had been but couldn't finish the words; his voice was so weak. I took over for him, recapping the little intake of food, the bleeding diarrhea, severe weakness, and the hours and hours of sleeping. He ordered a CT scan but wanted him to get some labs and a bag of magnesium first. When the labs came back, we were all shocked. They looked the same as his last visits; no changes. How could he be this weak and there be no changes? Maybe the CT scan would show something. Roger asked for an Ativan prior to the scan, and hesitantly they gave him one on the condition he stayed in the wheelchair because of weakness.

The men in the CT scan area practically picked Roger up and placed him gently on the scanning table. Unbelievably, Roger promptly fell asleep. When the scan was done, we were sent home to wait for the results. I got him home, gave him his medications with a large cup of broth and crackers, and he went to bed for the night. I beaded for a while to collect my thoughts then joined him.

2

Carry Me

It was day +40. As soon as I got up, I called for the CT scan results. Roger was so weak he could barely walk to the bathroom without me holding him up. He had asked me to carry him to the bathroom all night long. I was heartbroken with worry. The watery diarrhea was back and was bright yellow with a stench so bad it burned my nose. His rectal area was so inflamed he said it felt like acid every time he went. I put a handful of petroleum jelly on his rectum to help prevent the stool from burning so bad. It helped a little. I told all this to Soter when I called for the CT scan results. He said the scan results looked better than the last one he'd had quite a while back. He said, "If Roger becomes confused or unable to keep fluids down, take him to the ER. If he spikes a temp, take him to the ER. If not, call back in the morning with an update." If I had been home, I would have already had him in the ER, but under these circumstances, all I had to go on was what the clinic NPs were telling me to do. I didn't know what was normal or not normal, and as far as I was concerned, this was a classic case of C-Diff right down to the smell. All nurses know the smell of C-Diff, a bacterial infection whose symptoms range from diarrhea to life threatening inflammation of the colon. It commonly affects older adults in hospitals or long-term care, and typically occurs after the use of an antibiotic. I would assume this was not normal and we should go to the ER, but I hated to take him to the ER to sit amongst a bunch of sick, germy people, only to have the BMT doctor called and us sent home with, "Yeah, you feel crappy. It's part of the process." I hated this! My poor baby was in so much discomfort and he wouldn't eat anything because he didn't want to have to go to the bathroom!

At 10:30 p.m., I took Roger's temperature, and it was at 101.4. That was the ticket to the ER. I called the on-call BMT doctor and told him I was taking him to the ER. I asked the doctor if he could call the ER and let them know we were on our way. He said he would. Roger was miserable. All day he had been literally crawling from the bed to the toilet, and his voice was so weak I could barely hear him. I got a bag packed in case we stayed overnight. With most of his weight bearing down on me, I helped him to the car. I needed to get him a cane whether he liked it or not!

We arrived at the ER at 11:20 p.m. and found out no one had called from the BMT clinic. Once again, we sat in the little lobby, cold and worried while we waited our turn. We had not been bumped up, we were not special, we were just like the rest, waiting our turn. I was livid, but I kept it to myself. At 12:15 a.m. they called Roger back and took his temp, which was now up to 102.3. They gave him a bed pan for a stool sample which he was able to give, took blood cultures and six additional vials of blood, and left. I asked the CNA to close the door while we waited and she did. We waited and waited. Finally, the door opened abruptly and a woman burst in the door, startling us. I was using the side of the gurney as a pillow as I sat in the chair next to the bed. Roger was fast asleep. She thrust a tall, plastic jug at Roger, and in a heavy accent she said, "Drink this, all of it, and they come get you." She had started to walk out the door when I stopped her. I asked what he was drinking and for what reason. She said, "CT scan." I told her he'd just had one. She stood there a minute then said, "Wait" and left. A couple minutes later, she came back in and took the jug from the night stand and said, "Wrong patient, never mind" and left.

I looked at Roger and said, "What was that? It's a good thing I questioned her. If I hadn't been here, would you have drunk that?"

Roger said, "Yes, I would have drunk that."

I looked at him and said, "Your kidneys would have shut back down. There is no way they are ready for another hit like that." I was mortified! I knew I couldn't leave him, I had to be present and mentally alert at all times. I crawled up on the gurney with him and just held him. We were in that dark room for hours. I dozed off a few times, which helped a lot. Just that little ten minutes here and there cleared my mind.

At 7:00 a.m. the results were back. After eight hours in that chair trying not to fall asleep, my left shoulder was killing me from trying to get in a comfortable position, and my butt was numb. Roger's hip bones and sacrum were killing him. The ER doctor said it was C-Diff, and the drug of choice was Vancomycin, six times a day. We were told that it would take at least two days to notice a difference. She also mentioned the Cyclosporine levels, which were at 70. I looked at her and said, "That's weird. Just five days ago it was 98, two days later 214, and today 70? How can that be?" I explained the rollercoaster ride Roger had been on ever since he started this medication. I asked if he could be put on Tacrolimus.

She said she would discuss it with the BMT doctor, but in the meantime, he needed fluids. I asked about the rest of the labs and she said, "I have his last set of labs from two days ago. His labs tonight are actually better than the ones from the other day, but he needs fluids, his kidneys need fluids." I was shocked that his labs looked better. Nothing made sense anymore. She told us to sit tight, he would be getting 2000cc of IV fluids, and in the meantime I was to go get his Vancomycin from the pharmacy to take home with us. Roger asked for pain medication.

They gave him some and before he fell back to sleep, I got up in his face and said, "I will be back shortly. Question anything that they might try to give you while I'm gone." I held his face, looked in his eyes and said, "What did I just say?" He repeated it so I kissed him and went to the pharmacy.

The pharmacist came to the window and told me there was a problem with the insurance. They were not paying for the Vancomycin, and it was $1200.00. I looked at her in disbelief but didn't say anything. She waited for me to say something as I just stared at her, my mind in total chaos. Finally, she put her hand on mine and said, "Give me a few minutes, I'll be right back." I waited for two hours. Several times the pharmacist came out and told me she was still waiting for a call back. I told her I would be back later, that I needed to get Roger home.

When I returned to the ER, Roger was sitting up drinking juice. I said, "Wow, you look chipper." He said the fluids made him feel so much better, and his head felt so much clearer. We were discharged, headed home, and both went straight to bed. Because I couldn't get the Vancomycin yet, the ER gave him an IV dose before we left so I knew he was covered for a bit. I needed at least three hours of sleep then I would head back to pick up meds. If I didn't get us home soon, I would fall asleep at the wheel!

At 1:00 p.m., the phone rang, waking me from a dead sleep. I fumbled with the phone, dropped it then finally answered it. It was the clinic checking up on Roger. I told them what had transpired in the ER, which they were aware of since they had already received the ER reports. I explained that he felt better after the IV fluids, but he was still in bad shape. The NP told me that they were changing medications again. Roger was to begin taking the Tacrolimus, discontinue the Cyclosporine, add the antibiotic Bactrim, and take the Vancomycin until it was gone. I asked about the Bactrim. I was told it was part of the study protocol, and started on the 42nd day to prevent pneumonia. They then gave me a new clinic schedule. Roger was to be in the clinic every day for blood draws to monitor the Tacrolimus levels. As soon as they were at a therapeutic level, we could return to our original clinic schedule. I wrote everything down, said thank you and laid back down.

Roger heard the phone conversation since he was only six inches away from me, and his only remark was, "Every day again. Great..." I wasn't sure how to feel about all this. I hoped the Tacrolimus was easier on his system and that his body would manage it better than the Cyclosporine. All this medication was bad for him, bad for anyone. To think it was keeping him alive was such an oxymoron. It was so hard to wrap my head around what was going on in his body, how it was able to function at all. What an amazing machine the human body is!

I made Roger some lunch; broth and crackers with a G2 drink. I gave him his afternoon meds with a pain pill then put the urinal next to the bed so he didn't have to try to walk while I was gone. I headed to the pharmacy. When I arrived, the pharmacist had seen me come in, and came out into the waiting room and asked me to come to her window. She said the insurance company finally agreed to pay for the Vancomycin if it was in liquid form. If we agreed, they would pay the $54.00 for it. The pill form was $1200.00, but the same liquid medication was $54.00. What a difference! I agreed. She said she was glad Roger was switching to the Tacrolimus. I told her what had happened with the Cyclosporine, and she said she had noticed the dosage difference over the past few weeks and was not surprised at all. She said the original dose had been calculated wrong by the clinic. It was so nice talking to her. She asked me how I was doing and, of course, the water works started. My pockets were always loaded with tissues so I pulled out a handful. She laughed which made me laugh. It felt so good to just laugh! She hugged me and said, "You're doing good, Robin, you are a good wife." It was wonderful to hear. I don't know why, but it was just wonderful!

Roger was still in bed when I got home, and there was no pee in the urinal. I made myself a sandwich and fruit, and Roger a bowl of soup with crackers, his protein drink and a glass of water. I sat on the bed with him and we ate. I told him about the medication costs and that the pharmacist was really nice to me. He put his hand on my cheek and ran a finger down under my chin, raised it and said, "You are a good wife and I couldn't do this without you. You're my angel!"

I got choked up and said, "I love you so much, Roger!"

I put the dishes in the sink, texted everyone that we were headed to bed, would check in the next day, and not to call that night. I was asleep before my head hit the pillow. Of course, the kids texted me, "Goodnight" a few hours later, which woke us up, but it didn't take much to go back to sleep. I was up a few times with medications and helping Rog to the bathroom, but for the most part it was uneventful.

Day +42

The alarm sounded at 7:30 a.m. Roger sat up on the side of the bed as if he had been awake for hours, but he hadn't. This morning I was up and at 'em too. I was so ready to get him to the clinic. I looked over at him sitting on the side of the bed, bent over as if he was looking for something on the floor, and asked him if he was okay and ready to go to clinic.

He looked at me and said, "Heck yeah, get me there!" I laughed, he chuckled. I packed the bags and told him we were also having breakfast at the clinic. For breakfast I brought some instant oatmeal and cut up fruit; for lunch, two peanut butter sandwiches, cheese sticks, protein drinks and G2. I had my day set. A few books, my beads and Roger's medications, and off we went.

The NP saw us right away. Roger was still pale and hunched over in the chair, just staring at the floor. His temperature was 99.8. She asked him how he was doing, made a little small talk about the C-Diff infection, and went over our new schedule. She skipped over all the details of the past few days and the ER visit and started right in on all the upcoming changes. First, Roger would get another 1000cc of IV fluids and a 4 gm bag of magnesium. I was given a written script for the Tacrolimus and the new clinic schedule. We were also told that Roger was going to start getting an IV solution called Intravenous Immunoglobulin, or IVIG, a solution made from human plasma to treat immune deficiencies. It contains immunoglobulins from the plasma of approximately 1000 or more blood donors. This was amazing to me. A mixture of blood plasma from one thousand people was going to be given to Roger to boost his ailing immune system. I asked if this was protocol. I was told it was not protocol, but it was a product that some patients need when their immune system is a little sluggish. The clinic would need to put in an insurance request for the IVIG first. It cost over $10,000 a bag and Roger was going to need a few bags. Also, Roger would be having a lumbar puncture and a bone marrow biopsy in a couple days. These two tests would determine if Roger's cells were all gone and how the new cells were progressing in his bone marrow. It would also determine if any rogue leukemia cells were wandering around. I asked about the C-Diff, and was told, "It happens."

I asked, "Is there a manual on the different setbacks that normally occur with transplant patients? It sure would be beneficial to know when something pops up whether to worry about it or know, *It happens, it's part of the process.* There should be a manual."

I was told, "Each patient is different. If a manual was given out like that, it would be harmful to the patients and families. Everyone would assume a setback was normal and not take the onset of symptoms seriously. Patients just need to present as setbacks happen. It's part of the process!" I was being broken like a wild horse and I didn't like it at all.

Roger got all snuggled into his clinic chair with his memory foam pillow then swallowed his handful of meds and breakfast. We saw Shawn walk in, but he hadn't seen us. Roger pushed all the finished breakfast stuff off his tray onto my lap, sat back quickly and closed his eyes. I was like, *What the heck? Why did you do that?* Then it hit me as Shawn crossed over in front of us and sat down next to me. Roger was going to sleep. Shawn was my problem today.

When Shawn left, I noticed in one of the clinic rooms next to us, two people I had not seen before. Along the walls of the infusion room are private rooms for patients who are really sick. Either they are being quarantined from us or us from them. In this room, the wife was going on and on about a cruise her and her husband were taking in a few months. She was on the phone talking loudly about the trip and all the arrangements that needed to be made. The couple looked to be around 70 years old. She was planning and calling people with lists of things to take care of. It sounded like a group of people were all going on a trip together. Her husband was in the clinic chair and she was in the little blue chair. He was the patient. The way she was giving orders to the people on the phone made me think, "I know who wears the pants in that family!" Then I heard that he was having a bone marrow transplant and they were receiving the preliminary testing schedule, EKG, pulmonary tests, echocardiograms, dental work up, etc. Throughout the consult, she continued to ask when her husband would be okay to go on the cruise.

I thought, *Oh my, she is a newbie! Cruise in three months? No, no, no, no, no!* The NP said there would be no cruise any time after the transplant.

The wife said something like, "He's okay. He's a tough guy." The NP asked if she had been present during any of the previous consultations with the doctor, then the door closed and I couldn't hear any more. I thought about our beginning days. It had been months since Roger was diagnosed, and so much had happened. I too thought Roger was going to sail right through this with no problems. Boy, did I think wrong. This was the toughest thing a person could do in a lifetime and *if* they lived through it, I had a feeling the last thing he was going to want to do was go on a cruise after his transplant. A floating petri dish of all kinds of bugs. I am truly germaphobic now!

After about 30 minutes, the couple and the NP came out of the room, and the husband was asked to take whatever empty chair he wanted in the transfusion room. If a patient gets up to go to the bathroom or to see the NP, a RESERVED note is put in the chair. He picked a seat directly in front of us. The wife looked at me then at Roger then back at me. I knew what she was thinking, and so did Roger; thinking he was much older than me.

Roger said, "She's my wife."

I asked her husband, "Are you having a mini transplant?" I assumed they were due to his age. Ages forty and under get the full dose of chemotherapy and the full radiation dose. Over forty, you get a mini, which is a lesser dose.

Her husband gently said, "Lower level, yes."

I said, "So did we."

She said, "OH, GLAD YOU'RE STILL HERE!" and walked off. Roger and I just stared at her, and Roger chuckled out loud. She had a rude awakening coming as her life was going to be turned upside down!

I looked at Rog and quietly said, "I feel sorry for her husband. She is going to be a nightmare." Roger dozed back off. I watched the older couple out of the corner of my eye as I beaded and listened to their conversation. She kept telling him he would be just fine and the "trip of a lifetime" on that cruise ship was going to be just what he needed to feel all better. I have never wanted to say something so bad in my life, but I didn't. I kept to myself, calculating when we would see them again and wondering if they would still be married.

Diana, my friend of almost 33 years, called. I was happy to hear from her. She asked me how I was doing, but as I started to tell her she cut me off and started in on her life, as it usually went. She started complaining. She'd had this big, beautiful pool and backyard oasis built and she was not lying out in the sun and enjoying it like she should but planned to start using it more ASAP to help with her stress. She said, "I'm just exhausted, Robin. This is show and sales week. I have been so busy making cinnamon rolls and shish kabobs for our evening barbeques. Today I had to go through a crap-load of wines, trying to pick out the right ones for the meals. The photographer has been staying with us for a few days like she does each season, so I have to entertain each night. I still don't have a dress yet for the big party. UGH, I still need to do that. I am just exhausted!"

I said, "Yep, lying out by that pool is the best idea to help with that stress, my friend." I love her, I do, but she is so self-centered. Her husband has given her a beautiful home that looks like a castle. He had the backyard beautifully landscaped to entertain all his friends and family, her hair was always streaked with perfect highlights, and her nails were manicured every other week. Her clothes were plentiful and the food and wine she consumed was comparable to a king's palate. I just don't think I could complain about my perfect life to my best friend who was fighting to keep her husband alive from battling cancer. I didn't say anything, I just listened as I have done for over 30 years. When the phone call ended, we exchanged I love yous and hung up. I wanted to cry.

Not knowing Roger was listening, he said, "I love you." So sweet that he knew what I was thinking. I thought about my friends going on with their lives and enjoying the ambiance of it all. Betty often sent me pictures of Max, the sunset on the beach and all the pictures of the food they were barbequing while they watched the sun drop into the drink. She sent me pictures of Max out on the deck with them, sunbathing or sleeping soundly between them at night. Life went on for everyone around me. They had no idea what my shoes felt like. Part of me wanted to scream every time they complained or bragged to me about their doings, but I quickly remembered this was not their fault and took it as it came.

Roger finished his transfusion and we headed home. It was a long, emotional day. He was hungry! We were told in the clinic that his labs showed a very low protein level in his system so I needed to make sure I upped his protein intake. I made him a nice breakfast for dinner; egg omelet with some black beans and cheese melted inside. He ate most of it with a protein drink without any discomfort. I was happy; that's a lot of protein all at once. We watched a little TV together and went to bed. We both slept through the night.

Days +43 – +44

As the Vancomycin did its wonders, we continued our back and forth schedule to the clinic. Each day was IV fluids and magnesium drips. Roger was getting a little stronger, his diarrhea was becoming less, and the stench and acid smell was subsiding. He continued to eat better; two small meals each day with a little more protein but still didn't make it out of bed unless it was to the clinic. I prepared his meals – egg and fruit with a protein drink for breakfast, organic chicken with rice, veggies and broth for late lunch/dinner – and served it on a tray for him in bed. I offered him fluids all day long. I made sure he showered and got his medications on time, and just let him rest. I figured the next day we could try a walk if he was up to it.

Day +45

The was no clinic. I asked Rog if he wanted to try to walk. I wasn't sure how that would go since he had spent the last several days in bed when not at the clinic. He wasn't able to eat breakfast, said his stomach didn't feel well. I made a piece of dry toast with some juice for his medications. He asked for a shower before the walk. I helped him to the shower and proceeded to wash him. His skin was just hanging on him after such a huge weight loss in such a short time. What was most apparent was the loss of all his muscle. There is no bulk left. I was so glad he was overweight before he'd had the transplant. He balanced himself against the shower wall with arms raised overhead, leaning against it so the water ran right down his face and belly. As I washed him, I noticed weird purple/lavender streaks going down his legs starting from his knees. I asked him to look and he said, "Yeah, probably because I can't really feel below my knees anymore." The sensitivity in his lower legs and feet was absent now. I reminded him to be very careful.

He was able to make it once around the complex. We didn't talk during the walk, he just concentrated on putting one foot in front of the other. As I watched him – shuffling, hunched over, lower lip relaxed, showing his lower teeth like it had lost its muscle and was just hanging there, breathing heavily from his mouth, eyes focused on the ground – I began to wonder if we would ever make love again. How did one go from this state of health back to a normal, healthy, physical life? Although I saw it all the time on TV, cancer patients running marathons, boasting about their survival from the deadly disease, I have never seen a bone marrow transplant patient like Roger in any of those commercials. Nor have we had the opportunity to see any bone marrow transplant survivors in his age group at the clinic. Shawn was doing pretty good, but he was 20 years old and got his donor cells from his brother; very compatible and usually successful transplants, especially at that young age. I hoped that over time, Rog would get it all back, at least his quality of life. This was not quality at all.

The walk took everything out of him, causing his legs and hands to cramp. He said, "They cramp like a charley horse. Each time the cramps hit, it almost takes me to my knees." I knew this meant his potassium was low again. As soon as we got back, I gave him two potassium pills and massaged his legs for a bit. He went back to bed for the evening. I again brought him his meds and drinks throughout the night.

3

IVIG

It was day +46, and we were excited about getting to the clinic. Most days we just go through the motions, but today we were arriving with bells on our toes. Roger was getting his first bag of IVIG! I used to work at the blood bank years ago, and people would come in and donate their plasma. It would take two hours, with both arms tied to the chair while the blood drained out one arm, filtered through a machine then back into the other arm. I now have much more respect for the wonderful people who do this for us every day. Roger was excited to get his little bag of immune boosting cells. Hopefully this would do the trick to get his system back up and running because he was working too hard to stay on top only to be knocked down again.

When we got to the clinic, we were not rushed back like the two previous times. We saw a whole new group of people sitting in the lobby. It was as if it was our first day. We didn't recognize a soul, and there were more young people today. I asked what the holdup was and I was told it had to do with our insurance. What now? Finally, we were called back after nearly an hour wait. Roger was ready to get settled down for a long day's nap when the wind was removed from his sails – both our sails. He was down another six pounds and insurance had not approved the IVIG. I thought Roger was going to cry. I asked why the insurance didn't approve it and we were told, "It will go through, it always does, but some insurances take longer than others." So, no IVIG. All his bloodwork looked good except for magnesium, as usual, so he would get that. The NP was surprised his potassium looked so good since it had been on the decline for a while. I told her I had given him two pills last night due to debilitating cramps. She just looked at me for a second as I looked back, then she went on without a word about what I had done.

We were given a schedule for the next appointment. The IVIG should arrive by then so he would get that, and on the same day he would have a lumbar puncture to test for leukemia in the spinal fluid. We were told this was part of the protocol, along with receiving a dose of Methotrexate in the spinal fluid during the procedure. I asked what the Methotrexate injection into the spinal cord was for. She answered, "It's used in the central nervous system as a prophylaxis in patients with Acute Lymphoblastic Leukemia. If a leukemia cell has reached the spinal fluid, it could lodge in the brain and cause cancer there. So, it is a preventative measure." Chemotherapy right into his brain? Roger asked if there were any side effects and she said, "You shouldn't notice anything at all."

Roger settled in for his dose of magnesium while I beaded. The rest of the day and evening was quiet and restful.

Days +47 – +48

Tuesday was uneventful. Roger ate a little, rested a little, and repeated. He tried to get more fluids in but said his stomach just couldn't handle it. Before all this happened, Roger always had seconds and even thirds with each meal. Now he didn't even have room for fluids because his stomach had gotten so small. It was an early night. We were both in bed by 8:30 p.m.

The next day I headed to the warehouse store to get more G2 and protein drinks. When I got back, Roger was ready for a well needed shower. I asked him if he needed help and he said yes. His skin looked good, no rashes or broken skin anywhere. His rectal area was pretty much back to normal, just a little redness but no more pain or bleeding. The flaky skin was becoming less noticeable and the itching was gone. He was able to eat a nice lunch and 24 ounces of fluids. He decided not to go to bed but to sit on the couch and watch TV. I asked Roger a couple of questions since he seemed to be feeling pretty good. I asked, "How do you feel now?"

He said, "I just wish they would give us some sort of hope. All they say is 'Yeah, it's part of the process. Yeah you feel crappy, it's expected.' They never really told me what to expect, but as I go through hell they say, 'Yeah, it's to be expected, it's part of the process.' It would have been nice to know what I was really getting myself into. They should have never sugarcoated it. I still hear them sugarcoating it to the newbies all around us. It's not right."

I asked him, "What would you want to know?"

He answered, "I want to know when I am going to get off these drugs. When am I going to feel better? When am I going to know this transplant worked? When can I expect to go home? Where is the hope? All they do is push more drugs on me that make me feel like crap! Robin, no one told me I would lose 60 pounds, just a little weight. Soter said I would lose maybe 15-20% muscle mass – two weeks ago for the first time! You were there, he said, 'Don't worry about eating, just get the fluids in,' right? That doesn't make sense to me. Look at me. I have no muscle left and this concerns me, A LOT!" He was opening up for the first time. I hadn't known how he was feeling. I didn't know he had concern at all. It was great that he was finally venting.

Roger added, "You have to do the bills from now on. I can't do them anymore. I can't concentrate. It's like there is no connection. I look at them and I can't make heads or tails out of them. I used to be able to do them in my sleep and it's not like we have a lot. Something isn't right in my brain. No one told us about 'Chemo Brain.' I couldn't even comprehend when Soter said it lasts for years in some people. This is my life, my quality of life. And they are going to give me more chemo in my brain? What's going to happen to me? The hardest part of all this is thinking I'm going to lose my mind! What's going to happen to me?" I was barely able to control the tears. I climbed up in his lap. He was so bony, I immediately thought I would hurt him. I started to get down and he pulled me back up and buried his head in my shoulder and we cried together. It was heartbreaking. This man with an IQ of 140 was losing the one thing that he could always count on – his intelligence.

The afternoon was quiet after this. He watched TV while I thought about his quality of life. At home, he spent a lot of time in front of the TV. I wondered if, after all this was said and done and he was feeling much better, he would enjoy life more. Instead of sitting in front of the TV, maybe he would sit on the deck more, tinker in his garage man-cave more, lay out on the grass and just watch the clouds go by, read a book – anything but sit in front of the TV all day.

The day was trickling away and my mind was swirling with everything we had talked about. It was a restless night for me, and the next day was an all-day clinic day. Poor Roger, he was going to be poked and prodded all day. He fell asleep while I packed our bags for the next day then joined him in his slumber.

Day +49

Roger was up before me and was feeling pretty good. He showered himself, took his handful of medications, put a full bottle of pain pills in my purse, and headed to the kitchen. I watched him from the bed, so happy he had a bit of energy. I asked him to make me a crab omelet with cheese, onions and mushrooms, and a glass of champagne with orange juice in it. He said, "Coming right up!"

When he called me in to eat, I had a wonderful bowl of fruit, cottage cheese and a piece of toast with butter and jam on it. I joked saying, "Aw, the omelet looks and smells wonderful." We both giggled.

He said, "Thank you, and you're welcome!" He kissed me on the top of the head, sat next to me with a bowl of noodles in broth with some crackers on top and we ate. I was so impressed. I didn't make a big deal out of it, I was just happy I was seeing him with energy and making me breakfast. It was wonderful.

We got to the clinic at 8:00 a.m. The IVIG was there and ready for him. It was a six-hour IV drip. Roger asked how long it would take to feel the effects of the immune booster, as he called it. The nurse starting the IV said, "I don't know that you will feel anything at all really. It's mainly for your blood to help prevent another outbreak. You just got over C-Diff, right? Well it's for things like that." We looked at each other and didn't say anything. I guess we both thought it was the ticket to no more sickness in the future. Rog was just staring at her, and I could see the disappointment in his eyes. He had his six vials of blood drawn and waited for the call to radiology.

They transferred Roger to radiology and prepared him for the lumbar puncture. The tech getting the procedure tray ready for the NP looked at me and said, "You might not want to watch this. You can step outside in the lobby and I will come and get you when it's over."

Roger said, "She plays with beating hearts after surgeons crack open a chest, she can handle this." He looked at me inquisitively and cocked his head to the side.

I shrugged my shoulders and said, "I do."

He said, "Okay, you can stay until the x-ray machine is turned on then they will ask you to step out, but you can watch from the window with the rest of the techs if you'd like." We waited 45 minutes for the NP from the clinic to bring up the Methotrexate while Roger laid on the hard, cold gurney with just a thin sheet on him. Everyone was getting a little perturbed standing around in sterile gloves and gowns, hands clasped in front of them. Finally, it arrived. It was an uneventful and perfect procedure, but for Roger, it was painful and his bones were hurting. I watched as he clenched his fists over and over during the procedure, and I clenched my fists as I watched the vial of Methotrexate enter his spinal fluid. The previous night I had pulled up an abstract from 2010 that stated there was no convincing evidence that this drug was of any great benefit to the patient. The only problem was that the article was based on a study of children with leukemia. 99% of all information is on children, so what should I think about this? I had to trust them, it was all I had. When the procedure was done, I was able to sit with Roger as he lay flat for one hour to ensure the hole they took the fluid from and injected medication into was sealed and not oozing spinal fluid. We were left in a holding room while the hour ticked away. When we were alone, he said, "Give me a pain pill."

After 30 minutes, the NP from the clinic came in and said, "Roger, your numbers look good today. Your potassium is still good." She looked at me and raised her eyebrows.

I said, "Yup." She looked back down and continued after she jotted down that I had given him potassium, "You need to work on your fluid intake. It's very important."

Roger raised his hand up and said, "I'm drinking a lot! I'm drinking more than you say I should. Why do I need more? What's going on with the pushing of fluids?"

She said, "Your kidneys still haven't fully recovered, so drink. Also, you will have a bone marrow biopsy on Monday. You will have that in the radiology department. We need to decrease your Tacrolimus to 1 mg twice a day. Continue to take the potassium like your wife here prescribed. After the next lumbar puncture with Methotrexate, we will look at the kidney function again. If it looks good, we can decrease the Prednisone and you can go home." We looked at her and she looked back at us. Then it hit us. What? Go home? Like in real home? She understood our looks and said, "Home-home." I wanted to cry! I got up from my chair and jumped up and down, clapping my hands and just laughed with joy.

Roger, much more composed said, "Thank you – finally!"

She smiled and then laughed with us. She then said, "This is all very preliminary, but it is the next step if all goes well. On day +56 we plan to stop the CellCept, and on day +180 we can stop the Tacrolimus. Any questions?"

Roger asked, "How much longer do I need to lay here?"

At that moment, the tech walked in and said, "About 20 more minutes."

The NP said, "You have the new schedule, so after you're done here, they will take you back to the clinic to finish the IVIG then you can go home, *to the hotel*."

I laughed and said, "Wow, thank you so much!"

She left, and Roger and I started talking so fast. Then it hit us – wait, go home, then what? Just home? I looked at the schedule and it had us checking into the clinic once a week for blood draws and IVs.

Roger asked, "Do you think I'm really ready to go home?"

I said, "Well, we aren't discharged yet, we still have a few more visits. We can write down all these questions then ask them at the next visit."

He felt better, and I felt better. There was still a lot that hadn't been explained to us.

One of the clinic nurses came in to check on the IVIG transfusion and Roger's back where the lumber puncture was. The clinic had cleared out and we were one of the very few left. She asked us how we were doing. Boy, was that a loaded question, but we were ready for it. Even though we were ecstatic about the going home news, we were still confused about everything else.

I said, "We are both disappointed. When we started this journey, we were painted a much different picture of this BMT process. As time goes on, Roger's body continues to break down. He has had several trips to the ER, spent ten days in the hospital, a week of which was in the ICU, and all we hear back is, 'It's part of the process.' Well, that process almost killed him the first week after transplant due to a lack of communication within the hospital staff of doctors. Every time we question things we're told, 'We will cross that hurdle when we get to it' or 'It's part of the process.' What is the process? If you know there *is* a process then we should be made aware of the stages of this so-called process so when urgent symptoms come up, we will know that this is to be expected and not freak out. There should be a list of *things that might happen at this stage* for the caregivers and patients." She didn't say anything, just looked at each of us. I continued, "Roger got C-Diff, but we were told to stay home unless he fit the six concerns given to us on the front of the checkout sheets. Well, what if you know something is wrong and it's not on that six-point list? Do we assume it's nothing to worry about? Both times I called in when Roger needed help and got none, only to have him hit a crisis state a few hours later."

Roger said, "I am so tired of hearing 'It's part of the process.' I want to know when I'm going to feel better. They want to send me home. What do I expect now? If something goes wrong, am I supposed to jump in my car and drive two hours to get here or do I go to my ER? Will they know how to take care of me?"

The nurse was looking at Roger then at me. It was obvious she was at a loss for words. I said, "I'm sorry, but this is just not right. I got a booklet on what I am and am not to do as a caregiver for Roger. For example, wash food, wash hands, stay away from people, no eating out, watch for rash, temp, diarrhea, fluid intake, etc. Where's the booklet on expected symptoms, or WHAT constitutes *part of the process*?" Why are we, the families and patients, not privy to what to expect as time goes on? They say there is a 30-day goal, a 56-day goal, a 100-day goal, a 180-day goal. If these are goals, then you as the clinicians are aware of what occurs if these goals aren't met. This would then be the definition of *part of the process*, right?"

She nodded and said, "That makes sense to me."

I continued, "They blindside us at the most vulnerable moments with a stack of papers explaining a clinical study that, for the most part, says if you want to live, you must sign this document and let's get on with it or you will die. The next document thrust in front of us to sign explains that we have to sign this or you will have to mortgage your house if you want the medications to keep you alive. It's a no brainer, right? Once these documents are signed, everything else going forward seems to be a secret. It can't be that difficult to give us something that tells us *what* the process is, not just a hollow statement, like it's a secret that only the clinicians on the bone marrow transplant team can know."

The nurse had sat down and was watching me pace the room as I spoke. Roger clapped when I was done and said, "Exactly!"

I looked at her, she lowered her eyes and said, "You know, I have only worked here for two and a half years. I work in the infusion room and only deal with the IV therapies. I don't get involved with the rest of the patient's history. Maybe I should. I had no idea. I can truly understand your concerns. Roger does have a pretty serious leukemia. Just know us nurses back here will do anything for you. We love our patients and don't want to see any of them in any more discomfort than they have to be in." She hugged us both. The IVIG was finishing so she stepped out to prepare the paperwork and get what she needed to disconnect him from the bag.

Roger said, "Nice gal, but you know all we just got there was someone that let us vent."

I said, "Yes, I know. I hope we don't get black-balled back here because we spoke our minds."

He said, "Me too."

We headed home. I couldn't get the conversation off my mind. I went over it again and again, hoping I didn't just screw us up with the clinic. If I were her, I would have gone right to my supervisor and let her know about the conversation to get the patient help. I worried what might happen the next time we had a clinic day. If I was confronted, I would put all the blame on me and my neurosis on keeping my best friend alive. They could hate me, but I wanted them to love Roger!

Most of the evening Roger complained of back pain. He asked for a pain pill every four hours and I gave it to him. It was a sleepless night for both of us.

4

The Call and a Whole Lot of Confusion

On day +50, I had set the medication alarm before I went to bed, got up when it sounded, gave Roger his meds, then went back to bed. We slept until 11:00 a.m. I had hot flashes and bad dreams all night. Roger got up and went straight to the couch and started his love affair with the remote. He ate most of his breakfast and spent the next hour trying to get as much fluids down as possible.

I was so excited about going home. I was about ready to leave when Roger's phone rang. He answered and said, "Hi, Dr. Perses." Wow, the infamous Dr. Perses called Roger's phone! Were we in trouble? We hadn't seen this doctor of ours but briefly a few times. I could only think of him as the man who left Roger suffering in the lobby hallway without a hello or any emotion, just scurrying off so he didn't have to talk to us. Not a good memory! Did the nurse say something? Roger motioned me to come to the couch. I sat next to him and listened in.

The doctor asked in a questioning voice, "Roger, are you okay?"

Roger said, "What?"

He asked, "Are you feeling okay? Are you confused or have any pain?"

Roger looked at me with big eyes and slowly said, "I feel tired and pretty weak. I have pain in my back, but I feel pretty good considering."

The doctor said, "Roger, your lumbar puncture came back abnormal. For every drop of spinal fluid, there should only be 0-5 white blood cells present. Yours came back with 34." He was talking slow and methodical. Not his usual standoffish self. He asked, "When is your bone marrow biopsy?"

"Monday," Rog said.

The doctor continued, "We need to get another LP at the same time. This is very unusual. Maybe it's nothing, but it could be a sign of an infection or leukemia cells present in your spinal fluid. We are running a more sensitive test on the fluid right now to determine what kind of white blood cells they are."

Roger explained the C-Diff and the Vancomycin. The doctor said, "That would have nothing to do with these cells and where they are. I will see you on Monday. Let's see what the bone marrow looks like," and he hung up.

Rog looked at me and said, "I wonder what that's all about." I went to the computer and started digging for answers. I looked at the Living Strong cancer site and the NIH, Med Plus, and the Cancer Society sites. They all read the same; if white blood cells are found in the central nervous system fluid within two to four months post bone marrow transplant, they most likely were rogue cancer cells. They drew reference to patients with Ph+ALL, which was Roger's diagnosis. The words were ominous, direct and to the point. Treatment is chemotherapy to the spinal fluid and targeted brain radiation.

Roger was watching TV. I didn't know if he was watching it or staring at it. His words came back to me from the other day, "What is going to happen to me?" His one worry was losing his mind. He had complained lately about brain fog. Some of the patients in the clinic call it Chemo Brain. It is a common term used by cancer patients to describe cognitive impairment or cognitive dysfunction after chemotherapy. Why reasoning and mental impairment happens, no one knows. If Roger must have spinal chemotherapy, which is straight to the brain, and targeted radiation, this chemo brain he has now was going to get a lot worse. He was already getting Methotrexate infused into his brain and it seemed to be increasing the brain fog. If cancer was present in the fluid, I was sure the chemotherapy would be a much more radical type of medication, especially since we were in a teaching hospital that made money on clinical studies – studies that use medications that are considered experimental. In the clinic I had watched patient after patient use flash cards from the game Trivial Pursuit for memory recognition. I asked why and was told it helped with brain fog.

My mind was all over the place. How was he going to be able to handle this? He was so weak now and his weight had dropped into the 250s. When I met him, he was all muscle at 250. Playing basketball three nights a week kept him lean and mean. Now there was not much muscle mass left and the loss of weight had been so fast that he didn't have much strength. Brain cancer. I asked him if he wanted to talk about it. He ignored me and watched TV. I knew then he wasn't watching, he was in his head. I told him I needed to do laundry. He didn't flinch. I got the clothesbasket and left. I stayed in the laundry room while the clothes washed and dried. I called Diana, who was beside herself. She listened to me cry and go on and on. Finally, she told me she loved me and was there if I needed her. I sat and listened to the sound of the washer.

When it was done I took the laundry back to the room. I folded the clothes in the bedroom while Roger talked to his mom. I was coming to the realization that my life with Roger as I knew it would soon be gone. I had no feelings, I felt almost numb inside. I snuck into the cabinet and got out the vodka I'd hidden in there. I cracked the cap and drank two big swigs right out of the bottle then put it away. The evening was a blur; not because of the vodka but because of the thoughts of losing Roger. Brain cancer?

Day +51

The day started out just like the previous day. Roger got up and went straight to the couch. I asked him if he took his meds and he said, "No." I went and got them and handed him the box. He looked at it then looked at me. I took them out of the box and gave them to him. He held them as I went in and got him some juice then he took his medications. I asked if he was okay and he said, "I'm really shaky this morning." The doctor had told me to give Roger Baclofen for his shakiness when it occurred. I had started putting it in his meds three times a day as it said on the bottle because he seemed to need it often. I told him the Baclofen was in the group of meds he just took, and he thanked me. I made us some breakfast; an egg omelet with ground up organic turkey and a mixture of veggies. He got his usual assortment of protein drinks and juices with it. He didn't seem as weak today. I changed the sheets on the bed and put them outside for the housekeeper to pick up.

Roger was engrossed in his TV so I took this time to call Betty and check on Max. I told her about Roger and the test results. Her New Yorker bluntness came out. She said, "Well, your life as you know it is over if he has brain radiation and the leukemia is back. But look at it this way, you have Max." She is a cat fanatic. Cats, to her, were better than people. *The planet needs more cats and less people* was her motto. Maybe this was true, but I needed Roger. I knew her well enough to not take this personally, but I wanted sympathy, not reality. I hung up after talking to Max through the phone.

I asked Roger if he wanted to go on a walk with me. He did. He got dressed and we headed out to do a lap or two around the complex. I asked him how he felt about the LP results, but he didn't answer. I told him gently about what I'd read from the many sites.

He stared at the ground as he walked and said, "I'm going to wait and see what the second test results show."

I asked, "If you are out of remission, are you going to go through with targeted brain radiation and chemotherapy to the spinal fluid?"

He said, "Yes, I'm going to do whatever the doctor tells me to do. I'm not going to roll over like a dead cockroach. My brain fog is getting better. Over time, it will continue to get better."

I said, "Okay, I just wanted to know what you will be saying to the doctor when the time comes." It was his body, his journey, and his brain. I am his wife, his support person, not his judge and jury. Whatever he wanted to do was his decision. Part of me just wanted to go home and be with Max for a day. I just wanted to love on him, snuggle him, and feel better for just a day.

I mentioned this to Roger and he said, "If you go, I go with you, period!" I couldn't take him to Betty's house. She had five cats, horses and ducks, all carrying germs in and out of the house. I felt like I just needed a break away from all of this, some time alone to be in my own thoughts, a long, hot bath with no responsibilities for just one day. The more we walked, the more I was in my head and realized he wasn't going to let me out of his sight, and my time alone to just rest was not going to happen anytime soon.

The next day was uneventful. Roger watched TV and we walked around the complex twice. His stamina was getting better each day. I beaded, researched, and wrote in my journal, keeping my mind as busy as possible. The next day we would find out the white blood cells' origins and what kind of cells they were. I knew I wasn't going to sleep.

I laid there in the dark with Roger asleep next to me. I just wanted to sleep! One of the caregivers at the clinic recommended I purchase a book called *The After Life of Billy Fingers*. I had it on the Kindle and decided to read it. It's about the hope that love is present after death and that it is unconditional, is all one can hope for, a peace in knowing we have nothing to worry about. The thought of losing Roger, at that moment lying there right then, was a moment of peace. He would be okay.

Then I found myself asking, *Why me? Why is this happening to me? Is this my journey or Roger's? If Roger's, then why have I been brought along?* I started to think metaphysically. Maybe Roger and my soul made an agreement. Maybe I agreed to help him through this lifetime with heart disease and cancer. Maybe this was part of my mission here on earth this time around. Maybe it wasn't always about us individually but about our whole journey as souls and how we are linked together. I said out loud, "Why me, universe, why me?"

Before the entire thought left my mouth, I heard loud and clear, "Because you can handle it." I don't know where that came from, but it was there. Tears of emotion flooded me. I put the book down and turned out the lights. It was so dark in the room I couldn't see my hands in front of me. I don't know if my eyes were open or shut, but a motion picture started playing in my mind's eye. It was me and Roger on the beach. We were surrounded by the white sandy beach with dunes all around us, sun shining on us like a brilliant spotlight, the water gently lapping to shore. We were dancing all crazy like kids, twisting our hips and arms in the air, laughing and dancing all around, so happy, so uninhibited, just us, no one else, like we are the only two on the planet. It was a wonderful motion picture. I wanted to keep that show in my mind forever. When Roger got better, this was what I wanted to do with him. I fell asleep at peace.

Day +53

This was the day we found out the results of the lumbar puncture. It was also a big day for a follow-up LP and a bone marrow biopsy. During breakfast, Roger put the pain medication bottle in my purse as he did when he knew there was a day of pain ahead of him. I just observed, we didn't talk. He didn't try to engage in communication, even after I kissed him when we woke and I gently caressed his face and chest. He didn't look at or acknowledge me. I left him to his thoughts.

I drove Roger to the front steps of the clinic and he walked in on his own. I parked the car and walked up the hill to the clinic. I was nauseated. I thought at any moment I was going to throw up. I'd had a light breakfast, nothing unusual except for the carrot and pineapple juice. I wanted to stop in the bathroom and gag myself to get it over with then I realized my heart was racing and my pulse was at 120 beats per minute. I was having a panic attack! I bent over and breathed long, slow breaths until the wave subsided. I was so scared!

When I walked in, Roger wasn't where he said he would be. I went into the clinic and saw that he was having his PICC line IV dressing changed. When they were done with his dressing, they put him in one of the private patient rooms. We waited patiently, both wringing our hands. Soter walked in, said hi, and sat down at the computer desk like he usually did, and started bringing up Roger's records. His mood was nonchalant. Roger asked about the white blood cells and the results. Soter didn't turn around but said, "They are fine, no cancer."

I said, "What!" We were in shock! I looked at Roger and he was crying. I thought, *Why didn't someone call us and tell us the results instead of making us worry for days?* I got up and hugged Roger, kissed his eyes and said, "Oh, baby, it's going to be alright!"

Soter said, "The white blood cells are some kind of infection. We don't know what it is, but since you aren't having any symptoms, we aren't going to do anything. We will repeat the LP in four days and do a comparison. I will treat you again at the next LP, with chemo Methotrexate anyway." The relief was unbelievable. My stress, nausea, and the need to vomit were gone!

Soter prepared Roger for his bone marrow biopsy, asking him if he wanted Ativan or morphine. He said both and they gave it to him. Soter was swift and precise, his skills at this were impeccable. Before we left Soter said, "Tacrolimus level looks good. Stop drinking so much water; your sodium levels are WAY too low, and keep trying to get more protein in. Your levels are still way below normal."

When we were done, we headed back to the hotel. Roger said, "Let's go home for a couple days." I didn't argue. I packed quickly and away we went. He was silent in the car, drifting in and out of sleep. He was still a little groggy from the meds but at least his hip from the biopsy wasn't hurting him.

5

The Ranch Calls

As soon as we got home and walked in the door, Roger went straight to his recliner, picked up the remote, and that was that. I unloaded the car and prepared him some lunch. Mom was surprised but glad to see us. As much of a pain as she was, I was glad to see her too; someone to talk to about something other than Roger's cancer. We talked for a while then I got started. I had work to do so I went in and got a lesson from Rog on how to remove a partial board from the deck. He got down on one knee to show me how but when he tried to get up, he literally couldn't. I tried to help him, but he had no energy in his legs to bring himself up. I got a chair from the kitchen, put it next to him, and held it tight while he managed to slowly pull himself up. It was 98 degrees outside and with all the effort he was using, he started feeling lightheaded. I helped him back to his chair, and he apologized over and over for not being able to help.

For the next two days, I worked my butt off. Roger slept well with no problems and enjoyed just being in his house where it was cool. He caught up on all the shows he couldn't watch at the hotel. Here we had all the fancy channels and he was in heaven. I waited on him hand and foot. I begged him to come outside on the deck and talk to me while I worked to get some fresh air, but he always said no due to the heat. I wasn't going to fight with him, so I let him be. I made snacks and juice trays for him to graze on while I was outside.

Day +56

We got up early to head back to the clinic. I had thought about going back the previous night but Rog wanted to stay and let me rest. He'd done really well over the past few days. He was still having a hard time eating but managed to get down small portions of a little bit of everything. He stayed in his chair and refused to do any exercise. I couldn't pick him up, throw him outside and demand pushups like boot camp, but I tried. When Roger didn't want to do something, he just stopped listening to me. He literally ignored me.

I was happy to be heading to the clinic. I was excited about seeing Soter and getting more good results. With the bloodwork heading in the right direction, this meant the "goal schedule" we were given should be right on track. The biggest goal was getting him off the Tacrolimus and CellCept. This would mean the new donor cells were finally in charge, no longer in battle mode. He would be on the road to recovery. A glorious day for both of us!

When we arrived, we were told we weren't going to see any of the NPs. Today was test only. I was surprised and disappointed. I waited in the lobby while he got his test done. After two hours I started worrying. I asked the clerks at the desk if Rog was okay, and I was told they hadn't even started the test. Roger had been laying on the gurney on his belly, waiting for the clinic to bring the Methotrexate. Once again, the clinic made Rog wait. I knew he must be in a lot of discomfort, but there was nothing I could do. I couldn't get to him to give him a pain pill and I started to worry.

Finally, the NP from the clinic showed up, handed the vial over, and left without talking to me. When the test was over and he was being wheeled back down to the clinic, I looked at him, raised my eyebrows and looked at my purse. He said, "Two please!" I put them in his mouth, he chewed them up, swallowed, and said, "Thank you." I held his hand and smiled at him as we walked.

When we got to the clinic, I asked why we weren't being seen by the NP. I was told it wasn't planned to see them. Instead, a nurse we had never seen came in. She looked at Rog and said, "You are going to hang with us for an hour while you lay flat after your LP. I will come in and check on you frequently. If you need anything, just let me know." She was looking at his lab results on the computer screen and asked, "Are you a vegetarian?"

Rog said, "No."

She said, "You need to get your protein up. It's at a really low level!"

Roger said, "This I know. I'm doing the best I can. It's really hard to eat protein, it's so dense. I used to eat steak three times a week, now I can't even look at one. I eat eggs and chicken, beans of all kinds, and cheese when I can handle it."

She looked at me and said, "Should I set you up with a dietitian so she can teach you how to cook for him?"

I said, "No, I know how to cook for him. It's his mouth and belly that don't want to swallow or absorb the protein that I do get in him."

Roger said, "Soter told us to get the sodium and the protein up. The sodium is good, but I know the protein is not."

She said, "Your sodium is perfect, don't even worry about that."

He said sternly, "The sodium is good because she made me broths for weeks and I drank it. You tell me not to worry about it and I guarantee you the next time I come in here, you will scold me for having low sodium. So, what is it? Keep doing what I'm doing and try harder on the protein intake, right?" He startled her and me.

She said, "Yeah, okay, you can look at it like that."

He sternly said, "I was told that the Tacrolimus is preventing me from being able to absorb what I put in. At 180 days when I can get off it, my protein will go up!"

The nurse looked at me and raised her eyebrows. I said, "Soter gave us a schedule of goal dates. At day 180, he can stop the Tacrolimus and this bad cycle of nutrition malabsorption will stop."

She said, "Stop Tacrolimus? You're not stopping it. Most patients are on it for six months to a year and even longer."

I said hesitantly, "Soter gave us a chart that shows after 180 days, Roger will be weaned off these medications. When he is weaned off, will his electrolytes become more stable? Will he be able to absorb the nutrition better? They will return to normal, right?"

She looked right at me with a concerned look and said, "You seemed to be a linear person, but this is not a linear disease."

I could feel my emotions welling up inside of me. Were we given a bag of crap? Were we told this to pacify us? This nurse was saying it like it was – she didn't know us. Was this the truth, that patients routinely stay on this drug for longer than 180 days? My mind started jumping from thought to thought. If he didn't get off these meds soon, he would waste away to nothing. My tears started forming. I said in a shaky voice, feeling almost broken inside, "No one has said this to us about the Tacrolimus. I am not a linear person. I am telling you what Soter told us. He gave us a calendar that showed us a weaning-off schedule for the Tacrolimus and it ends in 180 days."

She said, "Oh, if Soter gave you that then go by that. I'm just a nurse. He's the one in charge of the patients. I don't know Roger or his history. Soter obviously knows him much better."

I started crying profusely, the tears were flowing and there was no way I could stop them. I had lost all control. I put my head in my hands and just sobbed. Every day it was something new, a new piece of info different from the last; contradictory. Why didn't they give you all this upfront, the 'what ifs' or possibilities of the reality of it all? "This is the goal schedule. At 180 days, we try to wean patients off the medications, but many don't make it to 180 or many need to stay on the drugs longer. Let's shoot for this goal and see how everything looks when the 180-day mark arrives." Is that too hard to say? No, it says keep an open mind, this disease has its challenges. Roger and I could handle that! Being told one thing only to find out another makes us feel like we had been lied to, given false hope. This was not good. Linear? What does that mean anyway? Wrapping my head around that one made me cry more.

I looked up and she said, "Do you need to see a counselor to help you get through this? Nancy and Karen are great."

I lost it even more. I was speechless and just wanted to leave. I said, "No, I don't want to see the counselors." She kept on and on about me needing psychological help to deal with all of this. I just stopped listening and softly asked her to just change his PICC line dressing and please not talk anymore.

Another nurse came in and said, "Roger, your magnesium is 1.1; looks like you get 4 grams today."

I said, "His magnesium at his last visit was 1.4 and they gave him 8 grams. Isn't 4 grams going to leave him still on the low side?"

She said, "We were told to just give him 4."

I looked at Roger, and he was looking at me. I blew my nose, sat back in the hard, blue chair, leaned my head against the wall behind me and closed my eyes. I was so, so tired. Why couldn't it all make sense? Nothing ever made sense here!

Roger slept through his transfusion while I took a walk and cried some more.

When we got home, I made Roger a nice meal of lentils, fresh steamed greens, and a protein drink. I couldn't eat. I took a big gulp of vodka, letting it burn all the way down, and went in and took a long hot shower. Roger sat on the couch with his remote and meal. He said he was sorry about a dozen times. I told him it wasn't his fault, kissed him and said, "I'm just tired, that's all."

Day +57

Every July 4th, Roger and I would spend the evening tailgating with friends. We set up the barbeque on the back of the truck and Roger cooked up a mean burger or steak. I made potato salad and garlic bread, and our friends brought hors d'oeuvres and desserts. We just vegged out in our lawn chairs, laughing, gossiping and carry on until the fireworks started.

I think I was in a state of depression. I was so lonely and wanted so badly to be with friends and family; I just needed to get out of that hotel for a bit. I needed us to feel a part of life – alive, stress free and cancer free. That's all I wanted.

Roger wanted to take a nap. I asked if he would like to take a walk first and he agreed. We walked around the complex twice and reminisced about the July 4th of years gone by. We had a ball reliving some of the most fun 4ths, and the conversation kept him so engulfed in memories, he didn't realize he had walked two laps. He was ready for a nap after the walk. I decided to go to the home and garden store to price out what I needed for the deck. I had decided to enclose the deck so Roger and Max could enjoy it bug free. I also stopped at the store and picked up a couple of nice, organic chicken breasts and some snow peas for dinner. Surprisingly, Rog loved and ate it all. Bed was early for both of us.

Day +58

At 11:00 a.m. a maid was at the door, using her key to enter. When she did, she was surprised to see us there. She said, "You are supposed to be checked out." I told her I would take care of it and headed down to the lobby to pay for another week. Hopefully it would be the last one, but just in case, I would let them know that we were not sure, to just keep the weeks coming. The manager was very nice, took my money, and scheduled us for another week.

Roger wasn't feeling very well and said he just wanted to sleep. I took his temperature and it was his usual 94.7. I told him I needed to get some groceries. He told me to go ahead, he was just going to be sleeping. I closed the curtains and made him drink some broth. He asked for some pain pills, saying his body was hurting all over, mostly in his joints, and felt a little nauseated so no breakfast that morning. I sat on the side of the bed with him and looked up Methotrexate's side effects. Sure enough, everything he was feeling were side effects. He told me to go shopping and let him sleep. I put the cell phone next to him and told him I would be right back.

I had researched all kinds of **proteins** that were available besides meat. His levels were dangerously low and I needed to get them up. His total **protein** level should be 6.4-8.2, but his was 4.0. If the body doesn't get an adequate amount of protein through diet, it will use its own protein from muscles or organs. Roger had no muscle, so the organs would be the next best choice. I had to get more protein in him. I was now giving him three 30 gram protein drinks a day, but if the body isn't absorbing them, what do you do? It's such a vicious cycle.

I bought yogurt, cottage cheese, quinoa, yeast flakes, dried figs, broccoli, avocados and spinach. It was not the traditional steak or chicken, but the next best thing and easier for him to digest. I relied on the plant family, which was better for him and easier to absorb, in the soups I made him. I had a feeling that after his body recovered from this he was never going to want to see a bowl of soup again!

I got back to the hotel and Roger wasn't doing well. He was nauseated and sitting on the bathroom floor in front of toilet. When I saw him there, I got so scared I dropped the bags and ran to him. He said he had been there awhile, trying to throw up. I got him some Compazine and a glass of warm water and put him to bed. He was complaining of headaches and body aches, and was a little confused about the time and place. He thought we were at the ranch and it was June. I brought him some juice and had him rest until the Compazine took effect. After 30 minutes, he felt better but wanted to stay in bed. I made him a small meal of quinoa with yeast flakes and steamed spinach. He was able to get a couple bites down but that was all. He was able to swallow the handful of evening pills and that was it for the night. He was going to sleep.

I sat next to Roger and watched him sleep. He was looking so thin, and his reserve was getting very low. My worry was compounding every day. I needed to talk to the clinic and get some help. Something wasn't right.

Rog tossed and turned all night, moaning in his sleep. I fell asleep sometime after 4:00 a.m.

Day +59

I awoke to Mom calling. I took the call into the living room, shutting the bedroom door behind me. She told me there was a problem with the water system. I hung up the phone, and standing behind me was Roger. He said, "Let's go."

I asked how he was feeling, he said, "Puny, but I'll survive." God bless this man. How did he do it? One minute I thought, *This is it*, the next he was ready to go. We headed home.

When we got home, I got Rog all set up in his chair with a blanket, a pain pill, and his remote. I made him a tray of snacks, two protein drinks, and a pitcher of water. He was set, and before I knew it he was asleep.

With a couple of days off from the clinic, we decided to stay at the ranch. For the next two days, I got a lot done. Roger came out a few times to watch but for the most part he could watch me from his chair through the sliding glass door and window. Every once in a while I would wave to him and he would wave back. He started feeling better after we were home for a day. He got bursts of energy and used his Prednisone voice, making everyone all nervous with his temper tantrum rages. I think he liked scaring everyone into submission.

PART FIVE

1

GVHD of the Gut

Day +64 was the big day. We were seeing Dr. Perses for the test results of the bone marrow biopsy and the repeated Lumbar Puncture. This would only be the fourth time we had seen him since this journey began and he was supposed to be our doctor! He walked in all smiles. We were so disillusioned by him; we just stared at him, no emotion from either of us. We were in our heads, praying that whatever came out of his mouth was good. He propped himself half on the exam table, half standing and said, "Bone marrow biopsy and spinal fluid are free of leukemia cells. The cancer is gone." It was so surreal. We just stared emotionless at him. He held his hands out, chuckled a bit and looked at us like we were supposed to be jumping for joy. I felt nothing. Roger felt nothing. I wasn't sure if it was pure exhaustion or we were waiting for the "BUT..." scenario, I don't know.

Roger finally said in a flat voice, "That's great news. Can we go home? And can I get off these pills?"

The doctor stood up and said, "No."

Roger asked why and the doctor said, "Roger, you have lost so much weight. Since your transplant, you have lost over 66 pounds in just two months. It might be caused by GVHD of the gut." And there's the *BUT*.

I said, "He has no appetite. He eats a few small bites but drinks mostly broths and protein drinks. Can he have the medication Marinol?" This medication is a synthetic form of THC found in marijuana. It is given to cancer patients to help with nausea and increases appetite.

He said, "Yes, I will prescribe this medication, but if there's no improvement in one week, I'm going to scope your gut and look at it. If you're doing better and eating, then no scope." Roger and I nodded. The doctor went over Roger's labs; the usual low magnesium but everything else seemed to be "on track." We stopped by the pharmacy to pick up the Marinol. While I was inside, Roger looked up the medication on his phone and seemed to be content with it. We drove home without talking. I didn't know what to say. I wasn't sure why neither of us were jumping for joy, but we were numb, just numb.

When we got home, I went into the bathroom and cried then washed my face. Roger took a Marinol and sat on the couch with his remote, waiting for the pill to take effect. After an hour I looked at him and he said nothing happened. He drank some broth, two protein drinks, ate a potato, and was able to keep it down.

As Roger watched TV, I researched GVHD of the gut. The symptoms are anorexia, nausea and vomiting. It is seen commonly in patients who received donor cells not from family members, and occurs within the first 100 days. It is accompanied by GVHD of the skin and liver. If this wasn't textbook then I didn't know what was. I hated the fact that I had to come home and research this. Why didn't the doctor just tell us this? Why did he need to scope Roger since it was obvious this was the case? I was so tired of all the games, I needed to get my head clear, I needed to clean. I cleaned up the kitchen and Roger's bathroom. I could barely even open his bathroom door. He had piled all his clothes on the floor and just walked on them. Why?

There was a knock on the door. I was handed an envelope. Roger was asleep so I went into my bathroom and opened it. We had to be out of the hotel at the end of the week. The insurance company had denied the claim that I had gotten pre-approved to take care of the hotel lodging. Our insurance had provisions for this! It was as plain as day in the policy, and I got approval prior to making these arrangements. I was told, "There really won't be any problem, all looks good." Well it wasn't, and it didn't look good! I couldn't deal with this right now, I just couldn't. It was another sleepless night.

Day +65

After two large cups of coffee, I woke Rog. This was another lumbar puncture with chemo Methotrexate into his spinal fluid straight to his brain day. I hated these days and so did Roger. The discomfort and pain he went through each time was almost unbearable. His hands hurt so bad after each procedure from clenching the sides of the gurney to help him get through the painful injections. His shoulders and upper arms trembled through the procedures. If he'd had a leather strap between his teeth, there would be holes in it. Roger was so different after each injection and seemed to be having more problems with comprehension and recall as the days moved forward.

While he was getting the procedure done, Karen, the counselor, found me and sat down. She asked how I was doing, which was a bad question to ask me. I just started crying. She said, "Robin, you have to talk about this. What's going on?"

I said, "So much is going on and right now it's pretty bad. I got a letter from my insurance company. They denied my claim for lodging and gas money. I had it all pre-approved, so they shouldn't be denying us. I faxed them the letter they asked for and they said they will look at it again. Our insurance plan pays for lodging and gas money for cancer patients and families up to $7,500. But for some reason they denied the payments to the hotel." Karen put her hand on my knee. I said, "We're going to have to move in with Roger's mom. We're running out of money. I just don't think I have the strength to do this."

She asked how Roger was. I told her, "He's not doing well. Not eating, no motivation, doesn't even clean up after himself, and I have to beg him to shower and walk. He is getting weaker and has lost so much weight. He sits in front of the TV and just stares at it. Many times I see him leaning over with his head in his hands. When I ask him if he is in pain, he says, 'Yes, I need a pain pill.' I encourage him to get up and walk to give his back and butt a rest, but he refuses. He is starting to have problems with memory. He was helping me with the bills the other day and I asked him to address an envelope for me and put a stamp on it while I wrote the check. He handed it to me with the address in the upper right-hand corner where the stamp goes and the stamp on the other side. Without him knowing, I fixed it. He's not able to give himself the insulin injections anymore. He has gotten the dosage wrong several times. Fortunately, I saw the mistake before he injected. Dr. Perses told us he has GVHD of the gut and that diagnosis isn't good. He doesn't talk to me. He really isn't a talker anyway, but I can't get him to talk to me about his feelings on what's happening to him. I don't know what's going on inside there. His Prednisone does the talking most of the time when he does talk." I went on and on until the tears were no more.

Karen never interrupted me, she just let me spill all that was pent up inside of me. When I was done and the tears had stopped, she gave me a hug and said, "This was good for you to let this out. Whenever you need to talk, let me know" and she left. I sat there for a bit and wondered why she didn't give me any advice or say something to make me feel better. The more I thought about it, the more I understood. She let me unload until the tears were gone. That's all she could do, there was nothing she could say to make me feel better, there was no advice to calm my spirits. There was no hope to give me, just an ear to let me vent to, an unbiased listener with no judgment. I did feel a little better. I felt like I had room inside of me again to take on the next challenge – moving to Roger's mom's. I hadn't noticed that the people in the waiting room with me had been listening. I blew my nose and looked up to see a few faces giving me sympathy. I half-smiled back.

The rest of the day was uneventful. Roger rested in bed while I packed up the hotel and started loading the car. It had been a long and painful morning for him. I asked Roger how he felt about the move. He didn't have much to say about it other than, "I'm glad she lives close to the hospital." Mom's house was about ten minutes further from the clinic but not too bad of a drive.

Days +66 – +70

Over the next several days, my plate was full. First, the well stopped working on the ranch. We were out of water. The estimated cost to fix it was $2,000.00. I had to be present when the well guy showed up to discuss the possibility of a new well and I was freaking out! I needed to go immediately, but I was in the middle of moving. We couldn't afford to stay in the hotel to keep Roger safe, let alone the cost of a new well. After I got Roger settled in at his mom's, I headed home to deal with the well. It was late but the well guy was there waiting for me. After two hours of diagnostics, three fixed leaks and a new well head, we were good to go.

Second, Todd, Roger's son, wanted to see him. He hadn't seen him since the weight loss and I was worried about how he was going to handle the changes. Roger was listless, weak, flat, monotone, and had no motivation, as if he was giving up. When I asked him, he said, "You never have to worry about that, I will never give up. You all just want me to smoke pot." Sometimes he says the darnedest things! Todd was bringing him some marijuana oil made specifically for cancer patients. It's supposed to help with all the things the Marinol was supposed to do but didn't. I hoped the visit went well and Roger was able to tolerate the oil. It had been known to really help cancer patients get their quality of life back.

Todd was blown away. The last time he saw his dad, he was 310 pounds. He walked in, swallowed, looked at me, and turned and walked out. Roger hadn't seen him come in. I wasn't sure if he was coming back, but after a few minutes he returned saying he had forgotten the oil in the car. I left the boys alone and worked on unpacking. They had a nice talk although Todd did most of the talking. He gave Roger the lowdown on the marijuana oil. It was a good visit. Todd never let on if he was concerned or shocked at Roger's appearance. His dad had aged 30 years, didn't have much hair, and his face was gaunt and pale. Todd is stoic, just like his Dad. When he left, he gave me a big hug and said, "I love ya." He never asked any questions.

Third, Roger's mom's house had no central heat and no air conditioning. The room we were staying in was either incredibly hot or so cold you could store ice cream. The mattress on the bed was 40+ years old and had slept at least a hundred people in its lifetime. There was no privacy, and I felt like I was transitioning from the frying pan to the fire. I hoped I hadn't made a mistake coming here. Thank goodness we had our own bathroom.

I needed to get Roger motivated. I needed to get him moving and I didn't know how. Living in this heat was causing him more problems. I just wanted Roger to get better so we could get out of there...

I explained to Rog that he needed to exercise to get his strength up so we could leave. He said, "I'm trying."

I said, "You're not trying. If you were trying, you would get up and walk to keep up your energy. You would put your dishes in the sink, you would pick up your clothes instead of throwing them on the floor for me to pick up, you would try to take care of yourself and be responsible for yourself. But you're not! You are depending on me to do everything except change the channel for you!"

He looked at me and said, "Fine, I will try harder." The next morning it was as if he'd never said it. I was getting frustrated!

The past few days, Roger had gotten weaker. I tried offering him broths, soups, rice and chicken, G2 drinks, and protein drinks. I even got out some cookies and pastries, which used to be his favorite, but still nothing. He was just not eating. He would only take a few small bites of food. When the food got cold, he asked me to take it away. The little he got in caused him nausea. The next day was a clinic day and I was thankful since trying to get him to drink was also becoming a chore. Why was this happening to him? He wasn't progressing at all. Was it the stress of the move and all the other crap that we kept getting hit with or was something going on inside of him related to this disease? They told us he was in remission, and you would think that was a good thing. Remission means you are better and get to go home and start life again, right?

2

HHV6 and the CDC

Day +71 was clinic day. We would get the test results from the follow-up LP. I was so glad! Part of me hoped they found nothing, but part of me hoped they found something so they could fix it. Rog seemed to be in a real bad place, and I wasn't sure what was happening. He wasn't able to help me help him. Getting him dressed and to the car took every ounce of energy. Roger never spoke, he just stared at the ground while I put his arms and legs into his clothing.

When the NPs saw Roger, they were shocked. They asked me how long he had been like this. I said, "We were here just a few days ago. You saw him. He has been declining by the day and getting weaker. We had a few busy days moving, but I did all the work while he rested. The problem is he can't eat. He is nauseated after every meal. I put a meal in front of him about four times a day with snacks to choose from. His body hurts so bad he doesn't have an appetite. Please ask *him* these questions."

Roger was so tired and weak he sat slumped over in the wheelchair just watching us talk. The previous night he needed to go to the bathroom and fell twice trying to get there. I helped him, but it was the most effort yet to just stay on his feet. I explained this to the NPs. They asked Roger how he was feeling. Roger said, "I want you to admit me. I don't know what is happening to me." I started to cry. I took his hand, looked at the NP, and pleaded with them to admit him.

The results of the follow-up LP were not good. The first LP showed 34 white blood cells, the second showed 20 white blood cells. The third, this last one, showed 36 white blood cells. They were on the rise again. We were told that the doctors were stumped and had no idea what was going on. They wanted to do another LP and send the fluid off to an outside lab for more intensive testing.

Soter left the room after he gave us the LP results saying he needed to call Dr. Perses. While he was gone, I asked Roger what he was thinking. He just looked at me funny as if he didn't know me and said, "Thinking about what?"

I said, "About being admitted and how you're feeling."

He asked, "Admitted where?"

I looked into his eyes and asked him, "Roger, who am I?"

He said, "Your name is Robin." I caught my breath. A lump formed in my throat that hurt so bad I thought I would pass out. I had a hard time catching my breath. He just stared at me.

Soter returned with the other NP. "We're going to admit Roger. He is too weak and deteriorating. I have ordered an MRI on his brain for today as well. But I have to tell you that we are really stumped. We're not sure what's going on. We're admitting him for GVHD and malnutrition. That's all we know for now. There's a bed on the cancer floor waiting for him. I'm not sure when the tests will start, but it's going to be a long night. He will be an add-on to a full schedule." I asked about the next step in the protocol. He said, "Roger no longer fits the protocol in the study." I didn't let that sink in. I didn't care. I was glad they were seeing him as I saw him – in trouble.

The first test was his lumbar puncture. His back was killing him and these needles constantly going in and out wasn't helping. He was taking pain pills often but they didn't seem to be working. Soter said he would increase the dosage of the OxyContin. They worked for about three hours then he asked for another one. That afternoon his face was puffy, his cheeks were ruddy-looking, and his joints were warm to the touch. I visualized all the toxic medications sitting in all the spaces, just festering in there. If he wasn't absorbing anything, where was it going? His liver was under attack so it wasn't filtering them. Where were the medications going?

He returned from the LP at 6:45 p.m. They got him all settled in the room and told us the MRI would be done tonight but not until very late. The nurses started him on IV fluids, and he seemed to be resting and content in his bed.

At 7:15 p.m., he asked me when he was having his LP. I looked at him and said, "You already had it. Your MRI will be a little later."

He asked, "When is the LP?" I asked him how he was doing and he said, "How are you doing?"

I said, "Okay..."

He said, "Oh, that's good," and smiled at me. I was a little perplexed at what was happening.

At 7:30 p.m., he said, "We need to hurry up to get to Dr. Perses' office visit."

I said, "We went this morning. He admitted you."

He looked around and said, "Oh yeah, I like it here."

At 8:10 p.m., he said, "When are we going to get the tire changed on the truck? My cousin is having a problem with the pit boss and I need you to take over so the NASCAR race will move forward. We need to make sure we don't miss that appointment." He'd said it with a strong voice, like he was someone else. I looked at him as he stared at me and tried to get up.

I gently said, "You're in the hospital. There's no NASCAR race."

At 8:15 p.m., he said, "My sleeve for the shower is right over there on the dressing table by my hair dryer." He pointed to something across the room and said, "See it, it's right there." I reminded him again we were in the hospital, and what he was pointing to was the nurse's device to check patients' arm bands. He just stared at me, back at it, then back at me. He put his head back on the pillow and rested for a minute. What in the world was going on? This was the same thing that happened when he was toxic from the Cyclosporine and had kidney failure after transplant. I started writing everything down.

"It's 8:30 p.m.," he said, "We better hurry up, we need to get the tires changed on the truck."

I said, "We don't need to get the tires changed on the truck."

He said, "Yes we do! Your cousin is having problems with her pit boss. You're going to take her place so the NASCAR race will go on!"

I said, "Do you think I will make a good pit boss?"

He said, "Oh yeah, a great one!"

At 9:00 p.m., I was really starting to get scared. The worry inside me was turning my stomach. What if the MRI of the brain showed something wrong? Could they fix it? Could they reverse what they had done to him? He sat up and started looking around the room and then at me. I said, "Rog, do you know where you are?'"

He said, "Yes, in the hotel." I asked him what hotel and he responded. I asked him if he was sure, and he responded, "Yes." then looked at the IV pole and said, "No." He scratched his head and said, "We are at River Bend." River Bend Hospital is in another city.

I asked, "Do you know where we are living right now?"

He said, "An extended stay hotel. You need to go to Jensen Beach and get that plumber and get the well fixed. I know it will be difficult, but you need to get the water fixed for your mom."

I said, "Jensen Beach?"

He replied, "Oh, I mean Lincoln City." I explained to him where we were and why, and that I had fixed the well three days ago. I reminded him that we were living with his mom. He just looked at me.

At 9:30 p.m., Roger's dinner arrived. It was a turkey sandwich, Jell-O, crackers, a milkshake and coffee. He started eating the Jell-O and asked me if I wanted his sandwich. I asked him to try to eat it, but he said, "No, I want you to have it, you haven't eaten today."

I said, "Neither have you and your body needs it more than mine." He handed it to me. I took half of it and he ate the other half and drank the milkshake. I was surprised and happy at the same time.

He then looked at me and said, "Oh, by the way, they kicked the boys out next door."

"Oh, what for?"

Rog said, "Because they were doing all that fighting." I asked if they left and Rog said, "Oh yeah, and it wasn't pretty." I asked him when this happened, and Rog said, "While you were gone shopping just a bit ago." He finished his meal, and I was amazed!

At 10:00 p.m., he asked me about the shipwreck coins, the ones that the woman just gave me. I asked what woman and he explained, "I'm talking about the woman that buried the two ships full of gold coins with you. There's a substantial amount of gold in them and I need to get those coins, Robin. I was dreaming that we are buying an amusement park. I know you're not happy about it but when we were kids, before we moved we really enjoyed the amusement park. I think it's a good idea to buy it." He was now making the dream seem like reality. He went on to ask me about the dinosaurs with the mustaches and how we were going to get them into the NASCAR vehicles.

At midnight they came and got him for his MRI. I told the nurses that he was claustrophobic and needed the Ativan first. They remembered and gave him 2 mg that was scheduled prior to the MRIs. I was so happy Soter had put that in the orders.

I waited in the room for him to return. I had made my little couch bed up, borrowed a pair of hospital pants and was resting when Rog returned. When he did, I was told it was uneventful, that he'd actually fallen asleep and snored. This was great news! No extra stress on him. He slept through the night, but had sleep apnea all night. He hadn't had that in a while.

Day +72

The nurses tended to Roger all morning. I used this time to call the kids and the moms. I explained to Roger's kids that he wasn't doing well and all that had been going on. They were upset and worried but didn't ask to talk to him. I encouraged them to visit soon. I was concerned that if anything happened, if the MRI was positive in a bad way, they should see him now while he was still looking like Roger.

I laid in bed through the morning and watched Roger sleep. He wasn't waking up. He was so groggy, and watching him like that was horrible. I started sobbing in my bed. What was happening to him? Nothing was making sense! It wasn't like he was the only patient in history that's had this disease. Someone else must have had these symptoms too. What did they do for those patients? I was so scared and frustrated. What if he didn't get better? What if this was it? He was losing his mind, living in a series of fantasy worlds of NASCAR, shipwrecks, gold coins and dinosaurs.

He didn't even look like Roger, his appearance was changing. A thought popped into my head, wondering if he was starting to look like the 20-year-old he got the blood from. Does that happen? Could such a huge change in the DNA source cause one to look like the donor? I must remember to ask this question. His youthful appearance of no wrinkles or blemishes had transformed into a long, drawn, aged look. When he woke up, he slowly moved his head, his eyes taking their time to catch up with the movement until they locked onto me. He smiled and said, "Hi."

I wiped my tears and said, "Good morning. How do you feel?"

He said, "How do you feel?" mimicking me.

I said, "I feel okay. I am worried about you."

He said, "Don't worry." He turned and stared out the window, just staring out at the clouds.

At 11:45 a.m., Dr. Perses, along with the interns, entered the room. I had been crying for a while. Roger seemed to be oblivious to me being in the room. Dr. Perses looked at me, clasped his hands behind his back and said, "Good morning! Roger, how do you feel today?

Roger said, "How do *you* feel today?" I put my head in my hands and cried softly while he examined Roger. The interns just stared at me and shuffled uncomfortably.

The doctor then stepped back from Roger and said, "The MRI was negative. We are going to do another LP and compare it to the last one. We just don't know what's going on. It might be one of the medications he is taking, we're just not sure." I blew my nose and said, "In the past, since almost all of your patients are in some clinical study following the same protocol, have you witnessed any medication that could cause white blood cells in the spinal fluid or these kinds of hallucinations?"

He wrinkled his forehead and said, "Hallucinations?"

I explained everything that had transpired over the past few days and all the scenarios Roger was living in. My voice wasn't strong. What was coming out of my mouth were weak, tired, and broken words between tears. I wanted to be strong and mad and demand him to figure this out, but I was so deflated, so deep in despair, all I had was a pleading hopelessness in my voice.

He said in a lighthearted way with a big smile, almost as if he was trying not to laugh, "We just don't know."

I asked again. He looked at me then at the interns and back at me. He clasped his hands in front of him and just looked at me. I said, "My point is, if you did, could we stop that med and see if the spinal fluid clears up?"

He said, "We just don't know. Every patient is different." He wasn't saying yes or no to my question. It seemed like an easy answer – do you or have you ever had a patient where meds caused this reaction? He was the one who said it first. He put it out there as a possibility, "a medication he was on," but when I took it further he didn't want to commit. I was confused. The tears just started rolling down my face. I looked into the eyes of each of the interns, and they were teary and watching me with great grief in their eyes. They were hugging their clipboards now and not thumbing through them.

I said, "Please, I don't mean any disrespect for what I am about to say. Doctor, you had cancer. You were young. You wondered if you could ever have kids, ever have a relationship with your wife again, wondered if it was going to kill you, and you were scared." He lowered his eyes and shifted his weight then looked at me again. I wiped my nose, "We wonder these things, yet we are old with different concerns but still scared and worried if this is going to end poorly. We go to the clinic and express ourselves, 'Roger is sick, no appetite, foul stool, pain in the gut and pain all over.' We hear, 'Yeah, you are going to feel crappy, it's part of the process,' then we are sent home. It's like an assembly line. One of the patients even said out loud to us one time, 'It's one-size-fits-all here, isn't it?' I realized we are not the only ones who feel this way. Doctor, we haven't really seen you since April. You sat down with the study consent form in your hand and quickly explained the study you wanted Roger in. You didn't go into detail on what to expect, only that it was pretty much his only hope. You had him sign a consent, under the pretense that we understood it. Since, we have only been seen in the clinic where Soter and Tammy, great NPs, don't get me wrong, say NEXT. Even the day Roger had his radiation you saw us in the lobby, and you recognized us. You acknowledged us, looked me in the eyes and scanned to Roger in his mask and gloves slumped over in his chair, waiting for a room, and you just ignored us and went on your way. I will never forget that moment. Now you surface again and just give us the runaround." I was crying and speaking at the same time. My words were catching on the lump in my throat as my voice quivered through each word, tears streaming down my face. I was trembling. "Roger is sick. Is this normal to be like this when all the bloodwork seems to be right on and okay, minus the spinal fluid results, yet he is sick, weak, confused and unsteady on his feet?"

Dr. Perses let out a big breath but didn't say anything. It was if he was looking for the right words. I said, "Don't think about the study. I now understand. This study is being done to allow people in the future to benefit from the drugs that show promise in those who are going through these clinical trials right now. We understand this is trial and error. After rereading the clinical study, now when our minds are clearer and the fear of Roger dropping dead any minute has passed, I realize it's not about us right now, and that is the hardest pill to swallow. It's very difficult for me to be on the other side of the coin knowing what I do as a nurse."

He lowered his eyes and said, "No, it's not normal. I really don't know what's going on. The white blood cells could be a multitude of things, yet the standard tests are showing nothing. His symptoms could be GVHD so I am going to restart the high dose of Prednisone and get those tests done ASAP to find out what is going on." He was sincere. He continued, "I'm sorry it feels like an assembly line in the clinic. I've been made aware you've had some mishaps down there. Soter and Tammy have been with me a long time and I really need their help because there are so many patients."

I said, "I understand we are one of many, but that doesn't give you an excuse to not see each patient as an individual. Yes, they are all on the same protocol but some of them are not fairing very well, Roger being one of them. You need to step outside the box and make an effort to now treat him off the protocol. You can't just say, 'Patient no longer fits standard procedure.' He is still alive and fighting every day! We are no different than you. We want to live. I think the system has forgotten that it's people you are treating, not a stack of signed papers that guarantee your salary. Yes, I asked Soter about the protocol. 'How does it treat patients like Roger now that he is so sick?' He said, 'Roger no longer meets protocol and is off the study.' So where does that leave us? Left out in the cold, begging to get back in for help? Are you really going to help him or is he going to fall through the cracks now, be a burden? This is my fear."

The others in the room started to talk to one another softly. I had forgotten they were in the room behind me. Each of them had big tears in their eyes. One intern said, "We're sorry it seems like we're not treating patients like individuals. It's feedback like this that we need to hear; to hear from the patients and what's really going on with them and their families. It allows us to try harder and not forget why we're here and what we're doing."

It was nice to hear. I almost felt like she was stepping in for the doctor because he too was getting choked up. Each of them shook Roger's hand and then mine. Dr. Perses said, "We'll get to the bottom of this, just give me some time. I'll be talking to my colleagues some more." They left the room, and all of us had a new understanding of each other.

Roger laid quietly in his bed, observing like he does. I blew my nose and asked him if I was out of line. He said, "When I get into or observe conversations like that, I think of a few things:

1. Did they listen and hear what I was trying to get across? I think yes.
2. Is this going to make a difference? I think yes.
3. Is it going to change how they take care of me from here on out and is it going to be for the better? I think yes."

"So, it was good. It needed to be said and I'm thankful for what you said. I feel better in some ways and I feel more depressed in others." He was clear and what he said was smart and logical. Where did this Roger come from? He did this all the time – one minute he was somewhere else then he was back with logic and precision. I just didn't get it. I climbed in bed with him and rested for a while.

At 6:30 p.m., I decided to head to his mom's to pick up some clothes and back-up food. I wasn't sure how long we were going to be in the hospital. It was nice to know I could take my time, that Roger was in good hands and was in the hospital. If anything went wrong, he was in the right place.

When I returned, Roger had already had his lumbar puncture. They must have taken him right after I left. He now had to spend the next hour flat on his back. They gave him his Ativan, so he was a little loopy. He said, "Boy, we have a lot to do to get ready to see Perses."

I realized he was confused again. I said, "You just had your LP and now you have to lay flat for an hour. I will sit right here with you." I pulled my chair close to his bed and held his hand.

He said, "We're already here? Huh. We don't need to go see Perses, do we?"

I said, "No, we're here in the hospital, just rest." He closed his eyes and settled into the bed.

A few minutes later the nurse walked in and Roger said, "Aw, it's that time again for my morning pills."

The nurse laughed and said, "Roger, what time do you think it is?" He stared at her, looked away a second then back to her. She said, "It's evening, young man!" She gave him his Prednisone IV and left.

He turned to me and said, "So we just have the LP to do?" I explained to him that he'd had the LP about 30 minutes ago. He said, "Then all I need is to have the transplant?"

I said, "You had the transplant a while back. Just close your eyes and rest; you have about 20 more minutes to lay flat then I'll get you something to eat." Hopefully this was the Ativan talking. It was so strange that he had these small windows of such clarity, then so much confusion a split second later.

He rested while I sat holding his hand. With his eyes closed, he squeezed my hand and said, "I love you."

"I love you too," I replied.

One of the interns from earlier came into the room and said, "We're going to put a rush on the spinal fluid test to see if the white blood cells are up or down. If they're up, we'll start new tests immediately. If they're down, we'll continue doing what we're doing and move forward on a biopsy." I thanked her, and she told us who the night doctor on call was and that she would give us the news as soon as it came in.

Roger turned to me and asked, "Is Janet upset about the robbery?"

I looked at him and said, "Fred and Janet got robbed about eight months ago."

He said, "No, they were robbed again two days ago." This wasn't chemo brain. Chemo brain is described as a fog, as loss of train of thought. This was different, the wires weren't connecting. He was unaware of place and time most of the time, then out of nowhere he was right on track. I was worried. What was this?

The night shift doctor came in a little early and told us the white blood cells were at 27 and a sample had been sent off to a special lab that dealt with unusual bacteria and viruses. She said we should get the results back on Monday. I asked her if the white blood cells were causing the confusion. She said, "The bacteria/virus is causing the confusion. We need to find out what it is then we'll treat it." She checked Roger's eyes with a flashlight and said, "Enjoy your supper," as it had just arrived. He ate everything.

During dinner, he started all over about needing the tires to be changed on the truck for the NASCAR race, and was upset that I wasn't taking him seriously, as well as that I wasn't taking the job as the new pit boss seriously. I said I was, but we didn't need the tires changed. He suddenly switched gears and told me that tomorrow I needed to go dig the holes for the well to get the water flowing. I asked him to look around the room and tell me where he was. He did and said, "We're at the hotel, wait… no, no, no, we are at the hotel." I pushed the IV pole over and he changed his mind, "We are at River Bend Hospital and we live at home." I asked where home was, and he said Tigard, then changed his mind. He started getting upset, telling me to get to Jensen Beach as soon as possible to pick up the plumber. He then said, "You know, they kicked those kids out who were fighting all the time. We should have a quiet night."

I said, "That's great! When you're done with your dinner, you need a shower." He agreed. My head and my entire body were so tired, and it felt like the longest day of my life.

The shower was wonderful. I got into the shower with him, knowing no one would be around for a while. About 9:00 p.m., as soon as I got him back in bed, he began frantically looking for the remote. I just wanted him to rest, but it was obvious that resting wasn't happening anytime soon. I asked, "What's the matter? What are you looking for?"

He said, "The remote. I'm looking for the other remote." I told him there was only one for each room.

He said, "Then what is this? What is this for, this bottle of lotion?" It was the remote. I took it and held it in front of him so he could see it. He stared at it then took it back. He said, "Are you going to take the coins from the woman who just came in the room and offered them to me?"

I said, "No one came into the room, there is no woman." I rubbed his feet and looked at him.

He said, "Yes she did, and she has the coins. Robin, there's a substantial amount of gold there. I need it. I know you're upset about the amusement park, but you'll see. It will be great, just like when we were kids." Once again, I tried to reorient him to the time and place, but he wasn't having it. He was adamant that I needed the coins and that there was another big problem. "How are we going to fit the Tyrannosaurus Rex into the car with the eight of us?" I couldn't shake him away from these thoughts. I showed him my two mosquito bites. He said, "It's because you live half here and half there. They are going to bite you. But I don't have an immune system, they will really eat me, but you are half and half so maybe they won't hurt you."

I was exhausted. I felt like I had a two-year-old. When Tessa was two, I remember saying to her, "Please, just don't talk for five minutes. Give Mommy a break." Roger never talked, but that night he was talking up a storm about gibberish. I tucked him in and within minutes he was asleep.

At 11:00 p.m., the nurse came in for his night meds. She assessed him, checked the IV and asked, "Roger, what year is it?" This was the first time the nurses asked him about the time and place.

He said, "1994." She looked at me and I just shrugged my shoulders.

She said, "What is your wife's name?"

He responded with his ex-wife's name. I was stunned, speechless and on the verge of major tears.

The nurse looked at me. I was in shock, I think. She said, "Robin, her name is Robin."

He said, "NO, Sandy!" This day couldn't get over fast enough. My biggest fear had happened in front of me. What would I do when he didn't recognize me anymore? I took an Ativan from Roger's home bottle and cried myself to sleep. Roger was restlessly dreaming all night.

Day +73

This morning Roger woke as if nothing had ever happened, no confusion, and my name was Robin again. He was ready for his Ativan and said, "Let's get this show on the road." And with that, he left the room on a gurney for a series of tests; lumbar puncture, chest and abdominal MRI, and endoscopy of the stomach. Roger was gone all day. I hung out in the room and waited for him. I called the kids, and each said they would visit and spend some time with their dad. All three kids with their father – I don't think that had happened in years. He would be so happy!

The sun was setting and finally Roger returned. He got settled into bed and before I knew it, the nurses were hanging piggyback IV bags and connecting them to Roger. I asked what he was being given and was told Solumedrol. I asked what for and was told it just came through on the orders, and Dr. Perses was at the desk with Roger's chart and would be in shortly. Solumedrol is a strong steroid so I wondered what they'd found.

Dr. Perses came in, sat down and said that during the endoscopy, they found a large tumor encircling Roger's esophagus. They couldn't see it in the MRI, making it an accidental find. The MRI showed several enlarged lymph nodes in his back. He said, "I don't know if this mass in his esophagus is cancerous or not, but I took a biopsy of it and it should be back on Tuesday or Wednesday of next week. What we do know is that it's not an abscess and it's not an infection. We're calling it a polypoid tumor. I'm starting Roger on a Solumedrol drip, which is a steroid. I also found several ulcers in his stomach.

I think they're caused by GVHD. The steroid should calm them down. I believe the tumor is causing anemia, anorexia and the nausea. I will get the complete results back next week on the biopsies I took. His lumbar puncture from the other day just came back. Roger has the herpes virus in his spinal fluid. We refer to it as HHV6. Dr. Ruffian from the CDC will be sitting down with you and discussing the medication therapy he will be started on for it."

I said, "CDC, the Center for Disease Control?"

He said, "Yes, they deal with these types of infections." I asked how he got it. He said, "This virus shows itself in people with low immune systems. Roger has a very low immune system."

I said, "Okay, so he has a tumor on his esophagus, ulcers in his stomach, enlarged lymph nodes in his back, and the herpes virus in his spinal fluid, all at the same time?"

He stood up and said, "Yes, he does. I'll be talking to Dr. Ruffian more about the HHV6 and a few of my colleagues about the mass. I'm not sure how to proceed on the mass just yet. There are not a lot of doctors that remove these types of tumors in the esophagus, especially ones this large. I'll be back tomorrow with more information." He shook my hand and left.

Roger, who I thought was sleeping said, "Shoot me now. Looks like I'm staying awhile." Roger tried to eat mashed potatoes and some soup. He got down a couple bites but just wanted to sleep. I spent the night researching polypoid tumors and HHV6.

Polypoid tumors can be benign or cancerous. If they're cancerous and operable, long term survival is poor because they usually metastasize to the brain, the lymph system, and the liver. Chemotherapy and radiation is started with a prognosis of six months. This is a rare location, but more and more people are being diagnosed with them. If it is benign, it's removed as soon as possible and that's the end of it. I sure hoped it was benign!

HHV6 is a form of the herpes virus. Most of us carry this virus in our systems from youth. It shows itself in the form of a canker sore around the mouth area. When the immune system is compromised, it takes this opportunity to rear its ugly head. But when it makes its way to the brain, encephalitis occurs. Encephalitis is inflammation of the brain. Symptoms can be headaches, nausea, vomiting, confusion, disorientation, memory loss, speech problems, hearing problems, hallucinations and coma. It's treated and the patient is fine, but it can return at any time. In the studies I read, the drug of choice is one called Ganciclovir. I wasn't sure why the CDC would get involved, but I guessed I would find out.

I couldn't sleep. The nurses kept coming in and out, checking on Roger and hanging more IVs. They always asked me if I would like or needed anything. I just loved the nurses on the cancer floors.

My mind was going in all kinds of directions. I started to think about the ranch a lot more. How was I going to be able to take care of it and my mom all by myself? Here I was with no job, living on Roger's pension, being very frugal and living in the hospital. If I lost him, what was I going to do? How was I going to keep the ranch? It was my dream property! I had spent my whole life waiting to live on a little ranch like this, but the bills were piling up. I knew of at least one more surgery, this polypoid mass, had to come out.

No doctor in this hospital performed this surgery so I wondered where we would have to go to get it removed. I wished I could just rewind the clock and it would all go away! The stress was really starting to get to me, and I felt so tense all the time. It seemed that every time we turned around, something else went wrong. Roger must stay strong – he had a rough road ahead of him. I needed to help him stay strong!

One of the night shift nurses came in with a hot chocolate. She said, "You need to drink this and get some sleep. Tomorrow is a big day."

I said, "Thank you! A big day?"

She said, "Yes, you know this already. Now sleep – he needs you to be rested." She shut my light out, took my journal and set it on the little table, patted me on the head, smiled and left.

Day +74

Roger was started on Ganciclovir IV. We were told he would be on it for 21 days, the usual course. It's for the treatment of encephalitis caused by HHV6. It was explained to us that how and why it worked was still somewhat of a mystery, but it had been successful and was now a followed protocol. I was glad. This morning Roger seemed oblivious to all that was going on around him. He sat in bed, looking out the window or staring at me. When I asked him questions, he just looked at me with no answer. Sometimes he said, "Huh?" and I repeated the question with no response.

Todd showed up this afternoon. I was so happy to see him, and Roger was happy too. Whenever a nurse walked in, Roger respectfully introduced us to them, "This is my son, Todd, and this is my wife, Sandy." They smiled and looked at me with sadness in their eyes. I just held my breath and let it out slowly, trying to calm my nerves. Todd was shocked at first, but after the third time he just looked at me and said he was sorry. I went for a walk and made my way to the cafeteria for some strong coffee and a sandwich. I left the boys so they could catch up. When I left, Roger was telling Todd about the gold coins.

The rest of the night was uneventful. I stayed on my computer researching while the boys watched TV.

Todd stayed all night and slept in a recliner the nurses brought in for him. I was happy he stayed. I didn't get much sleep because my back and hip were killing me. I wished I could get down on the floor to stretch and do some yoga, but to lie on a hospital floor is asking for a lot of trouble with germs. I stretched in every position that didn't require me to get on the floor and tried to release the tight muscles that way.

The visit with his daughter was short but really nice. Roger's eldest would be staying for a week. The visit was a little embarrassing as Roger continued to refer to me as his ex-wife, Sandy, in front of the kids, but they didn't say anything. They just acted as if it was normal. The nurses worked around us and got used to me being called Sandy. One pulled me aside and said I should remind him who I was. I told her I did, it was just where he was in his mind right now. I heard, *I'm so sorry* so many times!

The kids heard all of Roger's stories about NASCAR, the shipwreck, and the amusement park. He also told them that I was very against it and wasn't going to be in the picture for very much longer. My heart sank when I heard him talk like that. I sure hoped this worked so I got my Roger back.

Dr. Ruffian, the infectious disease control doctor, came in and introduced herself to everyone. No one had been looking in her direction or had seen her come in, but her big booming voice rang over all other voices in the room, "Hello, I am Dr. Ruffian!" We all jumped. She was a woman with an abundance of confidence, a fiery redhead with a presence that commanded attention. I used to work with a cardiologist like her. Kind of God's gift to the world and they wanted whoever was in their presence to be made aware of it. She leaned against the wall and explained that Roger had HHV6 in his spinal fluid, and she had prescribed Ganciclovir, a medication that had shown good results. She explained that Roger would be on it for a while and during that time, she would order bloodwork to follow the progress. She asked Roger all the usual questions; time, place, who's who in the room, etc. She asked him some personal questions regarding his habits and what he did for a living. I think she was listening to his answers, looking for confusion. We all listened, and after about 50 minutes, we understood HHV6 and the side effects of the medications; tiredness, flu-like symptoms, skin rash, loss of appetite, and numbness in hands or feet. I was about to ask how we would know he was having side effects when he already had these symptoms, but she was on her way out as each of the kids thanked her.

Just before dinner an on-call doctor from the clinic came into our room. She explained that Roger would be discharged tomorrow if they could figure out how to order the Ganciclovir for IV home therapy. I was in shock! Going home? He had just started all these new medications and was still confused. What about the ulcers and all the tumors they found? How was I going to take care of him? What if something happened?

I didn't feel comfortable, and I think the doctor saw my concerns. She said, "Roger is in a very fragile state and the longer he stays in the hospital, the probability of him getting additional infections grows." She explained that Ganciclovir had a few bad side effects in transplant patients. Dr. Ruffian had also explained this to us. It lowers the platelet count and the white blood cell count, and causes bone marrow suppression, which wasn't good. His donor cells were finally picking up steam and the transplant was finally starting to take.

She was very understanding when I said, "This is too much too soon!"

She said, "Don't worry, quite a few things need to be handled first so you go home without stress – like medication refills and training you on how to give Roger this medication at home via IV, is a start." That part didn't bother me. What did was all the new medications they *just* started him on and everything they just found inside of him. We still didn't have a clear understanding of what was going on, but they were sending him home? Even his insulin was out of whack since he was started on the high doses of steroids.

The kids all left after dinner with lots of hugs and I love yous. Roger returned to watching TV. I had to shut down. My head was so full and nothing made sense, so I shut my phone off and fell asleep. I slept for seven hours straight before waking with a start. A nurse was talking softly to Roger, asking him how he felt and so on. She looked over at me as I was searching for the time. She said, "Go back to sleep. We got this. Rest!" So I did.

Day +75

The discharge planner informed us that the medication Ganciclovir had been approved by the insurance company for the 21 day protocol recommended. I would be giving him a dose twice a day. The medication would be in the form of baseballs; a small baseball-sized container with an IV line on it. Each one is pressurized. When I connect the unit to Roger's PICC line, the unit will create suction and the medication will be administered slowly over 20 minutes. When the baseball was empty, flat, it was complete. Simple enough. I would receive a week's worth each Monday, and they would arrive via courier to Roger's mom's door. They were also adding a medication for his ulcers, Budesonide, 3 mg three times a day. His insulin and his Prednisone had been increased, and I was to pick up these new medications at the pharmacy prior to discharge.

A NP from the clinic stepped in and told us that at the next visit we would be given the biopsy results and further instructions on what to do about the polypoid tumor. In the meantime, we were given a new clinic schedule and told to stay quiet and away from people while the Ganciclovir was being given. We were to follow the same clinic protocol as normal. It was a lot to take in, and I was extremely nervous for a couple of reasons. Roger thought I was someone else and I was taking him home when he was so sick. What if I missed something?

When we were alone, I asked Roger how he felt about everything and he said, "Fine. Are you going to be able to do this for me? Do you want me to tell them you can't so I can stay here?"

I said, "No, I'll be okay. I'm getting pretty good at this." I laughed a bit and he just stared at me.

I started packing up the room, getting ready to leave when Dr. Ruffian walked in. I needed some good news. She started talking in a very professional, stern, slow voice, as if I was a child needing extra time to comprehend what was being said to me. She went over the Ganciclovir and how they hoped Roger's body would react to it. She said she would be following his daily bloodwork and if any changes needed to be made, she would be the one to make them.

When she was done being bossy, I requested, "Can you go over the side effects of this drug? Anything I should be made aware of, just in case he has any adverse reactions. He already has all the side effects you mentioned."

She looked at me then at Roger, put her hands on her hips and said, "I went over *that* and what to expect from this medication for an hour yesterday! I will go over the bloodwork daily and take care of anything that comes up!"

I looked at her and said, "Yes, you did. You came in here and gave me a whole hour of your time. You gave me a lot of information all at once, prior to the medication being started. Now he is going home with it and I'm responsible for getting it in him and taking care of him while I do that. I'm now in need of some *extra* advice and maybe I can ask a few questions this time!" I was pissed and I didn't give a darn if I was taking up a bit more of her time. She was supposed to be my advisor. What was her problem?

She walked closer to me, looked me in the eye and said, "What?"

I stepped into her and said, "I understand that you need to monitor his bloodwork while he's receiving this medication and that you will make the appropriate changes as results come in. But we're not going to be here for you to get daily blood results so what's the plan after discharge?" It was obvious that there was a pissing war beginning.

She said, "I read my patients' lab work every day. I get them on my pager, my email, and my desk, even when I'm on vacation. I'll tell you when and after I get the results what to do. If I see anything alarming, I'll let you know!"

I stepped back, took a breath and said, "Listen, I'm a nurse, we're going home. There will be no bloodwork for you to look at every day because we won't be here to have bloodwork drawn for you, and no results to forward to all your devices, so what is the plan?"

She looked around the room and saw the bags being packed. She said, "You're going home? WHO TOLD YOU THIS?"

I dropped my head, took a cleansing breath again and exhaled, "Dr. Cook told us last night. You just missed the discharge planner who is working with the drugstore to have 21 days of Ganciclovir baseballs delivered to our front door."

She said, "21 days, who said 21 days? I will decide how many days he gets this medication! As I explained to you yesterday for an hour, I will monitor the blood results. If they're positive, I will continue the medication. If they're negative, I will decide if and when he needs to stop it." I raised my hands and shrugged my shoulders at her. She said, "I'll get to the bottom of this," and she stormed out.

What am I, a child? Don't ask questions? So, no advice? What now? Once again, there was obviously no communication between the departments in this hospital. No one ever knows what the other is doing. I'm exhausted! I looked at Roger. I had almost forgotten he was in the room. He was sitting up with his hands folded on his chest, smiling a huge smile. I lost it. I started laughing so hard and couldn't stop. He was laughing too, in his deep, baritone chuckle. When we finally regained our composure, I told him I was sorry. He said, "It's okay, you're very entertaining. I needed popcorn for that one."

I said, "Who am I?"

He said, "You're Robin, my wife." I kissed him gently on the lips. I felt like a million bucks!

I went to the nurse's desk to get an update on the discharge and ask when the best time would be for me to head to the pharmacy. The doctor was at the desk. I told her what happened with Dr. Ruffian. She crinkled her nose and forehead and said, "Oh boy, let me look into this. I'll meet you in the room in a bit." After about 20 minutes she came into the room and said, "You're being discharged for a few reasons. First off, like I mentioned before, we need to get you out of here, Roger. There's a bad bug going around and the hospital is full of it. If you get it, it won't be good. Also, we don't know what to expect on the biopsy results and we won't have them for a few days. It's better for you to wait at home for them, not here. If the results come back cancerous and you're here, you could end up being seen by a breast cancer on-call doctor. We have a private specialist we want you to see, not someone from here. But we'll cross that bridge later. The Ganciclovir won't be ready until tomorrow, so you'll stay here tonight and be discharged in the morning. Go ahead and get what you need from the pharmacy now. They'll close soon. All the orders are written so you can leave as soon as you're ready in the morning. Any questions?" I asked about side effects to look for since he already had most of the side effects now. She said, "The big one is his confusion. If it gets worse, call immediately. He has encephalitis, so most side effects will be from that, not the medication." Wow, okay. She left and so did I. I got to the pharmacy just in time. Another shopping bag full! I have so many bottles of pill and needles, I could open a pharmacy.

PART SIX

1

A Change of Scenery

On day +76, all the nurses said their goodbyes and out the door we went, Roger in a wheelchair and I stressed out. We got settled into Roger's mom's home. Being in bed for a few days had made Roger's legs even weaker. Thank goodness for the wheelchair, but climbing the four stairs into her house took almost twenty minutes with Craig's help.

I could see in Craig's face that he was really worried about his dad. But he, like all Rog's children, doesn't talk much. They keep their feelings to themselves, no matter what they are. The apple doesn't fall too far from the tree!

I made Rog a bed on the recliner in front of the TV where he would stay for the next three days except to go to the bathroom. Craig spent his time talking and watching TV with his dad and doing little chores for Grandma. The medication procedure was simple and Roger was tolerating it well. Each day he seemed a little less confused and a bit more alert, which made me happy! He ate little, but he ate. I watched the boys get reacquainted and left them alone unless I was serving medications or meals.

Day +79

Roger had gotten up last night to go to bathroom and somehow cut the back of his wrist, creating a pretty good gash. It didn't need stitches, but it was a good one. He didn't wake me, he just crawled into bed and went back to sleep. This morning, the sheets were covered in blood, and it scared me when I awoke to find the bed like this. "Where are you bleeding from?" He told me it was his wrist and held it out for me to see. It looked horrible! He said something on the wall had caught him. Sure enough, there was a small nail sticking out from the doorframe going into the bathroom. I pulled the nail out, cleaned up his wrist, and put antibiotic cream and a bandage on it. I explained to him that his immune system was so compromised that if things like this happened, he needed to tell me right away so it didn't get infected.

That afternoon, Roger walked around the property a couple of times. He did pretty well although his body and hands were really shaky. He could no longer do anything that required a steady hand, and giving himself insulin was impossible. Trying to get the little strip or stylet into the machine was impossible. His legs weren't as weak, but he was unsteady on them. I asked him to use his mom's cane, and it took a huge argument to get him to use it. Mom had to remind him that she fell not long ago on the uneven cement, so using the cane was a good idea. We took it slow, and it was nice to get out in the fresh air. After he walked, he went right back to his chair and found his favorite friend – his remote control.

It was a nice, uneventful weekend and Roger was doing great with the Ganciclovir, no side effects. The baseballs fit perfectly into his shirt pocket so moving about was easy. I worried that his immune system wouldn't be strong enough to heal his wound, but it was doing great.

The summer heat was bad that year with it being between 95-99 degrees. I wanted to get him out walking more, but he said the heat killed him. It killed me too! I spent the week researching and figuring out ways to make his life better while he and Craig watched TV.

When it was time for Craig to head home, he promised to call more. Rog had tears in his eyes as Craig left. I was so thankful he took the time to stay and help with his dad's care. It had been a nice week for all of us.

Day +84

Roger said he was feeling pretty good that morning, better than he had in a while. He looked better too, more alert. I think the medication was working. We had a nice breakfast with his mom and headed to the clinic for a post-hospital checkup.

While Roger was getting his labs done, I left the clinic and decided to take a walk. I started thinking about my life, how I never thought I would be in this place – living in hospitals, hotels, and with Roger's mom. When I married Roger, I thought my life was going to be perfect. We were barely married two years when he had his bypass surgery, and he never really recovered from that before he went right into leukemia. Why did we buy the ranch? It just seemed like a lot of work to me now, the joy was gone. I didn't know how I was going to be able to do it all without losing myself.

When Roger was done with the lab work, we met with one of our doctor's NPs. She said everything looked good with his bloodwork. She said, "Roger is doing well and if you want to make a trip home in the next few days, it should be okay, just be careful." Roger had complained about the heat and said he needed to get out of town. The NP had just given us a free ticket. I stopped at the little store in the hospital lobby and got him some snacks to eat on the way home. I knew he would be hungry and I needed to give him his insulin.

That night's dinner was simple; soup, fresh steamed veggies and some garlic toast. He ate it all, which was shocking. He talked to his mom through the whole meal and it was nice hearing his voice. I just sat and listened to the two of them sharing their ailments with each other, and took a picture of the two of them together. They looked like husband and wife, the same age. It was so sad to see, but I'm happy I got the picture.

We laid in bed and I asked him if he really wanted to go home. I said, "You know what's going to happen. I'm going to be working most of the time, catching up on everything." He said he understood but needed to get out of his mom's house. When his brothers visited, they were complaining about their bumps and bruises to him – a bad knee, a bad ankle, heart palpitations, can't work because of all these horrible health issues – as if any of those ailments were of any significance. I wondered if they knew that Roger would trade all of their ailments for his if they would agree to it. I wondered if they got the fact that their brother was sitting in front of them fighting for his life.

Day +85

We got up early and headed home. On the way, we talked about everything. Rog was articulate and making sense. He still had short term memory loss but when talking about the past, as in years ago, he remembered everything.

I asked him when my birthday was. He said he knew Sandy's. I said, "That's good, what about mine?" It took about 20 minutes, but he finally got it and he was pleased with himself. He said he wanted to try to mow the lawn when we got home. I said, "Absolutely not. Are you crazy, Mr. Clark?"

He smiled at me and said, "We'll see." The man could be so irritating!

The wood had been delivered yesterday, a few days late and delivered halfway up the driveway. Roger told me to use the tractor, and he wanted to help so he drove the tractor up and down the hill while I filled and emptied it. All he had to do was drive it. He was happy for the first time in a long time, and I was happy he was outside getting fresh air and all the work was in the shade. I started to put the tractor away when Rog said, "No, I am mowing the yard." I had called Todd when we got home and told him to come over right now or Dad would be on the mower. No matter how much I grumbled and pleaded, Roger was not giving me the keys back. He mowed for about 25 minutes, with short sleeves, sun beating down on him, and no hat. What started out fun was turning bad, more and more bad by the minute. He was using all his strength to stay on the tractor and maneuver it up and down the hills. He had already been on the thing for three hours dumping wood.

Yelling over the loud tractor motor, I tried reminding him that every time we came home and he did something like this, we ended up in the ER or the hospital with diagnosis of exhaustion or dehydration. "Get off the tractor – enough!" I said. He ignored me. Todd showed up at that very moment. He had a long talk with Rog and before I knew it, Todd was on the mower getting the yard done. I was so relieved!

Roger didn't have anything left in him. He could barely stand, let alone walk up the hill to the house. Todd helped him and I was worried. If he did too much, how was this going to affect him? I helped him to the lounge chair on the deck, made him some lunch, and took his temperature. All was good. Roger rested on his lounge chair and watched Todd mow the lawn. I was glad he was feeling better and was trying, but this was the time to let his body heal, not challenge it. He was not happy with me, but I didn't care.

After a good meal and a good night's rest, we headed back. Roger had lab work we needed to get to.

We got back pretty early, stopping at the hospital for a quick blood draw then back to Roger's mom's. She was in the carport trying to clean up pine needles. I got Rog in the house to his recliner, started the Ganciclovir, and got him his cup full of medications and a snack then went out to help Roger's mom.

Roger was getting a little stronger. I wasn't sure if it was just his stubbornness coming through, but he was able to stand a bit longer and was steadier on his feet. His mind seemed clearer and his conversations had substance.

A little later, Rog went to lie down in the bedroom and after a while I joined him. He was pouring sweat. It must have been 98 degrees in that room and he was miserable. I had him take off his sweat soaked T-shirt, which he wore every day. I got a washcloth, put cold water on it, and rubbed it over his skin with the fan blowing on him. After about ten minutes, he fell back to sleep.

I woke him for dinner. A nice chicken breast, mashed potatoes and steamed veggies with a cup full of pills, an insulin pen, and a baseball of Ganciclovir all awaited him at the table as it did every night.

Day +87

We slept in. It was a day of rest, no clinic. We planned to head back home for a couple of days. This day was so hot, and we both used wet washcloths all day and sat in front of the fan.

Roger ate all his meals, took all of his seemingly one thousand pills, was poked six times in the finger for sugar levels, poked more times in the arms with insulin-filled needles, and had two baseballs of Ganciclovir infused into him. This was the daily routine – morning, noon and night.

He agreed to take a walk around his mom's property. He was getting steadier on his feet although he still suffered from shaky hands and a weak body, but at least he was getting better at holding it up. He wasn't as hunched over and wasn't shuffling anymore. His affect was still monotone and his look was one of a blank stare most of the time, but at least he was trying again. Sitting in front of the TV was still his favorite thing to do, but at least he was walking and exercising his body, moving the blood around. This gave me hope!

Day +88

We headed back home to spend a few days finishing projects. As soon as we walked in, Mom was at the front door with her purse in hand, asking me to take her to the hardware store. Roger was immediately in his chair with his buddy, Mr. Remote. I told him I would be right back, got him his snack, water and juices, and we headed out.

When we returned, Roger was in the garage, tinkering with the tools on his workbench. I was a little concerned he didn't stay in the house, but he did what he wanted. I asked if he needed help. He said abruptly, "I'm bored. You were gone a long time!" We had been gone two hours. Since we live 13 miles outside of town, at least 40 minutes of the two hours was travel time. I apologized. He said, "I'm going to get some shelves. Give me the keys."

I was surprised. I said, "You can't drive."

He said, "I haven't taken anything to impair me. I'm fine!"

I said, "Roger, you are so shaky and have a problem remembering what you are even doing half the time, let alone carrying 60-pound shelves to the truck." I was frustrated, and there was no way he could build shelves.

He said, "You spent all that time with your mom and now I need the truck."

I said, "Okay, let me take you." I felt bad and sad for him, but there was no way I was ever going to relinquish his truck keys to him. At that moment, I realized I was going to have to hide them from him because he would leave if he had access to them. After a small, intense argument, he agreed to let me drive him.

At checkout, Rog got out his bankcard to pay. After four failed attempts at remembering his debit code, I used my card and we left. It was a good thing I went. Once we got home, I helped him put the box of shelves in the garage and left him there to try to put them together. He fired up the TV on the workbench and sat down in his man chair. I had a feeling that was where he was going to stay. I left to work on the deck for him and Max.

I checked on Rog frequently and made sure all meds were on time and his belly had food in it. Each time, I found him watching TV in his man cave. I connected the baseballs and he gave me no inclination that he was aware I was accessing his IV. At least he was outside in the fresh, cool air.

Rog was able to eat all his dinner and when he was done, he pushed his dishes aside and went to his chair. No thank you or comment on whether he liked it or not. I assumed he did since it was all gone. Without a lot of talking, we went to bed and slept like babies.

We headed back to his mom's the next morning and settled back into the oven we temporarily called home. The heat was unbearable and I couldn't wait until we could go home for good. Throughout the day, I kept the fan on Roger while he sat in his chair. I dampened his arms, legs and neck with a wet washcloth so the fan breeze would feel even better. Roger just sat there. He didn't take his pills unless I put them in front of him, and he didn't get up for dinner to have supper at the table, he just waited until I put his meal in front of him on a TV tray. He didn't bring his dirty dishes to the sink, he just pushed the tray to the side of the chair. But he did go into the kitchen three times, searching the refrigerator for cookies he thought would be in there. He drank his fluids when I reminded him, and when I asked what he was so intensely watching on TV, he just ignored me. When it was time to do a finger stick to check his glucose level and insulin need, he shook so badly that after wasting five glucose strips, at $1.00 a strip, I took over and helped him.

He said loudly in my ear, "I will do it!"

I jumped and, for the first time, yelled back at him. I just lost it! I was so frustrated with him I said, "No, you can't. You need help! You have just wasted five strips and haven't even poked your finger yet."

He didn't say anything and he didn't look at me, he just looked at the machine on the table and waited until I finished. As I did the glucose check, I began to feel bad about my reaction. I knew I had been on the verge of yelling at him for days. I just wanted more from him. I wanted him to make as much effort in taking care of himself as he did trying to remember how to use the damn remote! As the days lingered on, his short-term memory was getting worse. Things that came easy now took hours to figure out. Gadgets that he bought for fun, he now looked at as if they were from a foreign country. He didn't ask for help, he got frustrated and threw things away, no matter what it was – batteries, computer, phone, and medication bottles – because he couldn't open it. I had to go through the trash cans several times a day to pull out everything he had thrown away. Tomorrow at the clinic, I needed to talk to the NP about this.

I was finally understanding and seeing what was going on, and it wasn't a good feeling. Would Roger, my genius, ever really return?

2

Going Home

During the day +91 clinic visit, I asked the doctor about Roger's memory and flat affect. We were told that the radiation and chemotherapy were responsible for this as well as the HHV6 in his brain. We were told that the encephalitis would resolve but sometimes there was residual memory loss that came with it. He asked Roger all the usual questions; how do you feel, how do you think your memory is, are you eating, pain level, and so on. Roger answered with, "I think I am doing a lot better. But I do have a lot of pain all over, especially in my joints." I just stayed quiet and stared at the floor. When they were silent, I looked up and found the doctor looking at Roger then at me. He made some notes on the computer, turned and said, "It's time for you to go home. I have talked to Dr. Moros. He's up-to-date on your progress and will be following you while you're home. You will need to continue the Ganciclovir, which we're working on having delivered to your home, and continue the blood draws in the hospital there. Dr. Moros will send us copies of the results, and if changes are necessary, we'll address them together. All your medications have been ordered and are waiting for you in the pharmacy. They have been sent to Dr. Moros's office as well. I will need to see you in the clinic every two weeks to go over your progress, but it's time. You're ready." I was crying softly, tears rolling down my face. I reached over and held Roger's hand while the doctor continued to talk. I could feel my body trembling. I asked if Dr. Moros was able to take care of Roger in an emergency situation or if we were we supposed to try to drive back if his temperature went up or he had other complications. He said, "Dr. Moros is capable. If an emergency occurs, he will notify me then we'll determine what's next." He reminded us to keep the PICC line clean and dry and to have regular dressing changes.

I was in shock! Roger was speechless and emotionless. Dr. Perses asked Roger if he was okay with going home. He smiled and said, "Heck, yes!" Roger had one more magnesium infusion to take care of in the clinic so I took this time go to the pharmacy and call the family.

When we got back to his mom's I packed up our belongings and stuffed the car to the gills with everything we had with us. We decided to leave in the morning so we could have a nice meal with his mom before we left.

Everyone was so happy we were going home! To them, it meant Roger had successfully survived a bone marrow transplant. I too took it as a great sign that all would be fine. It was time to just rest and let his body do the healing. I was so happy driving back home with ALL our stuff!

The next day neither of us wanted to do anything but sit out on the deck and breathe in the fresh air wafting up the canyon onto our back deck. We called Betty to prepare for Max's return. There was so much to do!

The first full day home I spent on the phone with Dr. Moros's office. We were informed that Roger had completed his Ganciclovir medication and that no more baseballs would be arriving. Roger and I were so happy! Every time we got to stop a medication, we were elated! It's funny how I had come to say "we" as if I was taking the medications too. I asked Roger if that bothered him, and told him it wasn't intentional, it was just that *we* were doing everything together now, so it just started coming out of my mouth as *we* instead of *he*.

He said, "I say it too, it just is." Okay, so it is. I got Roger's new clinic schedule for the hospital near home. From our house to the hospital where Dr. Moros's office and the cancer infusion clinic is was 32 minutes on a good day with no traffic. I felt good about that.

The first visit to Dr. Moros's office was especially emotional. He walked in, sat down, and looked at us with tears in his eyes. This was the first time he had seen us since the day he diagnosed Roger in the ER and told me that Roger had maybe eight hours to live. I barely remember that night. Dr. Moros said, "Hello. I have to tell you that no couple has ever moved me like you two did that night in the ER. When I saw you with your head lying on his chest, holding Roger's hand, knowing what I was about to tell you, my heart was in pain. You two were so connected, and I have never witnessed such a connection. It was beautiful! But the look on your face was a look I'll never forget, when I told you what I told you."

The tears were rolling down my face. Roger reached over, wiped my tears and took my hand. We just looked at each other and smiled. I blew my nose and said, "We have been through a lot since we last saw you."

He said, "I can see that. Roger, how are you doing?"

Roger replied, "I've been better, but I'm making it work."

I said, "Thank you for letting us come home and for taking over his care." I asked all the questions regarding emergency care if anything was to happen, medication refills, IV care, follow up procedures, and finally just gave him the list with all the questions. He went through each one. After he finished, I was so content and relaxed, and felt confident that being home was going to be just fine. The doctor shook Roger's hand, gave me a hug which I so needed, and told us that we were in good hands.

When we left the room, he sent Roger to the lab to get his bloodwork done and asked me to stay a minute. He said, "How is he really doing? How are you doing?" I caught him up on Roger's mental status and stamina, and told him not to worry, it had been a lot worse. But I did ask, "Will he ever get his youth back? People keep asking if I need help with my dad when I push his wheelchair into places. This kills Roger."

He said, "Everyone is different."

I said, "I am far beyond being appeased, I need honesty please!"

He replied, "No, I don't see that right now. Robin, his body is dealing with GVHD of the gut, the liver and the skin. I'm not a transplant doctor, but I take care of a lot of post-op transplant patients. Roger is really going through a lot right now. Just do the best you can."

Days +96 – +101

During these days of being home, I did nothing but work on the property and get Roger back and forth to the clinic for his follow ups.

Roger's weight was resting at 240 pounds; he had lost 75+ pounds in 101 days, and his strength was very limited. As the days of being home passed, Roger's stamina had gotten a little better and he was more motivated. I believe that him watching me work from sun up to sun down encouraged him to want to help me more. With the front porch in need of a cement foundation, Roger decided to try to put the mixer together for me. I set up a nice, comfortable chair in the garage, opened the box, and gave him the instructions then left him alone. What should have taken a few hours took four days. Roger spent the afternoons in the garage trying to figure out the directions to put the cement mixer together. Occasionally, something would tell me to check on him and each time I found him in need of help. The instructions seemed foreign to him; just two pages and six steps were confusing. The upper part of the machine just needed to be mounted on the stand, but Roger's brain was not computing. He said, "I'm reading this and understand it, but I can't do it. Between my brain and my hands, something is not syncing. My hands are shaking so bad I can't hold the screws. Robin, something's not right!" I helped him at each of these moments then let him be for a while to try to figure it out as he asked me to do.

I walked in on him trying to saw a piece of the metal frame in two. I said, "Before you do that, can I see the instructions where it says to saw the frame in two?"

He said, "It doesn't say to saw it in two, but it won't fit so I'm making it fit." I carefully showed him where the problem was. Most of the time I found him staring at the instructions in his hands, and sometimes he was reading them out loud to himself. He did this for hours, but honoring his request, I let him be.

I could see what was happening to Roger as the days lingered on and his body and mind got weaker; he was going to need tools to make his life easier. His determination was getting stronger, but his body was still aging every day. I likened it to a microwave. When you take the food out, it's cooked but it's still cooking inside, drying up the food, shriveling the skin of the potato, and all the life inside the food. Roger was taking handfuls of medications; these medications and the lingering deterioration effects from the radiation were killing him. I hated it and none of it made sense to me.

My priority was to get handicap bars and toilet seat lifts put up in the bathroom, and a front porch with ramp and railings added. All the walkways around the property needed leveling so he didn't trip and fall, and his man cave needed to be clutter-free so he didn't fall over anything. Plus, the new menu of organic foods and spices needed updating so mealtime was easier and healthier. I needed to box up most of my cupboard items and give the prepackaged, preservative-laden food away. Roger's body was no longer getting any of it. If I was going to help save his life, it must start with the food I was putting in him. Cancer cannot live in a clean body!

The kids, knowing I was going home with Dad, took the attitude, *Mom can do anything. Roger is home, so all is good. Vacation time for us!* I didn't hear from any of them the entire eleven days.

Roger surprised me during the day with, "There's a movie playing. Let's go." We dropped everything and went. It was great. We used to have what we called, "two movie Tuesdays" at the local theater. Tuesday is $5.00 movie day. We would take in two movies, two big buckets of popcorn, and a soda refill. It was our thing. This day was a little different. This Tuesday we wore surgical masks to prevent Rog from getting sick, had a small popcorn with no butter and no soda, but we had a blast!

That night, as I laid there in the darkness, I listened to Roger's soft breathing. He held my hand as he slept, something we did whenever he wasn't sleeping in a hospital bed. It felt good, but at the same time my mind was reeling with thought. I was tired. I felt like life was bearing down, suffocating me. There was so much to do, and all I wanted to do was sit on a white sandy beach with an umbrella drink and listen to the distant sound of steel drums and the gentle waves of the ocean in front of me. I seemed to be falling into a pit of despair. The movie was a great distraction, but it was just temporary. The kids were so busy with their own lives, and part of me was happy they were on their own and doing well, but part of me wished they knew me better – the part of me that hid and cried, that was sad and lonely, who needed help and a hug, a big hug. It was disheartening how people just assume I can handle everything. The fact was, I was drowning!

Roger finally finished putting the cement mixer together. Now I hoped the mixer worked. Fortunately, Roger did great, and the mixer worked beautifully! We worked together and got it done.

I was finally able to take care of Roger's needs. The bathroom situation was first on my list. Roger's legs had become so tiny and weak. He, being so tall, going from a standing position to a sitting position on our low toilets was getting difficult. His legs didn't have the strength to push him up. When he called me in to help him stand up from the toilet one morning, I knew this was now a priority. When I was done, everywhere he turned in the bathrooms he had help. I found him in the bathroom later that day, crying. I asked if he was okay and held him. He said, "This is the best present you could have ever given me, Robin. It was so hard to stand up. Now it's so simple. Thank you so very much!" Amazing! I wish I had known it was so difficult, I would have done it sooner.

Day +116

After a few visits to the new clinic, we had gotten to know the nurses pretty well. They were a great group of nurses and it makes all the difference in the world when you have loving people around you when you're going through something like this. Sometimes it was the nurses that got me through to another day.

I found it mind boggling to see cancer patients reclining in the easy chairs receiving an infusion of chemo drugs, snacking on chips, candy bars and fast food. I wondered why they didn't get it. How did they expect their bodies to heal if all they put in it was crap? I watched them mindlessly sticking their hands in the bags of chips over and over as they watched TV or read a book while the poison was trickling in. I had done so much research on diet, the benefits of organic foods, and on the foods that caused cancer, and there they sat, consuming these foods while the doctors proclaimed to cure them with poison. Poison on poison. No wonder we weren't curing cancer! Every time we left the clinic, I found myself wanting to find the nearest airplane and get on it, no matter where it was going. Just take us somewhere else, please!

I watched Roger lose more weight. He was down to 230 pounds and getting weaker. I spent a lot of time with him during meals, making sure I fed him only what he wanted. Whatever he was craving, I made him. Trying to get him to eat was the worst part of my day. He had started to veg out with the TV again. For a while he was hanging out with me as I dug holes or leveled paths, showing me areas to fix or how to fix them. He showed me how he wanted his man cave laid out to make it easier and safer for him, and together we got the little jobs done. Like a team, him as the foreman and me doing the grunt work. He pointed, I did. But as the days lingered on, I was noticing confusion and the flat affect again. I wondered if the HHV6 was coming back. I hadn't asked if the medication killed the virus or just put it back in dormancy. If it stays in us, creeping out in times of immune deficiency, did that mean it was still in him? I planned to talk to the doctor about it.

Day +117

It was a long night and I couldn't sleep. I started realizing that there was going to come a day when all of this was going to be gone. Roger would be gone, the house would be gone, and I would be on my own again. The thought made my chest hurt.

As the sun rose and peeked in through the windows, Roger woke up. He turned to look at me to find me looking at him. He said, "Good morning." I reached over and kissed him. I lingered for a minute, hoping he would kiss me like he used to. He didn't try, just quickly hugged me and patted me on the back. I looked into his eyes and I *saw* the Roger I married, deep in his eyes. But his body language was not matching the warmth in his eyes, which I didn't understand. This was the man that relentlessly fought for me for months with his charm and charisma until I gave in. I could see him in there, but he didn't play outside anymore. I missed being touched, kissed and snuggled.

I let him rest and take his time getting up. His breathing was labored and it was hard for him to catch his breath with just the slightest bit of movement. I got up and started the morning routine with breakfast and getting his pills and insulin ready. He still wasn't out of bed so I went in to check on him and he said he needed help getting up. He held onto my shoulder as I helped him to the side of the bed. He got really dizzy, laid his head against me, and took several deep breaths. After a few minutes, he was able to stand. I got him dressed as he stood in front of me then I helped him to his chair.

It was a long day. He couldn't do anything for himself without getting winded and having slight chest pain. I called the clinic and they scheduled a CT scan for tomorrow afternoon. They told me not to worry, to just keep him quiet.

Roger slept most of the day. He was pale and his breathing wasn't getting any better. Any activity was a struggle so he only got up from his chair to go to the bathroom. I tried to get him to lay in bed to rest and get his feet up, but he said it was too hard to breath. I stayed in the house with him; nothing seemed important but making sure he was all right. Mid-morning, I got a call from a local GI doctor who we had an office visit scheduled with to discuss the polypoid tumor wrapped around Roger's esophagus. Was this the reason he was having difficulty breathing? Was the tumor growing? The CT scan couldn't happen fast enough!

I Can't Breathe

It was now day +118, and Roger's CT scan was scheduled for 12:00 noon. I had him rest and fed him breakfast in bed with all the usual medications. Getting him out of bed and dressed was almost impossible. Our bedframe was an old California King waterbed frame with a mattress in it. To get out of bed, you had to lift yourself up and over the hardwood frame. Trying to get Roger's body up and over this frame to a standing position was extremely difficult to do without his help. I don't know how we did it, but we did. We made it to the car and off we went. Hopefully this scan would give us an idea of what was happening.

Roger made it through the CT scan. He got a burst of energy that lasted for about 30 minutes, which was perfect timing, allowing us to get him on and off the CT scan table without much difficulty. But that didn't last long. By the time we got to the car, he was once again out of breath. He was so pale and using too much energy to breathe. The muscles and every blood vessel in his neck were noticeable, and each breath came with severe chest discomfort. I knew I needed to get him to the ER, to Dr. Moros. As I drove, I called the clinic, put them on speakerphone, and told them where I was headed and why. They told me to stay on the phone until I got there. I was panicking inside and used every ounce of control to keep my voice calm and steady. Roger couldn't breathe and he couldn't answer any questions. I started to wonder if I was going to get him to the ER in time. I yelled into the phone to call the ER and tell them we were on our way and to have stand-by at the door. The rest of the trip was all about keeping focused and not getting into an accident or freaking out. I was shaking and breathing for Roger. He was bent over with his head in his hands with saliva dripping from his mouth as he concentrated on every breath. The nurse on the phone spilled off all kinds of questions which neither of us answered.

Within minutes I had sped through every light and screeched into the ER parking lot where a team was waiting for us. They opened Roger's door before I even came to a stop. Three men pulled Roger from the car onto a gurney, slammed him into a sitting position and took him away. I was sobbing as I clutched the steering wheel with my head resting on it. I stayed there by myself, alone for a few minutes before I heard the nurse's voice calling my name from the phone. She said, "Robin, park the car and go inside. They need you now!" I slammed the car into drive, found a parking spot, and ran through the doors where a nurse was running toward me. She grabbed my hand and pulled me, running down the corridors into an ER room. A doctor was waiting, and I was already getting Roger's medication sheet out of my purse and handing it to him before he had a chance to ask for it. All he said was, "Did he take all these meds this morning?" I replied yes. "When did his symptoms begin?"

"Yesterday, but they got worse today. He just had a CT scan done."

The nurse looked at him and said, "I got it." She went to the computer and brought up the scan that was done minutes before. The doctor looked at them and left.

I asked the nurse what the doctor had seen, but she said nothing, just pointed to several areas that looked like blood clots. I said, "Oh no, he is having a pulmonary embolism!" She looked at me quizzically. I said, "Nurse," sat down in the chair and just sobbed. She knelt beside me and said she would go see what was happening with him.

Before I knew it, an hour had elapsed. I sat in that chair going over everything in my head, where we were and how we had gotten here. I had a bad feeling that the next doctor I saw was going to give me really bad news. The ER doctor finally came in with Roger in tow. He was hooked up to three IVs and breathing a little better. He was still pale, almost grey, but it was a color I had gotten used to. The ER doctor notified us that Dr. Perses had requested that Roger be sent via helicopter back to the BMT hospital tonight. I looked at Roger and he said in a breathless voice, "No." I explained to the doctor that whenever Roger's health was in an emergency medical state, it took that hospital's team days or weeks to decide what to do. The continuity of care was horrible, and he ended up getting worse before he got better.

He left and when he returned minutes later, he said, "Dr. Moros thinks we can take care of this here. He has written orders for a CDC doctor, Roger's cardiologist, and the pulmonologist to see him tonight. He said. "Roger, you will be admitted, and we will continue blood thinners until you are stable enough to leave. You will be on blood thinners most likely the rest of your life, young man. But in the meantime, hold tight while we get you that room." Within a few minutes, Roger's cardiologist was at the bedside asking all kinds of questions regarding his chest pain. A few minutes after he left, the pulmonologist was interviewing Roger.

When he left, I heard all these familiar voices in the hallway outside our door. I looked out and the ER doctor, Dr. Moros, the pulmonologist, and the cardiologist were all going over a handful of documents, discussing Roger. The BMT hospital had faxed a handful of Roger's records to them. They merged over to a table, spread the papers out, and studied them. A female doctor showed up, and the conversation began again. I sat back down and looked at Roger in disbelief. He asked what was going on and I told him that all the doctors were talking with each other right now about him. He smiled, closed his eyes, and drank in the oxygen from the mask he was wearing. The CDC doctor then came in and talked to us about Roger's transplant and the several medications he was taking. At the end of the interview, she told us that after a brief pow-wow with all the other doctors, Roger would have a full work-up in the morning, consisting of sonograms of his neck, groin, legs and underarms for additional clots. "In the meantime, rest, enjoy the oxygen, and we will all see you again in the morning." She lightly touched my shoulder, gently patted Roger's covered toes and left. Roger slept through the night and I eventually fell asleep on my little couch bed. All night, I vaguely heard the beeping IV machine and the nurses coming in and out.

I was awakened with a cup of coffee, a handful of sugar and cream, and a big smile from Roger's morning nurse. As the CDC doctor promised, the whole team arrived during rounds *together*. They took turns talking and asking all kinds of questions, starting with an explanation of Roger's progress since the transplant. I answered every question, finally asking how long Roger would be there. They said, "Most likely two days." I asked why this big team. They said it was because we didn't want to go back to BMT hospital, so they needed to prepare themselves for the next time.

I said, "Next time?"

Dr. Moros said, "Yes, for the next time. Patients with this type of transplant have known histories of getting blood clots and several other complications as time goes on."

I understood. The tears started flowing as I said, "Thank you so much. You have no idea how much this means to us. It doesn't usually happen like this." They all shook both our hands and said they would reconvene after the ultrasound was done.

The ultrasound tech did the test right at Roger's bedside. I asked him a lot of questions while Roger slept. The tech, as usual, said he couldn't discuss what he saw but he would explain what he usually saw in patients with blood clots. It became perfectly clear that Roger was full of them. His lungs, his legs, his groin, and one under his right arm. It wasn't long after the tests were complete that Dr. Moros showed up and verified what I had seen on the scan was indeed multiple blood clots. The plan was IV therapy to replace fluids and stabilize blood thinners then go home.

Roger's cardiologist showed up and said, "Rog, it's not your heart this time." He gave Rog two thumbs up and told him to get up and move about more, then left. Each doctor came in and said the same thing and ended with, "Roger, you need to walk more and do foot exercises while in your chair. If you don't, we will see you again for the same diagnosis." Roger agreed to exercise more.

While Roger ate his breakfast, I wrote in my journal. Every time we went to the BMT hospital, it was days of anticipation merging into worry and frustration to downright anger. No one talked to each other. If Roger had been flown there, they would have repeated all the same tests, wasting time, and he would have been put on some freaky experimental drug along with the blood thinners. It would have taken days to get the test results back, days of different doctors lingering around with different ideas just popping in and out of our hospital room. We were told a month ago that Roger needed a GI consult ASAP to determine if the tumor around his esophagus was cancerous or not, then when they gave us the appointment, it was for two months down the line and we were still waiting. Within 24 hours of being seen in the ER here, every doctor that was necessary to consult with showed up, talked to each other, came up with a game plan, and established a relationship with us for "next time." He was given a definite diagnosis and was started on the path to recovery, all in less than 24 hours. I was so happy!

Roger laid in bed with his remote, breakfast, oxygen and IVs, and he was breathing without effort. This never would have happened at the BMT hospital. I loved the nurses there but the "teaching hospital" concept, with the broken recorded message of, "It's part of the process" needed to be re-evaluated and deleted.

We hung out at the hospital for a few days, and walked the floors to build Roger's stamina for the trip home. I decided it was time to put all my attention on Roger and not the house for a while. I needed to have a routine with him. Breakfast and meds, then a morning walk. Lunch, meds, and an afternoon walk. Dinner, meds, and some chair exercises. I was going to need to stay on him and get him into a routine that he could handle. I couldn't just let him have his way anymore – it was time to get serious. I needed to help motivate him.

Day +121

One by one, our team of doctors came in and said their "goodbyes and good lucks," giving Roger high fives like they had just won a ball game. We expressed our deepest gratitude to each of them with happy tears in our eyes. We left with a new list of medications to add to the old list. I would be giving him abdominal injections of a blood thinner called Lovenox for a while. Once his blood was thin enough, he would be weaned onto Coumadin/Warfarin. He was also given pulmonary inhalers and antibiotics.

All Rog said about the new injections was, "Going to have to pick and choose now. What goes where? Arm or gut – insulin or Lovenox?" I was given a sheet with several lab dates on it to have Roger's blood drawn. I had dealt with patients on this medication in the past. For some, it took weeks and sometimes months to regulate, getting the blood thin enough but not too thin to prevent future clots. While we were in the ER, we were told by Dr. Moros that Roger's type of leukemia caused blood clots. This was shocking to me that it wasn't "part of the process" to check each patient for blood clots. We now had a standing appointment at the lab twice a week.

When we got home, Roger settled into his chair as the routine began.

Day +126

It was our first day back to see Dr. Moros for a post-hospital checkup. He told us he had notified Dr. Perses regarding all the decisions and treatments that transpired during Roger's hospitalization. I cringed and said, "Did you tell him we refused to be seen there?"

He said, "Yes, in a roundabout way. He was fine with it; not happy but fine. I sent him a copy of all the records, so he has them. He agreed with the course of action we took. He wants Roger to have a VQ scan, which is a profusion scan to show us how the air is circulating in his lungs. One of the embolisms caused an infarction in your lung, Roger, which is a dead spot, very similar to having a heart attack, but in your lung not your heart. This scan will show us if it has recovered or if it caused permanent damage. Your bloodwork shows me that we need to increase the blood thinner, so today I will prescribe a stronger dose of the Lovenox. Same procedure, just a stronger dose. Repeat the bloodwork in two days. Other than that, you look pretty good. How do you feel?"

Roger said, "Good, considering." We were given a two week follow up and sent on our way.

Day +136

The days were all flowing into one. Since we left the hospital, Roger had had seven changes to his blood thinner. The car seemed to know how to get to the lab on its own. The doctors seemed to be baffled by his body's inability to stabilize the Coumadin he had previously been changed to. One day it was too thin, the next not thin enough.

I had become so consumed with Roger's disease and everyday life that I had completely lost my own. Each day began the same and ended the same. I spent a lot of time crying and feeling sorry for myself. I felt like I had lost myself and didn't know who I was anymore. I had a routine, like a robot, and Roger and I didn't talk much. We didn't have conversations because two minutes into them, he had lost interest or was thinking about something else because his mind couldn't focus long enough on any subject. His brain fog was setting in more and more.

I decided to go outside and work in the greenhouse. I figured a couple of hours out of the house would be a good idea, knowing if I didn't get outside, I was going to go crazy! Roger didn't want to walk today, but I needed to get him up and outside. I asked if he would wash the cars; he wash the top and I wash the bottom. He agreed. I could see him from the greenhouse and he was doing great. I looked out again and he was gone. I went in and he was in his chair, saying he was done.

In the past, we used to talk for hours about all kinds of things. We laughed, argued, debated, shared, and found common ground on any subject. He was so intelligent and easy to talk to when he *wanted* to talk. Now he just stared, with no expression. His body was like a tall, wintery tree with no leaves or tiny branches to fill in the bald spots. Just a spindly, old, tired tree, waiting for spring, hoping it wouldn't be cut down because of its lack of beauty. His beard was snow white, long, and in need of trimming, and his hair was thin. His arms were full of bruises and purple patches, and peppered in multiple adhesive bandages and gauze wrappings that covered the many skin tears. He could no longer wear his rings, they just fell off. His size thirteen ring should now be a size ten. I told him I would get it resized but he told me not to bother.

I asked him if he was giving up and he defiantly said, "NO, I will never give up!" It felt at that moment as if he didn't care about my life, but only depended on me for his. I fed him, drove him wherever the next appointment took us, medicated him, reminded him, bathed and dressed him, cleaned the house, paid the bills, washed his clothes, and for me he did nothing, absolutely nothing. All I really wanted him to do was to take more action in trying to get better, to push himself to walk and get the exercise he needed to keep his blood circulating, to try to make a meal for himself or get his own drinks. Just help himself with his needs, not wait for me to tell him to do these things. Sometimes I could feel him glaring at me, almost as if he just wanted to tell me to shut up. I needed to take my life back and feel alive again!

Day +139

This was bill day. I decided it was time to downsize EVERYTHING. By reducing and changing the phone plan, downsizing the cable channels, and changing the insurance plan so the deductible was higher, we could save $300.00 a month. Something had to give.

The next appointment would be to see the GI doctor. They would remove the esophageal tumor, hopefully without any complications. I was extremely worried about Roger going through this big surgery when his body was so weak. My father had had a similar tumor, one they called Barrett's tumor. When he had his taken out, they had to cut through his back then flip him over and cut through his chest to get it out. That was in 1991. I hoped they had perfected it since then. I didn't think Roger could go through an invasive surgery like that.

4

Mayo Clinic

It was day +141, and we saw Dr. Paul, who turned out to be Roger's GI doctor from years ago when he'd had 13 polyps removed from his colon. Roger had forgotten the doctor until we were sitting in front of him. The bone marrow transplant (BMT) hospital had sent Dr. Paul all the pictures they had taken of the tumor. He studied them for a few minutes, turned in his chair, looked at us and said, "The BMT hospital sent you to *me* to take this out?" He stared at us in disbelief. I told him yes and he said, "There is *no way* I am going to touch this! There are only two men who are qualified to do this surgery. One is at the Mayo Clinic in Minnesota, and one is at the Mayo Clinic in Seattle, Washington. I know the guy in Washington. He has been dealing with this type of tumor for over 30 years. They are very rare. What I am looking at is not only a huge tumor but there seems to be a tumor within the tumor and all the lymph nodes are infected as well."

Roger asked, "Can you call him?" He left us in the room and almost an hour later, he was back. He had sent the pictures via email.

The plan was to have Dr. Paul's partner go back into Roger's esophagus and take a few more biopsies and aggressively measure its size. He said it was the only way the doctor in Washington would be able to make a decision on how to proceed. He explained that there was a big possibility they would have to completely cut it out from above the tumor to below the tumor, then reattach both halves of the esophagus together. He went on to tell us this was a very serious surgery. He asked Roger if he was on blood thinners, and Roger told him he was. I asked why he asked that question and he told me, "These tumors cause serious blood clots." I wanted to faint. Roger said, "I do have blood clots, lots of them!"

Dr. Paul said, "I need you to stop the blood thinners today. My office is scheduling the procedure for biopsy this Friday. You okay with that?"

Roger said, "I'm as ready as I'll ever be." Dr. Paul asked why we had waited so long to be seen and Roger said, "We took the appointment that the BMT hospital gave us and that is today. We were told we couldn't get in any sooner and the tumor wasn't cancerous. They told me it wasn't something I needed to worry about with all the other stuff I'm dealing with." Roger chuckled.

Dr. Paul said, "How do they know it's not cancerous? I can't tell that from looking at these pictures."

I said, "I was told they biopsied it and there are pre-cancer cells only."

He just said, "Hmmmm. Well, good thing the emboli didn't kill you then." He left the room and returned with all the information for Friday. Roger needed to stop the Coumadin, just when his levels had finally started balancing out. Dr. Paul explained that we would be staying at the Mayo Clinic when the surgery was scheduled, which was a couple hours away, and that I needed to look into hotel arrangements. Most likely the surgery would require a few days stay and there wasn't a place for me to stay in the rooms.

I drove home, my mind swirling in all directions. I asked Roger how he felt about everything. He said, "I'm worried if I can make it through this surgery. This sounds pretty intense. I just can't catch a break! Every time I turn around, it's something else. What did I do to deserve this? I'm just tired, Robin."

I said, "We'll get through it, we always do. I'll be there for you! Whatever you need." I left him to his thoughts. He stared out the window with his head resting in his hand against the car's window frame.

My thoughts swirled. Where would I stay? How would I pay for lodging, food and gas? If push came to shove, I could stay in the car and wash up in Roger's room when the nurses weren't looking. For that matter, I could bring an ice chest full of food, keep it in the car, and go down and eat when I got hungry. As I thought it through, I began to feel better.

But Roger was down to 231 pounds and this surgery was going to steal more of it, for sure. How do you eat after a surgery like this anyway?

Day +144

The day had arrived – another biopsy and measurement of the tumor. I was told to stay in the waiting room and that the procedure would only take about an hour. After what seemed like forever, the doctor finally came out and said the tumor was huge and needed to come out as soon as possible, but it was not cancerous. He said he'd had a piece of tissue sent to the lab to confirm this during the procedure. He explained that the pre-cancerous tumor was referred to as a Barrett's tumor, and the cells looked very suspicious. He apologized that it took so long. What he thought was going to be an hour procedure took four hours. He told me the tumor was encircling the lower portion of the esophagus and sitting on top of the stomach. He thought it could be peeled away and removed. He explained that this tumor was creating a protein that caused blood clots, and that after it was removed, Roger might be able to stop the Coumadin. I asked how Roger did and he said, "Like a champ. That is a strong man you have there. His story is going to read like a long novel some day." I told him it already did! I thanked him, he shook my hand and excused himself, letting me know that the doctor was waiting for his call.

Roger was groggy but smiling. He said, "Hi, babe. I love you."

I caressed his face and hair and said, "I love you, too. It looks like all went well."

He groggily said, "I'm glad it's not cancerous, I really can't do radiation again." I kissed him gently, and he closed his eyes and rested.

When we got home, he slept the rest of the day and night. I woke him for medication and fluids only.

Over the next week, we got calls from both hospitals. Surgery was scheduled for October 6. The BMT hospital's GI team had decided they could remove the tumor. After talking to Dr. Paul, Roger decided which surgeon to go with. The Mayo Clinic's doctor had been published on two tumors that were even bigger than Roger's. He had successfully removed over 30 of them, but only three were this big. The surgeon told Roger that if he needed to pull in a thoracic surgeon to help him get the tumor out, he would. Roger felt confident with his decision. I think he was feeling empowered knowing he was calling all the shots, and his attitude changed over the week of waiting. We talked about his upcoming surgery, both hopeful its removal would bring some sanity and health back to his body. While we talked he was more playful with me; teasing me like he used to. He chuckled, which made my heart go pitter-patter.

When I saw him like this – strong in his words and mind – it made me believe that we were going to pull through this after all. He asked me to sit on his lap and I did. I felt his boney legs and worried I was too heavy for him. He pulled me closer and said, "I'm fine." He kissed me gently, a nice, soft, loving kiss. It felt so good to be in his arms!

The days were kind to Roger for a while. He was holding his own.

Day +155

We got to the Mayo Clinic one day early. It was going to be a one-night stay. We asked if there were any restaurants close by and were told that just down the hill was a great one. I asked Roger if he wanted to walk and he did. What was right down the hill to the usher was about a mile downhill, so how were we going to get back up? Roger pushed himself. I asked over and over if he wanted me to go back and get the car, but he said no. When we finally got to the restaurant, it was full with over an hour wait. Roger didn't want to wait so we had to walk another two blocks to another restaurant. Roger couldn't sit down fast enough. He immediately took out his phone and started playing with it, totally obsessed with the thing. I think he was hiding behind it. He was exhausted from the walk so I told him I would get a cab to take us back, but he said no. When it came time to order, Roger needed to go to the bathroom. As he walked away, the waitress said, "Can I get your dad something to drink?" Roger heard it, looked at me then walked away.

I couldn't let it go. I said, "He is my husband. He has leukemia and we are here for surgery tomorrow. When you see a couple like us, don't judge or assume. He's only six years older than me." She apologized and when the meal was over, she paid for it. And I let her.

It took us two hours to walk back to the hotel. We stopped at every corner and rested on benches, planter boxes, anything he could sit on. He was sweating profusely and getting weaker by the step. He was so pale and exhausted, yet he wouldn't let me call a cab or go get the car. I hated it when he was like that! When we got back, he laid down and went right to sleep. He slept like a baby and so did I.

Day +156

Roger was prepped and ready for surgery at 6:30 a.m. We were told it was going to take several hours but if all went well, he would be going home tomorrow. I kissed him and off he went. I decided to find a quiet place to write in my journal.

The surgery was a great success! They removed three-quarters of the tumor and were able to do so by peeling it away from the outer stomach wall and the esophagus. I was told that to remove it all could cause scar tissue that could potentially close off Roger's esophagus, so a second surgery would be scheduled about six weeks after the esophagus healed. Roger spent that night sleeping off the anesthesia and I returned to my room. I took a long, hot bath and crawled into bed for a long night's sleep.

Amazingly, Roger had no repercussions from the surgery. He felt nothing at all – no pain and no difficulty swallowing. It was as if it never happened. For such a scare, there was no trauma at all and we were so happy!

Day +166

It had been five and a half months since his transplant, and the few weeks following the tumor removal Roger had started feeling better and decided to stop several of his medications. Before the removal, he was scheduled to start tapering off several of the medications, but that was put on hold until after the surgery. After spending an evening researching the side effects of all his medications, he became adamant about stopping *all* medications, telling me he wasn't thinking straight. He was so angry that his mental status was declining again, and realized that *most* of the medication side effects caused mental decline. The drugs on the chopping block were Tacrolimus, Noxifil, Norvasc, Baclofen, insulin reduction and the sleeping pill. The pills he was taking at this point were:

1. Acyclovir 800 mg twice a day
2. Amlodipine 2.5 mg once a day
3. Baclofen 10 mg three times a day
4. Tacrolimus .5 mg twice a day
5. Fluconazole 400 mg once a day
6. Gabapentin 300 mg three times a day
7. Insulin sliding scale 5 times a day
8. Levothyroxine 75 mg once a day
9. Imodium as needed
10. Lorazepam 1 mg three times a day
11. Magnesium 400 mg three times a day
12. Metoprolol 50 mg twice a day
13. CellCept 500 mg four tablets twice a day
14. Prednisone 25 mg twice a day
15. Compazine as needed
16. Simethicone 80 mg twice a day
17. Triamcinolone acetonide 1% to feet twice a day
18. Oxycodone 5 mg three times a day
19. Noxafil 300 mg a day
20. Ambien one at night
21. Bactrim DS twice a day
22. Arginine 1000 mg three times a day
23. Vitamin C 1000 mg a day
24. Provigil 200 mg a day

Tacrolimus was his immunosuppressant drug that helped prevent organ rejection, or GVHD. Its side effect is that it depletes magnesium. He was taking magnesium both by mouth and IV infusions. If he tapered off Tacrolimus, then he could taper off the high doses of magnesium too. Noxafil is an antifungal drug that helped prevent fungal infections caused by a weak immune system. Norvasc is a blood pressure medication. Baclofen is a muscle relaxant that helps with his leg and hand spasms. Insulin is for the side effects of the Prednisone, and Ambien was his sleeping pill. To put this in perspective, if he tapered off the Tacrolimus, there was a huge chance the GVHD would flare up again. If he stopped the Noxafil and was exposed to anyone with pneumonia or any other fungal infection, he was at risk and it could be fatal. His blood pressure was actually very low, so I wasn't worried about the Norvasc, and he really didn't need the sleeping pill. But when the spasms started, he was up all night. I planned to talk with Dr. Moros about the tapering that Roger wanted so badly.

Day +167

Dr. Moros called the BMT clinic about medication tapering and all was a go. We were to start tapering off the Tacrolimus and the Noxafil first. Roger could stop the Baclofen, the Norvasc, and the sleeping pill right away if he wanted.

During the doctor's appointment, Roger complained that he had been having severe chest pains again, although he hadn't told me about it. I had noticed that he'd been asking for more pain medications, telling me he was having joint pain. Dr. Moros did an EKG and saw a few changes so he ordered a CT scan of Rog's chest and a consult with his cardiologist.

When we got back in the car, I asked him about it and he said he hadn't wanted to worry me. He said, "I can see that you always have a lot on your mind and I didn't want to add to it."

Along with the mental decline and the new chest pains, Roger's eyesight started to decline. After an appointment with the eye doctor, a new prescription and two new pairs of glasses were ordered.

Day +172

After a few days, for some reason Roger's chest pain had subsided and he was feeling better.

We continued tapering off Rog's Tacrolimus. He seemed to be doing okay with the decreased dose so far. He had an appointment with his cardiologist soon. Hopefully it would be a quick, uneventful visit since he wasn't having the chest pain as much.

PART SEVEN

1

This is Your New Normal

It was day +177, and first thing that morning I called Dr. Moros's office and left a message that Roger was having a lot of gas, belching and discomfort in his stomach, along with a loss of appetite. I was more worried about the pain in his stomach. Dr. Moros looked at Roger's medications and his recent scans from the GI doctors showing Roger's stomach lining then returned our call. He said that everything looked good from his point of view and that if he got really sick, go to the ER. He also said it was a good idea to contact our general practitioner and reestablish a relationship with him for these minor things.

I said, "Roger hasn't seen his GP in over two years."

He said, "Well, it's about time he does." He went on to say that he would see Roger for cancer-related symptoms but not for aches, pains and gas because there wasn't really anything he could do for that. I called and was referred to Dr. Moros. The last time we were at the BMT clinic, we were given a three-month follow up appointment. Other than that, we were to go to Dr. Moros. Roger no longer met the criteria of the clinical study so getting help from the clinic was not as easy as it was in the beginning. Plus, they knew we weren't happy with them and that didn't help. But when we needed help, we needed someone to pay attention. I called our family doctor and made an appointment.

Our family doctor called to talk to me about Roger and his upcoming appointment. He had been receiving copies of all of Roger's medical records and treatments all along, which I didn't know. After a lengthy conversation, he said exactly what I thought he would say, "Robin, there is no way I can make changes or prescribe medications for Roger at this point. His medical status is pretty critical and he needs to be followed closely by his oncologists." He then added, "Change his diet to strictly organic, no dairy, no flour, and no wheat or sugars. This might help him digest his food better and be easier on his stomach. At this point, Roger is really not digesting foods so make it as easy as possible for him to do so with a diet change. This change will reduce the inflammation in the lining of his GI tract." If it's in the diet, I could do it. I had been doing it for months, I just needed to be better at it!

Day +182

It was now six months post-transplant, and the past week I had started the new cooking regime with Roger. He told me what he would eat, so I stuck to that list. His diet was darn good already, but I would watch the flour, wheat and dairy better. If he wanted sugar I let him; it was his only treat. He was doing a bit better. His gas was gone but the pain and nausea were still there, just not as intense. His weight dropped down to 225. It was a battle to keep weight on without carbs. At first it was about keeping his body clean so the cancer didn't have anything to feed on, now it was a whole new story. You would think after six months I would have it down pat. Every week something else popped up, making his life miserable when it came to eating.

He said, "I would rather lose weight than be in constant pain." So, I pushed on. I had a few vegetarian cookbooks. I had him pick out recipes then I prepared them for him. It was a lot easier that way. With him making the choices, he never refused. I noticed his energy level was dropping a bit more and he was losing strength each day. Without carbs for energy and weight gain, he was wasting away. His body was so tiny. It sounds crazy to think 225 was tiny, but Roger was a large boned, barrel chested, 6'7" man. 225 pounds was really skinny for his frame.

That afternoon we went to see Dr. Moros for a follow-up on the bloodwork and blood thinner, which was still a problem. I wasn't sure if his body would ever get it right.

Dr. Moros asked Rog how he was doing after he made a shocking comment on his weight, "Pretty soon I'm not going to be able to see you. Your weight is really too low." I explained the diet he was on and that it was our family doctor who suggested it. He recommended this diet to reduce the inflammation in Roger's gut that was causing the discomfort.

He asked Roger if his stomach was better. Roger said, "Yes, it is, but I just want to get back to normal."

Dr. Moros bluntly, without a pause said, "Roger, this is your normal. You will never see the Roger who sat in here a year ago ever again." No one said a word for what seemed like eternity. I looked at Rog. He was staring at the doctor who was staring at him. Roger was trying to understand what he was just told, and the doctor was standing firm with his eye contact so Rog could process the truth. The tears just started rolling down my face. I couldn't breathe and a major hot flash kicked in. I needed to get out of the room, but I was cemented to my chair, unable to move. Dr. Moros finally broke the silence and asked Roger if he needed any refills on any of his medications then proceeded to make a follow-up visit. He asked how I was doing on tapering the medications. I said, "Good," and we left.

The rest of the day was in silence. I knew Roger had a lot to process and it was harsh. I felt so bad for him and there was absolutely nothing I could do. I just let him be and brought him things as he needed them. As we were getting into bed, he looked at me and said, "I can't believe this is it, this is my new normal. I wish they would have told me this is what would happen to me." My heart was breaking, but I knew this was it. I knew this was his normal. As much as I wanted to believe he was going to make a big turn around and be the Roger I'd married, I knew deep down it wasn't ever going to happen. It was a knowing I didn't visit often, but it was becoming more and more obvious.

At Roger's cardiologist appointment, his EKG showed enough changes to warrant a treadmill test. Rog explained that he didn't think he could walk the treadmill. The doctor took his pulse and said, "Can you walk for a minute?" Roger said he would try. The medications kept his heart rate so high that walking on the treadmill to increase it would only take one minute.

The results were normal, for Roger. We were told that most likely the changes were caused by the radiation or the transplant itself, and were not life threatening. Roger let out a sign of relief and said, "There's that break I've been looking for!" I cheered!

When we got home, Roger went in to take a nap. He usually sat in his chair and dozed, but this time he went to bed. I tucked him in and said I would be back in two hours.

Roger slept through the night. He didn't want dinner, he just wanted to sleep. This wasn't good.

Day +201

It had been awhile since I'd written in my journal.

Roger's stomach pains were a little better, but the nausea was still present. It seemed to be worse right before he ate. If he could just stop eating, he would have in a heartbeat!

We got a call telling us he was scheduled back at the Mayo Clinic for the final removal of his Barrett tumor. I asked the doctor if the portion that was still present could be causing his symptoms, and he said possibly. The surgery date was scheduled and it couldn't come fast enough.

Roger was doing pretty well, holding his own and trying to stay healthy for the upcoming surgery. His only complaint was the stomach pain and nausea, and he got chilled a lot. He had no fat to insulate him so he snuggled in a blanket with Max on top of him and let me wait on him all day.

Day +206

The past week had been a rough one for Roger. His stomach continued to hurt more and more and he seemed to be weaker. He complained about a scratchy throat and sounded a bit congested but didn't have a temperature. I hoped he wasn't getting sick!

Roger was quiet all evening. He just sat in his chair and watched TV with a drawn face. I sat with him a while and asked how he was feeling. He said, "I feel off. I have no energy at all and my chest feels tight." I asked if it was chest pain or something else. He said, "It's my lungs. They feel like they are filling up." I took his temp and it was still normal. I made him some tea with honey and a teaspoon of whiskey in it and had him sip it slowly. After he was done he said he felt a little better and asked for more. I made him another cup. He smiled and talked a bit more, but I could tell he was really not up to company. I asked if he wanted to lie down and he did. I got him all settled in bed with the TV, a pain pill, and more tea with just honey. He apologized and I told him there was nothing to be sorry for, to just rest. I kept the door ajar so I could hear him if he called out.

2

Pneumonia and Encephalitis

By day +209, Roger's throat and lungs started burning and his congestion got worse. He woke with a temperature so I called Dr. Moros and he sent us to the ER to get a chest x-ray. Dr. Moros was on call so he showed up in the x-ray department to look at Roger's scans. The diagnosis was pneumonia. My heart sank and I felt like I was going to faint. The doctor looked at me and immediately got me a chair. My heart was racing and I felt like I was going to pass out. Pneumonia was the death card for transplant patients. Once it set in, it was a downhill slide.

Roger took my hand and asked me if I was okay. I said, "Yes, just give me a minute."

Dr. Moros got me a glass of water and started in on what to do next. He said, "The scans show pneumonia but it's not really bad yet. I am going to start you on Zithromax for the next seven days. Stay in and away from *all* people. I want to see you back in my office in a week. If your breathing gets any worse, Roger, I want you back in the ER immediately. Do you understand?"

Roger said, "Yes."

I asked the doctor why he wasn't keeping him in the hospital and treating him more aggressively with IV antibiotics. He said, "Because he will get sicker if he stays in the hospital. He's safer at home."

I stopped at the pharmacy, picked up the medication and went straight home. We didn't talk much on the drive. When we got home, Roger went to his chair and turned on the TV. I sat down next to him and asked if he wanted to talk about what he was just told. He said, "There's really nothing to talk about; it is what it is." I asked if he was hungry and got him what he asked for, took his temp and it was still up so I gave him a couple Tylenol too. I made him a cup of tea to soothe his scratchy throat and let him be.

Throughout the night, Roger tossed, turned and coughed a lot. I propped him up on pillows so he could breathe better.

Day +214

Five days later, the Zithromax wasn't working, the pneumonia was getting worse, and his appetite went to zero. We were back in the ER. He was put on a 14-day cycle of 750 mg of Levaquin, which is a pretty hefty dose, but they still didn't keep him. Roger was eating about two cups of food a day and his weight was down to 211. I called the doctor and told him what was going on. He was glad he was switched to Levaquin but said the loss of appetite was most likely caused by the chemotherapy and radiation. I was told to do my best to get him to eat, that it should pass. He would drink the protein drinks and Gatorade but everything else was a fight, and he stopped picking out dishes for me to make him. He said it made him feel sick and nauseated just looking at the pictures. Needless to say, his surgery was postponed.

The neighbor up the road educated me on a product called Simpson Oil and gave me a booklet to read. The studies had shown that it not only helped with appetite, but its main benefit was that it shrunk tumors, killed cancer cells, helped reverse the damage done by radiation therapy and chemotherapy, and was a great pain reliever. The key was getting enough of it into the patient to work. The goal was to get 100 grams in the patient in a three-month time-period.

After reading the pamphlet and doing some research on the computer, Roger was okay with taking the oil. He was very anti-drug use, but he knew he needed to do something. I bought the oil right away. The dosage was a small, rice-sized sliver of oil on a cracker several times a day. The first dose, as little as it was, caused him to feel woozy. Not bad enough to prevent him from standing and walking on his own, but lightheaded. He was okay with that. It also reduced the pain in his joints and hands, which was a blessing. So, the regimen began.

Day +228

It was day +228, seven and a half months since the transplant. Over the past two weeks, Roger's routine had been getting up between 10:00-11:00 a.m. and going straight to his chair where he sat until midnight. He just stared at the TV, watching the same shows over and over, not realizing he'd watched the same shows the day before. They were all new to him. His memory was fading, and his affect was flat, with no expression. When I addressed him, he looked at me with such an innocent look, like he was a child learning for the first time. He was having problems remembering how to use the remote control, just staring at it, trying to figure out how it worked. He had forgotten how to turn on the computer and his phone was nowhere near him, like it no longer existed. When I left the house, I had to put the number in and show him where to press to make the call go through. I was really getting worried. Thankfully we were to see Dr. Moros that afternoon. His pain had subsided since he started the oil. It took a few days to get used to the feeling, but he was finally getting pain relief. Roger was getting sicker and sicker, and he started having panic attacks if I was away from him for more than an hour.

Dr. Moros was shocked at Roger's weight and mental status. He asked me when this had started, and I told him about nine days ago. I told him about the Simpson Oil and he said that had nothing to do with this. He asked if there were any other changes in his regimen and I said no. He left the room, and thirty minutes later he returned. He explained that he had just been on a conference call with the surgeon at the Mayo Clinic and Dr. Perses. It was decided that the surgery was postponed again and that we needed to be seen at the BMT clinic Monday. They were scheduling another lumbar puncture and CT scan of his chest and brain. I had a feeling the HHV6 had returned since this was how it started before. When his memory started failing, in the back of my mind I knew this was possible.

Dr. Moros asked Roger if he was depressed since these symptoms are seen in a lot of his depressed cancer patients. Roger said, "I get depressed sometimes, but not all the time." I told the doctor that I couldn't be away from him longer than an hour without him panicking, and unless I gave him his food, fluids or pills, he was oblivious and just didn't remember that these things were important. About the only thing he did for himself was to go to the toilet. Roger put his hand in mine and said, "I'm sorry."

I barely got out, "It's okay," when I lost it and the tears started rolling. I stepped out of the room and went to the bathroom to wash my face. When I returned, the doctor was inputting information into the computer. He said to keep everything the same until after we were seen at the hospital.

On the way home, my mind was in a whirl of emotions. The thought of *whatever* they might find in the CT and brain scan made me feel like I was drowning. I was so tired. I had no time to myself and I seemed to never catch up. I couldn't remember the last time I stayed in the shower long enough to shave my legs. I hadn't dyed my hair in a long time either, and my grey roots were shining through big-time. I didn't wear makeup anymore – I just didn't feel like putting it on. Mom said I looked ragged. I was getting so depressed watching the love of my life dwindle away. And now this…

Day +231

Dr. Perses was surprised when he saw Roger. He looked at Roger then down at the chart. He commented on Roger's 105 pound weight loss since the transplant almost eight months ago. Roger said in a flat tone with no expression, "One heck of a way to lose weight. I wouldn't recommend it."

The doctor chuckled but that didn't last long when he realized Roger was just staring at him; no smiles, no joke. He cleared his throat and said, "Today we need to do a CT scan as well as a lumbar puncture. I need to see if the white blood cell count is back up in your spinal fluid." Roger just stared at him. I looked at Roger then at the doctor. He asked, "Roger, are you depressed?"

He answered, "Sometimes I get depressed, but not all the time." He asked about our tapering off the medications and how that was going, and asked for a summary of Roger's mental status. Rog looked at me to answer him.

I did, and asked if he had any idea what was going on. He replied with, "We're going to try to find out. One problem I see in your bloodwork is your protein is extremely low and your kidney function is poor. How are you doing on eating and drinking fluids?"

Roger looked at me again to answer. I explained his aversion to food right now and that I had to remind him to drink fluids all day, every day. I said, "Sometimes he gets his fluids in but sometimes he doesn't. Both are a fight right now." Right then the tech knocked on the door to take Roger to the CT scanner; the office appointment was over. I got no answers. Both tests were uneventful, and we were told that Dr. Perses would call with the results when they came in.

Day +234

A few days later Dr. Perses called to tell us Roger's spinal fluid was clear. The CT of the chest showed that the pneumonia had left scarring but for the most part, both lungs were clear, but his brain scan showed the encephalitis was back. He again started Roger on Ganciclovir, and the baseballs would start showing up at the house soon.

Rog was the same; slow, flat affect, monotone voice and lethargic. He sat in his chair, watched TV, and refused to do anything else. Eating was still a chore.

Day +238

When the baseballs showed up at the front door, I got Rog started right away. The days had just melted into one, all the same for the most part except for Roger needing more pain medications. His hip bones hurt so bad and were sticking out so much he looked like a skeleton. He couldn't stay comfortable in bed long enough to fall asleep. I purchased a 4" memory foam pad to put under us on the bed which seemed to help a lot.

Day +260

After the 21 day therapy with the baseballs, we were able to stop the Ganciclovir. With each infusion, Roger continued to show signs of recovery, and his appetite was finally returning although just small portions. His emotions returned, and he was up walking a bit more, mostly because I reminded him about the pulmonary embolism he got from being so sedentary. His blood thinners were still a nightmare, with the dosage still all over the place. His poor arms were so speckled with black and purple bruises. It looked very painful, but he said the spots didn't hurt, they just looked bad. It was nice to see him trying again, and he started to help me a bit more by getting his own medications and drinks throughout the day. The best part was that I wasn't nagging him all day about drinking fluids. This really took a load off my shoulders. He also started taking an interest in tinkering outside again, which made me happy. He needed the fresh air! It was a slow recovery, but he was on his way. The Ganciclovir once again did its wonderful job!

Day +280

The past few weeks had been almost a miracle! Once again, he surprised me. Roger had gotten better and better. He was so thin, but he was holding his weight at 210 pounds. He was eating well; actually really well. He could get in two good-sized meals a day without pain in his stomach, and his intake of pain pills was down too. He was crying a little more; I think just realizing how much his life had changed and how he looked was getting to him. He didn't look in the mirror anymore, saying he didn't recognize himself. His memory was getting a little better since I had been giving him Provigil in his morning coffee without him knowing it. For some reason, he had an issue with this medication, but I noticed it really helped him focus. With it, he had more stamina, was more alert and in control, and had a lot more energy.

He was up and outside doing things again. He brought in wood for the stove, made kindling, and he helped me build tables for the art room. It was a challenge to get upstairs, but he did it! He had even been helping outside. He reminded me all the time that, "In a couple of years, I will receive my social security. Everything will be easier on us." Roger, in his mind, was going to live forever. He would never talked about the "what ifs." He was still using the Simpson Oil and it was helping with his pain and shakiness. He had given me hope the past few weeks. He was alert and having conversations with me again.

Even though Rog was feeling much better, he didn't get too far away from me. Lately, he'd had extreme anxiety if I didn't go to bed with him or quit working and come inside with him when he was ready to stop. I was gone the other night and after two hours he was almost in a panic. He wanted me home now and was shaking with fear. He told me later that he was horribly lonely. I encouraged him to find me when his anxiety hit and I would help him get through it, no matter what. I also explained that his anxiety couldn't rule my life. He said he understood and wished he could get a handle on it.

I could feel my age creeping up on me; my stamina was waning. I found myself more tired, just wanting to go to bed, but when I got there I couldn't sleep. I dreamed of going out and doing things like wine tastings, movies, walks by the river, and calling friends and visiting them, but Rog tired easily and we were worried about him getting sick again before surgery. His final tumor removal was coming soon, another quick in-and-out procedure.

3

Clumsy Me!

On day +289, I was sitting in the hospital lobby waiting for Roger. He was having the surgery to remove the final portion of the tumor. He had been very anxious the past few days. He was doing so well that he didn't want anything to disturb his newfound happiness called "energy." We had arrived the previous day and Rog drove all the way there. It was hard to believe, but Roger had started driving again although I only let him when I was with him. That way if he got tired, I could take over, which happened a few times. His mind was clear and his mental status was back. His short-term memory was still a little hazy but for the most part he had been great!

Roger's surgery was a success, and after a few hours of recovery, we were back in the car on our way home. He said there was no pain and he didn't notice anything was done other than a sore mouth from being hinged open for so long. I was so happy, Roger looked great, sounded strong, and just wanted to be back in his own home.

Unfortunately I'd had a bad fall, landing on my left shoulder and tearing two rotator cuffs from the bone. Thankfully Roger was feeling better because the tables had turned and he was now nursing me. Him being able to drive was a blessing!

It was late when we got home. I fixed us a little supper and we were off to bed.

Day +321

I had been a little lazy on writing in my journal. I'd finally had surgery on the left shoulder and had been recovering from that. I was thankful that Roger was feeling good and some strength had returned. After the surgery my surgeon said, "I need you to understand that this is going to take at least a full year of recovery. You need to be very careful and stay on your feet until this heals, understand? No falling down."

I said, "I do."

He looked at Roger and said, "You got a tough one here don't 'cha?"

Roger said, "You have no idea." I busted up laughing. The combination of anesthesia and pain medication made that comment so funny to me. When the surgeon left, Roger said, "You did hear him right, didn't you? A full year to recover from this."

I thought about that a moment and said, "It's been over a year since your diagnosis and it went pretty fast. I'll be okay."

Roger, my hero! He had been cooking for me, doing dishes, helping me bathe and was cleaning the house. He took over all my chores. I think he was really enjoying being *my* nurse. I had been sitting around a lot. It hurt to move so we were spending a lot of time in front of the TV together, with him catching me up on all the programs he watched. I had no desire to know this stuff, but it became quite amusing listening to him get all worked up over some of the reality shows he was watching. Roger was happy.

About a week prior, Roger was taken off the Coumadin because his blood levels were not stabilizing. The doctors had become so frustrated and so had we. He was changed to Zyprexa, but unfortunately, his arms took a toll through the process. For some reason, the walls in this house seemed to jump in his way on a daily basis, causing him to go through adhesive bandages like crazy. I kept them in my back pocket and purse, his shirt and pants pockets, and in our coats at all times. He had at least five on at a time. Like a little kid, he wanted to see if the skin break was healing so he was constantly taking them off but when he did, the scab stuck to it, pulling it off and creating a bigger sore. It made me crazy! His arms were literally black and blue with scabs all over them.

Day +328

It had been a tough week. I was really having problems with my shoulder. Roger was still doing well although the new blood thinner was causing problems. His blood was still too thin. I had a feeling this medication would change again soon. I had taken a pair of men's long socks and cut the foot out so he could use them as arm protectors while he worked outside. He was never without them and they seemed to work well. His spirits were up and his stamina was still pretty good. He hadn't gained any weight, but he was holding his own although his stomach was starting to give him trouble again. Dr. Perses said at the last visit that he wanted Roger off the Prednisone. He wanted him on a steroid called Budesonide just for his stomach and intestines, but when I went to pick it up, there were two medications, Budesonide and Beclomethasone. Something just didn't make sense, although I was glad he was being taken off the Prednisone. It was eating up his body and I could see that even his teeth were taking a hit from the high doses. His gums had receded terribly.

Rog had been tinkering in the garage a lot, tending to his workbench and organizing it. Sometimes I brought him a beer and let him show me his new and improved workspace. He liked his time in the garage. In his man cave hideout, Roger turned on his TV and listened to it while he worked. I had made him a tall stool so he could rest periodically. He had no fat and his legs were so skinny that they tired out quickly. The stool was high enough that he didn't have to bend to sit down. His lungs got tight every once in a while, but I think that was due to the pollen in the pine trees. He could spend two to three hours outside before his stamina started waning then he returned to the house for a little nap to catch up.

Roger's 60th birthday was coming up and I wanted to do something really nice for him. I had planned a surprise trip to San Diego to be with his kids and grandchildren, and I hoped I could keep him healthy enough to get there. The plane flight was my biggest concern, but I would have him wear a mask and so would I. Planes are the worst for germs!

Day +336

The doctor bills were adding up from my shoulder, and Roger's hospital bills were piling up too. I sold some jewelry and Roger said he would sell a few guns to help. We planned a garage sale in the next week or two which should help. We thought about selling the travel trailer but that was our future lake home for the summer. We loved it there, but with all the bills, I had a feeling it might have to go.

Again, the blood thinner was changed. It was now Xarelto. Roger started breaking blood vessels in his eyes, and having blood in his stools and his sputum. I called the doctors but didn't seem to get anywhere. I finally called the pharmacist and she said that the combination of the Noxafil and Xarelto was an adverse combination when it came to thinning the blood. One or the other should be stopped immediately! Today at Dr. Moros's appointment, I told him what had happened. He looked it up and said, "Yep, she is right. Stop the Xarelto and follow up with the hospital on your next visit." This kind of mistake made me so mad! Why did I have to always be the one to figure out answers to Roger's medical problems when they arose? We were told that Roger needed at least one year on a blood thinner, no matter what. So, we waited for their next idea.

During the visit, Dr. Moros asked why Roger was taking Prednisone, Budesonide and Beclomethasone. Roger looked at me for answers. I told him that Dr. Perses had prescribed the latter two which would eventually replace the Prednisone. These medications were prescribed for GVHD of the stomach. He said, "They are all three steroids. That's a lot of steroids."

I said, "I was under the impression that while I was tapering him off the Prednisone, these two medications would eventually be the replacement drugs."

He said, "You're not tapering him off steroids, just Prednisone. These two are like taking Aleve and Ibuprofen; same drug, same outcome." I asked him what to do and he said just stay on the Budesonide, continue to taper down the Prednisone, and he would talk to Perses. He asked Roger how he was feeling. Roger told him pretty good and went over his new routine.

Roger was holding his weight at 217, and had been eating pretty well. I was keeping his diet very bland to help with his stomach pain; no seasoning at all. Roger used to salt his food before he even tasted it, but not now. So far, so good this week. I just never knew. Every day was a new day. The Simpson Oil seemed to be helping more and more. I had Roger tapered down to 7.5 mg of Prednisone a day now. I found that when it got to 5 mg a day, all broke down again. He stopped eating and the pain exponentially returned to his stomach. I was hoping that the Budesonide really did the trick and he got past the hill he fell off of each time we hit 5 mgs.

Day +352

We finally got *that* phone call from the BMT clinic. It was time for Roger's one year anniversary work-up since the transplant! It was so hard to believe it would soon be one year. We had talked about it a lot over the past week. Fortunately, Roger had been doing pretty well for a while now. His mood was pissy off and on but that was the Prednisone and all the crap he'd had to deal with. The biggest problem right now was his blood thinners.

For the big day, I cut his hair and trimmed his beard. I noticed black hair was starting to grow in and he didn't have one wrinkle on his face. He still looked 30 years older and had a ruddiness to his cheeks, but he looked different. He was really starting to look like someone else, which made me wonder again if the blood/DNA from his donor had started changing his features into what his donor looked like. It was weird because his jaw was thinner and his eyes were starting to take on a different shape. I asked him what he thought, and he said, "I don't recognize myself at all anymore. It's not me when I look in the mirror. I don't like it, so I don't look anymore." I stared at him for a long time.

We were given a list of tests that needed to be done at his one year follow up; bone density test, pulmonary function test, bone marrow biopsy, and a slew of blood tests. It would be a long day, beginning at 9:30 a.m. We planned to stay with Roger's mom the night before so Rog could get a good night's sleep. I was so excited and wondered what they did for the BIG ONE YEAR! I hoped it was nice – he so deserved a big congratulations!

PART EIGHT

1

One Year Anniversary Post Transplant

We arrived at the clinic a little early because we were both so excited! We checked in at the front desk as usual and it *was* as usual. I said to the receptionist, "Today is Roger's one-year anniversary since his bone marrow transplant!" She was looking at the computer and while doing so said, "Well good for you!" then she looked at him and said, "Here is your arm bracelet. By now you know what to do with it," and smiled at him. It was so anti-climactic.

We sat down amongst the rest of the cancer patients as I held his hand and smiled at him. I said, "I'm so proud of you! I'm not sure I could have been as brave as you've been through this whole process." He squeezed my hand and smiled back at me.

We thought we were going to see Dr. Perses first, but the pulmonary function test was first. Roger sat in the offered wheelchair and while the tech pushed Roger to his destination, I followed, bragging about his one-year anniversary. The tech was all over it. "Oh, my gosh! Right on! I am so proud of yoooou! Was it a good year or a bad year?"

Roger said, "A little of both." They carried on all the way to the testing room. Roger told him about his one-year adventure, his man cave where he hides from the women, and losing over 100 pounds.

The tech stopped and walked in front of Roger, twirled and said, "I lost a hundred pounds too! How do I look?" Roger and I both cracked up laughing and so did the tech.

Roger said, "You look a hell of a lot better than I do!"

He said, "Thank yoooooou," and skipped back behind the wheelchair and started pushing again. He said, "So you don't recommend cancer as a treatment for weight loss?" We both cracked up again, Roger with his deep chuckle, and the tech with his higher pitched laugh was precious, the best moment of the morning!

The pulmonary function test results were normal, actually better than the one he took a year ago, which was weird and amazing at the same time. The tech gave him a sticker when the test was over, one that you might give to a child, told him it was his congratulations present, and put it on Roger's hand. He wheeled us over to the bone density department, shook Roger's hand and said his goodbyes.

The bone density technician was not as fun, but gave Roger a high five and told him to keep up the good work. The test results came back normal as well. Next was the bone marrow biopsy back down in the clinic. I was excited about going back down. I couldn't wait for the group to see Roger and give him big kudos for his achievement. We arrived via wheelchair and were put into a room. A nursing assistant came in and took Roger's vital signs. She told him his bloodwork would be done first and took him into the lab. The technician looked at the orders, put on her gloves and said, "Hi, Roger! When's your birthday and what's your age?" Roger answered, and she proceeded to label the ten vials with a long strand of stickers. She asked how his morning was going, making a little small talk.

I said, "Today is his one-year anniversary since his bone marrow transplant!"

She gently said, "Oh wow, that's awesome." She pulled his arm forward, put the tourniquet on, and started filling the vials. She said, "Nice to see spring in the air." I was a little taken back. Why were we not talking about how great it was that he was a one-year survivor? I felt like the air was being let out of my bubble a little quicker than I wanted. I wanted him to have bells and whistles, confetti and a big cake or at least a cupcake. I said to myself, *She is just the phlebotomist. She doesn't know us. Maybe when we get back with the crew in the infusion clinic, the party will begin.* She finished up and put us back into a patient room to wait for Dr. Perses.

After 20 minutes, one of Dr. Perses' nurses came in, sat down in a chair across the room in front of the computer and started checking him in. It was the usual, "Hi, how are you doing? Did you get your lung and bone density test done? All your lab work done?" Roger answered with fine and yeses. She said, "Oh, today is one year I see." She turned her chair around and looked at Roger and said, "Congratulations, this is a big day for you!"

Roger said, "Thank you." I smiled and was slowly realizing this was just another day. No bells and whistles, no cupcake, no confetti. I was starting to feel bad for Roger. I wanted so much more from them. We had talked about this big day for weeks and groomed him up so handsomely for the crew to see him. I knew he was feeling the same way I was, but he was never going to show it. She asked how his year had gone and he replied, "Well, it was one hell of a way to lose over a hundred pounds. I wouldn't recommend it," and he chuckled.

She looked at his chart and said, "It's a good thing you had weight to lose," and smiled at him. I just stared at her. She turned back to the computer and started asking about his medications. She said she had a note from Dr. Moros about the Noxafil then said, "Stop the baby aspirin but restart the Coumadin. You will need to stay on it for life." She explained that the pulmonary embolism was not caused by the HHV6. I didn't know where she was going with this, but I listened and took notes like I always did. She continued, "Stop the Beclomethasone but stay on the Budesonide, and I want you to taper off the Prednisone completely. Your testosterone is at zero so we need to get you started on a hormone replacement therapy. I will get you set up with an endocrinologist. Soter will be here in a few to do your bone marrow biopsy then the doctor will be in to talk with you. Congratulations on your one year."

Soter came in with his assistant and said, "Hey, Roger, how are you doing? Looks like this is the big one! One year! How are you feeling?" He was talking while he moved around the room, getting all his instruments ready for the biopsy, interrupting Roger a few times as he talked to his assistant on things he needed then returned his attention to Roger.

He was asked to get up on the table and lay on his belly. Roger said, "Usually you give me something for anxiety."

Soter was surprised he hadn't gotten his Ativan and called for it. He said, "I will be back in a few" and left the room. They gave him 1 mg of Ativan. When everyone was out of the room, Roger looked at me and I was already on it. I had another Ativan and a 20 mg OxyContin ready for him. The wind had been knocked out of both our sails. We were expecting a glorious, celebratory day, but it was a day like all the rest. He took the OxyContin, chewed it up, and put the Ativan under his tongue. Thirty minutes later, Soter and the crew return. During all his previous bone marrow biopsies, Soter had to push and prod Roger's hip to find the right placement. Now, with his bony body and the past scars prevalent, it was easy to proceed. Roger held onto the edges of the bed and gripped them tight as the needle went in and the drill was screwed into place. Soter, with his body slightly over the top of the drill, turned it on and leaned into it firmly as it bore through Roger's hipbone then gave way into the marrow. If the grip bars were not made of steel, Roger would have bent them. His whole body tensed up as soon as the drill began to scream into rotation, penetrating his sore hipbone. I was so glad I kept a bottle of his pain pills and anxiety pills with me. So many times I had given him medication before procedures because protocol said the patients didn't need them. Therefore, the clinic didn't offer them or what they did offer was a dose that most cancer patients laughed at. They are so far into pain and anxiety meds that 1 mg is like taking a baby aspirin. So, I bring backup.

Dr. Perses arrived close to 30 minutes after the procedure. He and his assistant came in nonchalantly. He casually said, "One year, that's a big one. Congratulations." He sat down on the end of the exam table. His demeanor was so casual I would have bet $50 that he had taken an Ativan. He asked Roger how he was doing. Roger said fine. He commented on Roger's weight and referred to the lab work and the protein levels.

Roger explained that he was doing better on his intake, but meat just made him gag. He explained his new love for beans and rice and the Costco protein drinks. Rog said, "A month ago I weighed 211, now I weigh 217."

The doctor said, "Oh, that's good, that's good. Keep it up and drink more of the protein drinks." He reiterated the medication changes that we had gone over with his assistant earlier and asked if we understood. We both nodded yes. He said, "From here on out, the appointments will be every three to six months. You will be given a schedule before you leave today." He asked if we had any questions.

At this point, we realized that today, surviving one year, was not a special day to the clinic. It was just another day and I felt really bad for Roger. I had that one aching question that I had to ask, but I didn't want to ask it in front of Roger, especially on this day. At the same time, whatever the answer was, we both needed to know so I asked, "I noticed that on these papers you give us when we leave, in the appointment summary it says, "Your Health Goals (5 years) None. Is there any data now on patients living longer than five years after this diagnosis with the bone marrow transplant? Is the second phase of this study showing positive outcomes now? What are we to expect now – I hope smooth sailing?"

He crossed his arms and said, "No, not really, but after a year the statistics increase. At three years it increases to 80% and at five years up to 90%. This is an average across the board for cancer survival in general. Roger's immune system is strong enough to go in crowds, but still be very careful." I just looked at him and he at me. We had eye-to-eye contact for a good five seconds before he shifted his stance. He knew exactly what I was thinking and he knew what he had just said to me. "In general, across the board, cancer survivor's statistics are…" as he quoted.

"But Roger's cancer, there are no survivors at five years i.e., the word NONE on the paperwork?" I asked. He evaded the question and let the answer he gave be his final answer to us. Roger didn't say a thing, nor did his expression change. He said nothing to give us hope, nothing about the second phase or even the third phase that was getting started. Nothing! I felt awful and wished I hadn't asked the question. I was hoping for something positive, something, anything. But not today.

The drive home was so depressing. We didn't talk. He reclined his seat back, settled in, and got comfortable. I said, "I'm sorry, that was not what we were expecting. I don't get it! You would think that this one-year mark would be a big deal!"

Every time Rog had sat in the chemo chair, we'd heard, "If you make it to day 90 you're doing good, especially if you didn't get GVHD. But to make it to a year, *if* you make it to a year, wow! That's the kicker." I thought it would have been a big deal for the doctors to share with their patients the big one-year mark, especially since it still said NONE. Just letting the patients know they are proud of them and everything they had gone through would mean a lot. There should be a department for just that; one that gives out a cupcake and balloon. It would give the other patients going through hell hope that one year was attainable with just a small, congratulating cupcake! That hospital made billions so what would a few cupcakes and balloons cost a month?

I said, "I feel like we're in the Twilight Zone movie. Just know I am proud of you, and you are all that matters. This is our big day, a day for you and me to celebrate. No one else matters. It's your day! You did it!"

He said, "Thanks. I guess there are just too many of us to celebrate with. I never saw any celebration for anyone, did you?"

I thought about it for a moment and said, "Actually, no, I didn't." He closed his eyes and drifted off to sleep in seconds. I began to rack my brain, trying to remember if I ever saw a celebration. I was saddened to realize I hadn't. I decided I would combine his one-year transplant anniversary with his upcoming surprise 60th birthday trip. It would be glorious for him. I couldn't wait to tell him! He so deserved a celebration!

Day +370

Roger had been doing pretty well and it was nice when he agreed to go to the store with me to do some shopping. I asked him to ride the little cart they have for handicap people, but he wasn't having that at all. I hate to shop, and wanted to get in and out as soon as I could. All I could see were germs, and leisurely walking the aisles of the store was never on my agenda, but it was exercise for him so I leisurely walked with him. After about 30 minutes, he started limping and complaining of his heel and calf hurting. About ten minutes later, I was getting the car and taking him home. His foot was hurting so bad, I took his shoe off and he hobbled to the car with just his sock on.

When we got home he took his pants and socks off. His left calf was inflamed and swollen, and his heel was blue. I said, "How long has this been like this?"

He said, "I don't know. I just noticed it hurting. What is it?" It was an early case of cellulitis. I called the hospital to report it and was told I would get a call back. Three hours later, I called Dr. Moros and left a message. Two hours later, Roger was really in a lot of pain. I took him to the ER, and sure enough, it was cellulitis. They gave him a seven-day dose of antibiotics. I was glad we caught it early. If we hadn't, there would be no trip. For the next week, we babied the leg and kept it up. It only took three days for the swelling and pain to die down.

I got a letter in the mail with Roger's latest lab results from three weeks ago. He was now having complete lab work done once a month instead of every week. I looked over the lab work and noticed that his immune system marker, his IVIG number, was at 90, and normal is 400 to 600. When it was at 300, they automatically gave him a booster. At 90, his immune system was in real trouble. Why hadn't they caught this at the BMT clinic?

I called Dr. Perses' nurse and told her about the number. She was shocked and gave me a little lecture at the same time. She said, "Robin, it's not a good idea for you to be the middle man. I really need to have doctor to doctor confirmation on stuff like this. Calling about labs, swollen calves and Roger's many ailments is not a good idea. Please have Dr. Moros call Dr. Perses about this right away." I was very confused! Dr. Moros's office had these results a few weeks ago, prior to sending me a copy in the mail and nothing was said, yet the nurse was also saying this was serious? Roger needed a transfusion right away, especially if he was going on a trip via airplane. And why did it matter if I called and told them or Dr. Moros did? Somewhere the ball got dropped and I was the one who caught it. I said, "Okay, I will call Dr. Moros's office right now, inform him of the results that were overlooked, and have him give you a call."

Dr. Moros was shocked! He said he never saw this lab work and apologized. He called the BMT clinic then called us back saying that the IVIG was being ordered and we would be notified when insurance approved the transfusion.

Day 375

I got a phone call from the lab at Dr. Moros's office saying we missed his IVIG appointment yesterday. I said, "We didn't have an appointment. No one called us about this! I have been patiently waiting for the call." Why not call and tell us we were late, and they were waiting? I was so livid I could have screamed! The appointment was rescheduled, meaning he wouldn't get a boost until we got back. I hoped his immune system could handle the plane ride.

2

Happy 60th Birthday

It was Roger's 60th birthday and he continued to stay stable, although his appetite was still on and off. Some days he slept all day in his chair and others he watched TV and babied his foot. The cellulitis was gone and so was the pain.

Mom surprised us with a day out to lunch to celebrate Roger's birthday. He ate half of his half of the meal then enjoyed a dish of ice cream with a candle on top to celebrate. I could tell he was getting exhausted after a few hours so we headed home. Rog decided to take a nap. I joined him in bed, lying down next to him and asked, "Roger, would you like my present?"

He said, "Sure." I told him about the trip and that we were leaving in the morning. I had secretly packed our bags and prepared for the departure days ago. He started crying, he was so happy!

Rog's daughter had bought all the men tickets to the Dodger's game. I kind of wondered if I should have told him first just so he could prepare himself for a long day at the ballpark. I decided not to but explained to her that this might be too much, and to let the boys know to get him home if it became too much. Amy was good with that.

Needless to say, neither of us took a nap. We lay there, talking about the trip. Even though he was very excited, he was VERY nervous too. He asked about the germs rampant on planes, and his severe claustrophobia. I told him he could wear a mask on the plane and to just not go to the bathroom if he could help it. I too would wear a mask and take a small bottle of hand sanitizer with me, just in case. He asked me about his medications, food and sleeping conditions, and was content with all my reassurances.

Day +389

The trip was a huge success, but when we returned, Roger slept all day. I brought him broth and crackers with his pills. He had steak twice during the weekend and he was now having trouble with constipation. I asked him at the time why he was eating it and he said, "I want the kids to see me as they have always seen me, not sick." But now he wasn't feeling well. I got him stool softeners and kept the fluids coming. By the evening, with a lot of discomfort, he was able to pass some stool.

Tomorrow was IVIG replacement day. It would be an all-day event in the clinic at Dr. Moros's office. I brought lunch for us, a book, and a few ice packs in a little cooler. When the IVIG started infusing, we ate some lunch then he reclined his chair and went to sleep.

That night, Rog just wanted to sleep, no dinner, and just went to bed. I asked if he was okay and he said, "I'm just feeling a little off. My chest feels tight like it did when I had heart problems." Whenever he got this kind of discomfort, he went to bed and slept. If he didn't, he spent all his waking hours worrying about his heart. He'd had so many normal heart angiograms that the cardiologist wouldn't perform another one.

Day +424

It had been a rough few weeks. Physical therapy for my shoulder started and the exercises they were having me do were taking a toll on me. To make matters worse, I got bronchitis. Seven days later, Roger had it. I got Roger started back on the Levaquin as soon as the cough started. I had called Dr. Moros's office but was told to go see our family doctor. Our family doctor said he felt uncomfortable prescribing Roger anything due to his history, to call Dr. Moros's office back. Dr. Moros's office was supposed to call us back but didn't. I had a bottle of Levaquin in Roger's arsenal of drugs so I started him on it until the doctors could figure out who would follow him on this treatment. We never got that call.

A few days later was another round of IVIG and an appointment with Dr. Moros. I wanted to talk to him about this situation; oncologist versus family doctor and Roger's care outside of his cancer diagnosis. After the IVIG transfusion, Roger had his office visit with Dr. Moros who asked Roger how he was feeling. Roger told him about his cough, tight chest and the no return phone calls when we needed help. Roger said firmly, "We decided to take the Levaquin we had left from the last lung infection and I'm feeling better."

Dr. Moros looked at me, I looked back at him and raised my eyebrows, like *WHAT? You have something to say? Go for it!* He checked Roger's lungs and temperature and decided his lungs were fine. Roger complained about increased cramping in his hands and calves. The doctor looked at his labs and said, "Your testosterone is low. It's most likely the reason you're having cramps. I will put you on AndroGel and see if we can get that up."

I said, "His testosterone has been in the crapper for quite a while, years actually. We were told it was at zero a while back. He was supposed to have an appointment with an endocrinologist a long time ago but that didn't come to fruition. He has had cramps for over a year!" Dr. Moros increased his pain meds, gave him a script for the AndroGel, and sent us on our way.

Day +428

It was Roger's first dental appointment since his transplant. His teeth were hurting and his gums had receded quite a bit. During the appointment the dentist said, "Boy, Roger, this treatment has taken its toll. I see a lot of cancer patients and I'm going to be honest with you. You need four extractions and a gum cleaning. I won't do the gum cleaning because the infection rate is too high, but those teeth need to come out soon."

While he was finishing Roger's exam, I went in to talk to the finance department to figure out how to pay for this. I made the appointment and decided to worry about the money later.

Roger wasn't happy about losing more teeth. He spent most of the day researching implants and the cost of them while I got caught up on laundry and worked on getting all bedrooms ready for company to arrive.

3

Stubborn As a Mule

On day +430, my brother's wife and kids flew in to spend a few days with us. The plan was to find an apartment for my niece.

While here, we planned to take them to the fair, but I was a little worried about Rog. He was feeling worse but refusing to bow out of the festivities. It was a once a year, all-out hippie-fest outside of town. I thought Rog might not be able to make it. It was really dusty and his lungs were still not at 100%. I had a long talk with him and he said he was going, PERIOD! We had a few more days so I planned to baby those lungs while I could.

Day +431

Apartment shopping was a success, but when we got home, Rog was extremely tired. I could tell he was using every bit of his energy to stay alert. I went straight to him and gave him a kiss, and he asked for help to the bedroom. When we got into the bedroom, he closed the door and sat on the side of the bed. I asked him if he was okay and he said, "I just need to get comfortable with breathing." With every inhale, his neck veins popped out. I gave him his inhaler and after a few puffs he was doing much better.

I called the doctor's office and they sent us to get a chest x-ray and told us to keep the office appointment on Monday. I told the family we would be right back and headed to get the x-ray.

I pleaded with Rog not to go to the fair, telling him I would stay home with him. He was firm and said, "I'm going, we're all going, Robin!"

When we got home, I gave Rog a pain pill, his antihistamine, and his inhaler. I made him a cup of tea with honey and a teaspoon of whiskey to soothe his throat and open his chest.

At 10:00 p.m., I put everyone to bed. It had been a long day and tomorrow would be even longer. There were no complaints. Rog coughed most of the night.

Day +432

It was fair day! The morning was all abuzz and excitement was in the air. It was definitely going to be a warm day since the deck thermostat was already at 75 degrees and it was only 9:00 a.m.

Roger spent the morning in the bedroom, taking his time getting ready. He came out and sat in his chair, and I brought him his breakfast and set up a TV tray. He ate a little bit of the eggs, a few slices of bacon, and a pile of fruit. I was glad he ate. He looked so tired and was a little weak on his feet. The boys questioned whether he should go or not, but it didn't take long for the topic to end. Roger made it clear he was going. I felt so nervous, and something was telling me to stay home with him, but with all the excitement in the house, everyone talking at once and involved in several different conversations made Roger want to go and have fun even more. I understood this loud and clear, and stopped worrying. I knew he didn't want to miss out – it was his body and his decision so I stopped nagging and hoped for a great and healthy day for us all. I brought a blanket and chair for us to sit or lay on. I figured if he got tired, we could rest and listen to the music. We were out of the house at 10:00 a.m. and at the entrance gates at 10:30.

Roger showed signs of extreme fatigue early. He was wearing dark sunglasses so I couldn't see his eyes. Usually I could tell by his eyes if he was getting tired or not. I tried to get him to rest a bit on the blanket I brought and had placed on the grass in front of the concert area. He said no and continued to walk with us, asking to rest several times. I found a bench nearby each time. As the afternoon wore on, it became more and more resting and less walking.

I got Rog to the blanket and for a few hours we enjoyed the music. I looked at him after a bit and noticed his face seemed almost translucent, his eyes were puffy again, and he was exhausted. His breathing seemed labored, I could tell he wasn't doing well, and it was about a mile to the car. I began to worry about getting him to it.

The boys tried to get him to wait at the entrance while they jogged to get the car, but Roger said no and pushed through. The field was very uneven, making it a difficult walk for anyone to make. I had the older boys take Roger's arms on each side to help him balance, and he barely made it to the car. All the dust made me worry about his lungs.

When we got home I got Roger into a hot shower and had him cough up the crap he had breathed in all day. After his shower, he settled into his recliner and rested while I got dinner going.

I propped Rog up on pillows to breathe when we went to bed.

Day +433

I got up early and prepared a huge breakfast. Bags were packed and everyone was heading home. I was ready for some quiet and I knew Roger was too. He was having a tough time recovering from the long day at the fair.

As soon as the door shut, Roger let out a sigh of relief and told me he wasn't feeling well. I knew when I had to help him to his chair that morning that something wasn't right. His legs were weak and his balance was off. He was bent over as he walked, clutching onto me. He felt like he had lost more weight. I asked him to explain to me how he felt. As I watched him talk, I noticed that he looked older. Right at that moment, he looked as if he had aged ten years since Friday. His face was puffy and the bags under his eyes were full and protruding, hanging like near empty water balloons from under his eyes. His eyes were lifeless, and his expression was flat and emotionless.

I got out my stethoscope and checked his lungs; they were full of fluid and he was wheezing. I said, "I need to take you in."

He said, "Tomorrow I have an appointment, I will wait." I gave him a water pill and his inhaler and put him back to bed. I went with him, and we rested most of the day. I got up only to get him meds, insulin, and a bite to eat. He only got up to pee – and boy did he pee. By morning, he was coughing up chunks of pale white balls of junk. I couldn't get him to the doctor fast enough!

Day +434

Rog demanded to get a shower before his doctor's appointment. I think he knew what was coming. He had just enough strength to stand up and was barely able to walk to the shower. I put a chair in the shower for him to sit on while I washed him and gave him a quick shave. He was grateful since he had no strength to do it himself. I helped him to his recliner and finished dressing him there. His breathing was labored and his wheezing was more pronounced. He didn't want to eat breakfast, but I got a piece of dry toast and a protein drink in him to help with all his medication and insulin. I was really worried, and my insides were shaking and all in knots, but I kept focused. I hadn't seen him this weak in a long time. His lungs were filling up, but he didn't have a temperature, which I was grateful for.

When we got to the doctor's office, Roger needed a wheelchair to get in. He was hesitant at first, but I was able to talk him into it after I explained that I couldn't carry him and that he was being selfish putting himself in medical danger. He finally gave in and got into the chair. When Dr. Moros saw Roger he said, "You don't look too good, big guy. What's going on?"

Roger looked at me to explain. His head was drooped down and he was using all his energy to breathe. I explained the past few days; the trip to the fair and his decline beginning a few days before the fair. Dr. Moros just stared at him with his arms folded in front of him, and I could see his wheels turning. I said, "I want you to admit him." Roger shot me a look that could have killed, but I ignored it.

The doctor said, "I agree with her. Your lungs are full and given you were in a dust storm at the fair, there is a good possibility you have a fungal infection in your lungs. Your x-ray is not encouraging." After listening to his lungs, he said, "Roger, if anything, we can help you get that crap out of there with some breathing treatments. We also need to make sure that whatever caused this setback is given the right medications."

Dr. Moros left the room to make arrangements at the hospital across the street for Roger's admit. While he was gone, Rog said, "I don't want to go to the hospital. Why did you do this?"

I said, "What are you mad about? You knew this was going to happen. Isn't it why you demanded a shower?"

He said, "I fear them killing me. If you're not with me, I'm afraid they'll screw up again. You have to stay with me if I decide to go! And yes, I had a feeling I was staying this time."

He lowered his head, put his forehead on mine and said, "I'm tired, I'm really tired this time." The tears started to roll down my cheeks. He had never said anything like this before. I told him everything would be okay and reminded him that we were the two musketeers. He smiled weakly.

At 5:30, a bed was ready, with isolation precautions, on the oncology unit. Dr. Moros scheduled Rog for a cardiac workup, a pulmonary function test and a bronchoscopy with a biopsy. That night he was also having a CT scan of his chest. Roger still had no temp so this was a good sign.

After the CT scan, the pulmonologist came in and said the scans showed a lot of old scarring and quite a bit of haze that he thought was pseudomonas. Pseudomonas is found in everyone but usually doesn't cause a problem and, kind of like the herpes virus, stress activates it. When pseudomonas is activated, which occurs in immune suppressed patients, it can cause pneumonia. It's highly resistant to most antibiotics, and for a lot of transplant patients it can be fatal. Dr. Moros came in later and said he had looked at the scans and thought it was an Aspergillus fungus. Aspergillus funguses are molds found in dirt and decaying soils, as well as plants and building materials. It is even in household dust. Normal immune systems have a built-in protector from this mold, but immunosuppressed patients don't. There are 180 species of Aspergillus fungus. The problem with this fungus was that it had a nasty side, eating away at the lungs, leaving them looking like a sponge; lots of little holes and crevasses, which are nonreversible.

I waited until all the doctors had come in for consultations and the nurses had changed shifts. I headed home for a change of clothes and all my usual hospital paraphernalia.

When I got back to the hospital, Rog was in the middle of a breathing treatment. He was happy to see me, waved, and went back to puffing in the medication. After the treatment he was able to cough up some pretty big chunks of phlegm, and the nurse collected some of it and sent it off to pathology.

Rog and I talked a bit but before too long he slumbered off, wheezing as he gently snored. I made my bed on the little couch and I too was off to sleep.

Day +437

We just hung around in the room, waiting for tomorrow. Because of the blood thinners, there was a 48 hour hold on the biopsy. Rog had breathing treatments throughout the day. After the treatments and with a series of coughing spells, he could breathe for a few hours until it all started over again. He was literally exhausted from the coughing, his skin was still translucent, and I could see little spider veins all over his face. His eyes were bloodshot and his lips were grayish in color. His 02 sats were sitting at 89%. They had him on an oxygen cannula at four liters which scared me because four liters and sitting at only 89% isn't good. He didn't have the strength to get up to pee so he was using a urinal. He was afraid to have a bowel movement so he wasn't eating much.

While Roger slept, I researched the two different organisms, those the doctors had mentioned that could be the instigator of this lung infection. I compared the treatments and outcomes with people who had bone marrow transplants. I read some good outcomes and some fatal outcomes. Roger didn't seem to be in the fatal group and that gave me some relief!

It was a long night. Roger had two more breathing treatments and a lot of coughing. He was now bringing up green and yellow balls of thick, nasty phlegm. After he got up a very large chunk, his blood oxygen levels started rising, his sats were up to 94% on four liters, his lips were his normal color, and his wheezing began to subside.

Day +438

The next morning, Roger was very weak. Just raising his arms to adjust his 02 cannula was a chore. His face went from translucent to ruddy, and his nose was so sore and dry from the oxygen and cannula. I put petroleum jelly around the end and just inside his nose to help with the dryness, and he said it felt better. He didn't feel like talking or watching TV, he just wanted to sleep.

Dr. Moros arrived before his office hours to check in. He explained the pulmonary biopsy and said the best-case scenario was a bacterial infection, not a fungal infection. He said bacteria is easier to get rid of, but fungal infections were literally impossible to get rid of and the damage they did to the lungs was irreversible. Rog just stared at him and didn't offer any response.

The doctor asked if he was okay and Rog said, "No, I'm really tired. I'm not sure I'll get through this."

Dr. Moros touched Roger's leg and said, "Hang in there, big guy, you have been through a lot worse. I'll make sure they give you the good stuff so you can sleep the rest of the day." This was the day Roger was supposed to have four teeth pulled so I rescheduled that.

Early in the afternoon they came and got him for his biopsy. As they started to wheel him out of the room, Rog looked at the tech and said, "Wait, Robin, you have to come with me!" I picked up my book and headed downstairs with them. When we arrived, Roger was out of breath. He had been rolled down in a wheelchair, so it was weird for him to be out of breath, and his lips were bluish in color again. They checked his oxygen and he was at 85%. They increased the oxygen to five liters and his 02 sats finally started rising, settling on 92%.

The lung doctor showed up while they were getting Roger ready and he said, "I will try to scrape and wash out as much of the crap that is in his lungs as I can while Roger is under a mild anesthesia."

Roger was back in his room at 4:00 p.m. His temperature was 97.9, his blood pressure was 140/88, and his 02 sats were at 97% with four liters of oxygen via cannula. His nurse came in when he got back to the room and said she had read the doctor's notes. She said, "He REALLY cleaned out his lungs and they think it's Candida, a yeast infection." Roger had had thrush on his tongue and throat off and on for a while now, and used a nasty mouthwash when it showed up, which was pretty often. It didn't cause him any discomfort so most of the time I didn't even know it was there until I saw him gargling. I thought maybe it had made its way into his lungs so I was going to need to look that up. Rog didn't hear any of it. The anesthesia was still in his system so he was oblivious to us in his room. I hoped he could sleep through the night.

At 5:15 p.m., he started chilling and shaking like he was freezing. I woke him up and asked if he was okay. He said, "I'm so cold. Put my blankets on me," but he was covered up to his chin in blankets already. I found the blanket warmer cabinet on the floor, took four of them, pulled his covers back, put the warm blankets right on top of his body, and covered him back up with the hospital covers. The chills only got worse and his shaking was moving the bed.

Just as I was about to call the nurse, his pulmonologist walked in. He said, "Well, the preliminary results show Candida from his mouth to the bottom of his lungs. I scraped, cleaned and washed them out as much as I could. I have started him on Voriconazole IV. I have discontinued the Prednisone and added a different steroid, Hydrocortisone IV until discharge." Roger really started shaking and the doctor said, "He's going to have rigors and a temperature throughout the night and well into tomorrow. I've ordered Ativan and Oxycodone for tonight. As soon as I know more, I'll let you know. But you'll be here through the weekend for sure."

It took the nurse forever to bring him his Ativan and Oxycodone. Roger finally yelled at me to give him some from the bottles in my purse. I gave him 2 mgs of Ativan under his tongue. After about 15 minutes, he settled down a little. After the third Ativan and the Oxycodone was given from the nurse, his body finally rested and he went to sleep.

I looked up fungal infections of the lungs and after a long read, I realized that Roger could no longer be in contact with dirt, animal excrement, dust or decaying food. I knew we shouldn't have gone to that fair! How could I tell him NO and make it stick? How could I refuse him when he made decisions that I knew were bad for him? How could I keep him safe from these things when we lived on a ranch? I got to thinking that even if he didn't go outside, I did. I was going to have to undress outside and shower immediately after I worked in the garden, just to be around him. Life was going to change even more! I would have to get an HVAC before I brought Rog home, which would help keep the dust out of the air in the house.

Finally, at 8:00 p.m., Roger was feeling a little better, and at least the Ativan and pain medications were working. We were watching TV when he said, "Bill really likes the sharks."

I was like, "What?"

He said, "Yes, he just pushes them away."

I asked, "When?"

Rog said, "When he dives!"

I asked, "Bill dives?" I knew Bill didn't dive!

Roger continued, "Yes, he free dives and tank dives, pretty deep."

I asked, "Does Betty dive?"

Rog said, "I don't think Betty does it well, doesn't like it much." Betty doesn't dive and never has. She doesn't even go in the water. I started to get scared. Either this was the pain medication which he'd had in him for three hours now, or was it possible the HHV6 was back? He was falling in and out of sleep so it might just be the drugs. *Please don't be HHV6 again!*

The night was pretty rough. His blood pressure dropped to 90/50, pulse 131, and blood oxygen sats were 87. Even with the increase of oxygen to ten liters, his blood oxygen level stayed in the 80s. His face was beet red and the blood vessels in his eyes started breaking. I started to really worry. Rog asked for the urinal and urinated about 30cc. It was very concentrated, and he said it stung when he peed. The doctor was called, and Rog was given a 500cc push of normal saline, a couple pain pills, and a Tylenol. After a few hours, his B/P returned to normal. He was finally resting, but his oxygen levels remained in the 80s so the 02 cannula was changed to an oxygen mask set at ten liters. His level rose to 92.

A respiratory therapist came in and said, "I'm sorry, Roger got overlooked." She had his treatment ready and started it.

I thought this was strange so I said, "He had a procedure today."

She looked at me and continued, "He's supposed to get his breathing treatments three times a day like he does at home." She got the medication mist infusing into his mask.

I said, "He doesn't get breathing treatments at home." I had a funny feeling she had the wrong patient! I asked, "What are you giving him? I have a bad feeling right now."

She stopped the treatment and left the room to go check orders again. When she came back she said, "I apologize. I saw budesonide TID at 3 mg and I assumed it was an order for this drug as a breathing treatment."

I said, "He takes it three times a day, in a pill form, at home for GVHD of the intestines."

She said, "Oh, I didn't see the PO." PO means by mouth. She said, "I'll write myself up. I'm sorry." I looked up Budesonide in the lungs and it said it is contraindicated in patients with viral or bacterial lungs infections. This is why I stayed in the hospital with him!

Day +439

The pulmonologist came in bright and early the next day and said, "Last night Roger had a septic reaction to the procedure and this was the reason for the symptoms. I'm going to add Cefepime to his therapy." I told him Roger was allergic to Cefepime so he changed it to Penicillin. I told him Roger was allergic to Penicillin. He scratched his head and said, "I'm going to have to check and see what will replace those two. I discontinued the Budesonide, I heard about the treatment; it's okay. And as far as I can see, he doesn't have GVHD of the lungs, but the final tests will be back next week. Roger will be here until Tuesday or Wednesday of next week. Hopefully we'll have all the test results back by then."

Roger slept most of the day. He only woke every three hours for his breathing treatments and his meals, which he didn't eat. He just moved the food around the plate

178

with his fork and called it good. His face was in a perpetual worried state. His forehead was wrinkled and just stayed that way like he was in pain. Even when he was sleeping, he looked like he was in pain.

Day +440

Dr. Moros's on-call weekend partner showed up at 10:00 a.m. He introduced himself then promptly said, "I, in my ten years of being an oncologist, have only seen three ALL (Acute Lymphoblastic Leukemia) patients, and none that have had a bone marrow transplant. So I'm going to leave the particulars to your other doctors and have Dr. Moros see you on Monday morning."

I thought, *An oncologist that has only seen three leukemia patients in ten years? Where is he practicing? At the North Pole?* I said, "Okay. I need you to write IVIG orders for Roger and a blood test on his IGG levels. If they're low, I want him to get a few doses of IVIG while he's here."

He looked at me for a minute and said, "Sure, okay," left, and wrote the orders.

With the constant IV changes and breathing treatments, Rog wasn't getting much rest, or at least not good rest. I was exhausted too. I hadn't slept but a few minutes here and there. I called Roger's son and asked if he could take my place for one night so I could go home, wash, and load up on my supplies, but most of all get a good night's sleep.

He said, "Sure, I'll look at my schedule and see if I can come sooner rather than later."

The drug that was finally decided on for the lung infection was Levaquin. The other two drugs were the better drugs but being allergic to both stopped that pretty fast. The breathing treatments seemed to be working, his lungs were getting better, and the Levaquin should start working fast, especially since he was getting it via IV. It wasn't long before the new high-doses of IV steroids showed their ugly face. Rog got real snappy at me for something that didn't make sense. In a split second, I realized I heard the steroid yelling at me and I called him on it real quick. I snapped right back at him saying, "I'm not talking with the steroid, period! I have had enough for now and I'm tired."

He just looked at me a little startled. And that was that. The previous day, a dietician had come in to talk to Roger about his dietary habits and I told her, "We're pretty much vegetarians for the most part. We eat a little chicken sometimes." When he got his menu this afternoon to mark his requests for tomorrow's meals, he picked it up, read the heading out loud, "VEGETARIAN! Really?" and slammed it down on the table. I busted up laughing but tried to hide it, of course. He threw his head back on the pillow with his neck arched, looking up at the ceiling, and had a look of sheer disappointment on his face, like a little kid.

I just lost it. I had to leave the room. I walked down the hallway laughing so hard that if I hadn't found a bathroom, I was going to pee my pants. His facial expression was so funny! He looked like an eight-year-old that was just told to come in from playing outside.

When I went back to the room, he said, "Where'd ya go?" I lost it again. He just stared at me then started giggling too. My gut and face hurt, but it felt so good! Rog finally said, "What are we laughing about?" and it started all over again.

After a few minutes, I took a deep breath and said, "I love you, do you know that?"

He said, "I love you, angel." I felt like I'd just had spring cleaning in my body. It felt so good to laugh like that!

4

Pseudomonas and Aspergillus

Day +442 was a Monday and that morning Dr. Moros and the pulmonologist came in together. The cultures came back as definitely pseudomonas *and* it looked like Aspergillus was in there too. Not knowing how to treat it, they called in a specialist from the CDC.

My first thought was, *Isn't that a little overkill or are you not telling us something?*

They explained that it would take weeks, maybe months to get the pseudomonas at bay, but for now the drugs seemed to be working. They left with, "This organism is really stubborn!"

An hour later, the CDC doctor arrived. She pulled up a chair and got comfortable then started right in. "Yes, pseudomonas is in there. The Aspergillus is so minute that it's not really what I would call the culprit. The liver enzymes are up, and the gallbladder is showing elevated enzymes."

I told her that I had questioned the BMT clinic doctor about the liver enzymes about two months ago but was told it wasn't a problem at 680. I said, "All the studies I have read said that 680 is too high, but they didn't seem worried."

She was surprised that they had been elevated for so long. She continued, saying she thought it was the liver that had started the whole downhill slide. She ordered a CT of the abdomen and a series of new, more sensitive blood tests. She left saying she would be back after the tests were done.

At 5:30 p.m., Rog had his CT scan and blood tests. The nurse gave us the results. She said, "I never gave this to you, but the results showed an enlarged liver and some sludge in the gallbladder, but at 60, sludge is normal. Oh, and the doctor said she will be back in the morning."

I told Roger I needed to go home for a bit, clean up, check on Max and reload supplies. He was fine with that as long as I returned that night.

When I got home, I showered, reloaded my supplies, and put two potty boxes down for Max, as well as extra food and water.

I headed back to the hospital. Roger was resting and waiting for the respiratory therapist to come in. I made my bed, got in it, and started researching liver failure, elevated enzymes, and how they can snowball into this mess. After his treatment, we kissed and shut out the lights.

The next day, all the tests came back normal *for Roger*. I say this because if I'd had these lab results, I would be in the ICU, but for Roger they were fine. He had elevated liver enzymes, extremely low protein, low magnesium, extremely low IGG, poor kidney numbers, low O2 sats, low iron, lung scarring, enlarged liver, etc. Shocking for most to have all at once, but normal for Rog. We hung out until all the doctors came and went. We were told it would be a long road to recovery, weeks of antibiotics, and a whole list of rules about not being around anything associated with soil, mold, dust and dander. All a big NO-NO! His discharge was planned for the next day.

Day +444

My morning was consumed with discharge orders and a pharmacy run then I packed up the room and got a very weak husband home and into his chair. He needed a shower badly since he hadn't had one since admit and there had been a lot of sweating going on.

But there was no shower that night. Rog was barely able to get from the car to his chair using every ounce of his energy. He wouldn't eat, saying he was just too tired. I got him to bed and stacked his bedside table with fluids and snacks.

Day +448

Over the past few days Rog hadn't done well. He had tried to help me with things like putting clothes in the dryer and folding them. After he did, it took him at least an hour to recover, and his breathing was labored and shallow at times. His inhalers helped. I let him do a little only to help build his strength back up, but nothing that required any real muscle. Baby steps, as they say.

Meals were the worst! He was eating only a few bites. I went over a plethora of different meals for him to choose from, but nothing sounded good. I tried to keep him hydrated, constantly reminding him how important it was to get the fluids down to keep his lungs healthy. He just looked at me like I was treating him like a child, and truthfully, I felt like I was. But if I didn't keep on him, he wouldn't take in any food or drink. He would forget he was supposed to; he had no hunger signals and just didn't get hungry AT ALL! I weighed him and he was at 214 pounds.

The TV had become his buddy once again. As I worked on the chores, I checked on Rog every hour with fluids, pillows or a little snack, and kept the doors open so he could hear my voice.

At 2:00 p.m., I went in to check on him and he was in bed. I was shocked! I asked if he was okay and he said he'd had a bout of diarrhea and vomiting so I checked his vitals. His heart rate was 130 and his B/P was 90/58. I called the doctor and he told us to go to the ER now.

When we got to the ER, they were waiting for us. They took Roger back and his vital signs had gotten worse. His B/P was 88/44 and his heart rate was 168. They admitted him to ICU. Over the next four hours he was given 3500cc of normal saline. Diagnosis;

severe dehydration. How did this happen? I racked my brain about his intake. I had been giving him fluids all day, every day. Food, not so much; it was a chore to get him to swallow anything.

By morning, all vital signs were back to normal and his urine flow was better. He was very weak on his feet and two therapists were required to help him walk. He was able to walk 25 feet then had to be wheeled back in a wheelchair. They came two more times and each time he did better. Between the nurses and therapists, he slept. I laid in bed with him and watched TV while he rested. He seemed to rest best when I got in bed with him. The nurses didn't mind.

Day +452

Rog was doing so much better; alert, communitive and steadier on his feet. When Dr. Moros showed up, I asked what had allowed for such a change so quickly. I should have guessed – he had increased the Prednisone. He explained to me that he would go home tomorrow on 25 mg of Prednisone but if I started to see a downhill slide again, increase it to 50 mg a day until he was doing better, then taper back down to 25 mg. He explained that I would probably have to do this from here on out.

Since I had done this several times in the past, I had gotten permission as well as trust to do this kind of medication dosing by all his doctors. There was obviously an irritation with me from most of them, and I got that. I'm a demanding, outspoken wife who doesn't put doctors on a pedestal. I respect them, but I don't hesitate to challenge them if I see fit. What I do have from them is trust. My nursing background helped, but they also knew I had been with him 24/7 since the beginning and had kept a log of Roger's every turn. Sometimes they asked me what I thought was going on.

I headed home to get everything ready for the next day's discharge. I stopped by the store to pick up groceries and made a pharmacy run. When I got back to the hospital, Roger said the CDC doctor came in and interviewed him for three hours. He said she told him she was working on how this type of leukemia mutated like it does. Her interview started by asking him about his first job, and went through his whole life. When the conversation was over, she told him he most likely got this leukemia from the chemical Benzene he was exposed to when working a couple of years at a job he started when he was 17. He had told me once that if he had never become a cop, he would still be working there. And most likely he wouldn't be alive today. The number of employees that have contracted cancer while working at this company was huge! He said the interview was fascinating.

The CDC doctor scheduled Roger for a liver biopsy that evening. He was an add-on, so it was a late test. The rumor seemed to be that the liver was causing all the problems. When he returned to the room, I crawled back in bed with him. He slept until the next therapist showed up.

Day +453

It was discharge day, even with the liver biopsy pending. I was given a whole new medication schedule with an addition of new antibiotics and steroids. Several of his routine meds were put on hold until after the biopsy results.

Roger's legs were so weak. When he got up, he needed a large male CNA to help him balance. The help of the wheelchair was the only way I was able to move him. I was worried that I wasn't going to be able to get him into the house. This was getting harder and harder on me and on Rog.

Like on all discharge days, I headed to the pharmacy for the new medication run, packed up the car then went in for the last doctor's visits. I kept asking why they were sending him home so weak, and just like all the other discharges I was told, "He's better off recouping at home. He will just get sicker if he stays in the hospital." Yeah, yeah, I get it. It was up to me to get him through another recovery. I didn't mind, but it was so hard on my body to lift and move him. Plus, he had to hear me nag at him for at least two weeks to get up, move, eat, drink, take your medication, time to shower, etc. I hated that I was always the bad guy!

Right before we left the hospital, Mom called and told me the well was dry. Great, Roger was admitted for dehydration and now we were going home to no water! I postponed the discharge, called the well guy and ran and bought water, picked up Roger and headed home. Somehow I got him in the house and into his recliner. It was a chore and he was asleep in minutes. I placed water, juice and some snacks next to his chair, kissed him and told him I needed to prepare for the well guy.

Over the next few days, Roger rested and tried to regain his strength while I dug ditches, removed plants and prepared for the new well.

Day +457

This was my five month check-up with my surgeon. Needless to say, my shoulder was swollen and very sore. All the doctor said was, "Life doesn't stop for the caregiver, does it?" He refilled my pain meds and sent me on my way. Roger kept saying, "I'm sorry" all the way home. I felt terrible. When we got home from the doctor's visit, Rog went to his chair and just stared at the TV. He didn't want to talk or do much of anything. The trip took a toll on him. I let him be and just kept the fluids coming, caught up on laundry, and watched TV with him. After a few hours, he complained of not feeling well. He started having pain in his abdomen and was unable to walk to the bathroom without help. It was a drastic change. I took his B/P and it was down in the 90s again. I called Dr. Moros and he said to increase the Prednisone immediately, pound down the fluids, and keep the appointment on Thursday.

Roger wasn't happy about me giving him glass after glass of fluids. I gave him an ultimatum – drink the fluids or I would take him back to the ER. He gave me a hateful look, made some derogatory comment under his breath, and started drinking. I nagged him to drink all day, every day, and I was surprised he didn't hate me.

Day +458

It was unbelievable how Prednisone affected Roger. After increasing it to 40 mg twice a day, he had all kinds of energy. His legs were slow and still a little wobbly, but his mind was ready to go. After my shower, I found him in the garage tinkering. I asked him how he got the door to the garage open and he told me it wasn't easy. He was so happy! I got him some breakfast, coffee and a gallon of water, and took it out to him. He was so into what he was doing he didn't even hear me set his food down.

Rog stayed in the garage most of the day. He was happy in his element! He had his TV and a workbench full of stuff to tinker with. I checked on him and refilled fluids throughout the day.

Day +459

The next day, the biopsy results finally came back, and we headed to the doctor's office. Dr. Moros said, "Roger, you look pretty good right now."

Roger said, "Let's not take the Prednisone away. It seems to be my friend."

Dr. Moros smiled then said, "You have GVHD of the liver." We both shot him a look of, *What did you just say?* He said, "I need to repeat your labs and when they come back, I will give Dr. Perses a call and get advice on where to go from here."

I said, "So what does this mean?"

He said, "His liver is failing but his enzymes have been up for a while, so I need to converse with him first."

We headed to the lab then home, and waited for the call. And we waited... Rog was in his head all night. No garage, he just sat in his chair staring at the TV. I spent the day researching on the computer, and what I was reading was not good. If we didn't get this under control, Roger didn't have long to live. The only real line of treatment he was already on, but the big one was Prednisone. I had a feeling that it would be bumped up again. It was getting scary – GVHD of the gut, the skin, and now the liver. It had become almost systemic and was getting scarier by the day!

5

GVHD of the Liver?

The call finally came in the next day, day +460. It was Friday, and I was told both doctors were off until Monday. I asked the nurse what to do. She said she would try to get ahold of the on-call doctor, depending on what the lab results were. She said, "Keep Rog quiet for the weekend if you don't hear anything. If he gets bad, take him to the ER."

I asked, "What does BAD mean?"

She said, "Robin, you know by now what bad means. Just watch him and make sure he gets his fluids in and check his temp often."

No other calls came. It would be a waiting game for the weekend so I stayed close to Roger. His newfound energy was squelched and he didn't want to talk about it.

Day +465

I had left messages for days with no call back, no message, nothing! Roger seemed to be doing okay and holding his own. The only problem was his skin and eye color were changing to a greyish hue and he was still having right-sided abdominal discomfort and trouble keeping fluids down. He had a few episodes of vomiting, but no temp. I decided if I didn't get a call back by noon, we were heading to the ER. If this color change was due to his liver, he was in trouble!

At 11:30 a.m., Dr. Moros called and said to come to the office now to repeat labs. We did, and we were told to wait in the lobby for the lab results. After an hour, we were called back into Dr. Moros's office. He handed me the lab results. I was shocked! Roger's liver enzymes were at 1127, and his kidney function was off the charts.

I looked up at Dr. Moros and his face was almost in a state of panic and he was wringing his hands. He said, "The BMT hospital has a bed for you, Roger. I have already pre-admitted you. You need to go NOW!"

I asked a bunch of questions, "What does all this mean? Can this be stopped? Is it reversible? What are they going to do to him? What's the plan?"

He just looked at me and said, "Robin, your job is to get him to the hospital. Here's a packet I want you to take with you."

I looked at Roger who was looking at the floor. He looked up at me, crying. I got down on the floor and just hugged him while the tears flowed.

Dr. Moros was teary-eyed and said, "I want you to go right now." We got up and went.

Roger sat quietly with tears running down his face all the way home as I cried with him. We didn't talk. He stayed in the car and reclined his seat back as I ran into the house and got the pre-packed suitcase. It was always packed and ready. I threw in my journals and medication bag, made a quick scan of the fridge and started throwing food and drinks into a sack.

Roger slept the two hours to the hospital. He was admitted to the oncology floor and immediately hooked up to IVs. New medications were being pumped into him, but no doctors had been in yet. I asked what the plan was, and was told everything was on hold until the Stanford reports came in. I said, "Stanford?" Roger's biopsy and bloodwork had been sent to Stanford for testing.

At midnight, one of the BMT doctors showed up, explaining we would be here at least five days. She said she had no results yet to share with us. She said, "I will be here until the morning. Another doctor will take tomorrow and we'll have Dr. Craig for the weekend."

I asked, "Where is Dr. Perses?"

She said, "He'll be back sometime next week." This is why I hated this hospital! There was no continuity of care EVER! She apologized and tried to comfort us by saying, "The group had a talk about Roger before he arrived. We're all up-to-date." I was thankful Dr. Hart was on call.

I wished I had someone to help *me,* someone I could vent to that would just listen. I had isolated myself so much, just taking care of Rog that I didn't have anyone to help me. I didn't need or ask for much. It was so hard, I felt so lonely, and I was tired of all of this. I was getting extremely frustrated with the house and all the problems, the chores, the demands, the expectations, and those depending on me. I knew I was drowning in self-pity and I just wanted to scream! I felt like I was in a house with the doors shut, screaming at the top of my lungs, but those on the outside couldn't hear me. My life on this planet had been about taking care of everyone else, and I had forgotten what it felt like to do what Robin wanted to do; laugh, dance, listen to loud music, go to the beach and rock hunt for hours. I wanted to go camping, I wanted to be kissed passionately and held as if I was the most desired woman in the world. I wanted to play with my grandkids, be creative, sit by the fireplace in my own backyard and look up at the stars until the sun came up. I wanted to go wine tasting, to buy a pretty lacy blouse, visit a tropical island and drink blue drinks. I wanted to sit outside and listen to the birds while I enjoyed a perfect meal made by someone else. I missed life! I asked God to forgive me for being so selfish. Rog fought so hard yet continued to fail. How did he do it? How could he deal with this day in and day out? I felt so guilty having selfish thoughts all about me when he was going through hell. It wasn't his fault he got leukemia. I just wanted to go home.

At 4:00 a.m., Roger started coughing. I got up to check on him and his skin was covered with red, round, raised rings that looked just like ringworm, and he was itching all over. I called the nurses and one by one, the medications were discontinued. I didn't understand since all the medications he was on he had been on before with no reaction.

Why now? Finally, a nurse came in and said they thought it was Urticaria, a skin breakout with no known reason. They gave him 90 mg of Prednisone and Benadryl, and after a few hours he was feeling much better. He ate a great breakfast and even took a walk around the unit with help. I was surprised he wanted to walk, but he told me he was stiff and needed to move. I was happy to help him move! The double-edged sword was doing its wonders – 90 mg of Prednisone.

Day +467

The day lingered on and the IVs were all restarted; antifungals, steroids and antibiotics, but still no information on what was taking place at Stanford. All that was happening was a boatload of blood being drawn every few hours. If they didn't stop, he wouldn't have any blood left! The doctors were making rounds so we waited. In the meantime, they replaced Roger's PICC line and sent the old one to the lab for analysis. I was so glad they didn't leave him without one.

Day +468

FINALLY, the next day Dr. Hart showed up, sat down and said, "Well, we have determined that the instigator of all this mess was the pseudomonas. It looks like it created the problem with your liver too. Your liver enzymes are up, and this would be alarming for most patients, but not a patient with your history. They have come down a bit and are showing improvement, but it will take a year on these new medications to really see a difference. Pseudomonas is a pretty bad fellow. All your other labs look really good. Normally I don't see these numbers until you are a few years outside of the transplant. Your immune system did take a big hit and so has your liver, but the numbers are on the right track now. You should be discharged tomorrow or Monday. We'll need to see you back in the clinic a few days after discharge for more labs, so stay close."

After he left, I climbed up in the bed with Rog, and for the first time in a while, we talked about the future.

Day +471

The previous few days were tough, trying to get the medication schedule down to a science. Insulin was the biggest problem. He was taking such high doses of Prednisone which then increased the insulin dosages. I was poking his finger six times a day again, and trying to get him to eat three meals a day to cover the insulin med was just as difficult.

By the evening, I noticed Roger was getting weaker again. Getting up from his chair required my help. He was having abdominal pain and started belching a lot. And he was out of breath just standing up from the chair. Tomorrow we were back to BMT hospital for more liver tests and to see Dr. Perses. It was a night of pain pills and sitting up to get comfortable.

Day +472

It was a tough morning. With no sleep, only worrying all night, I wasn't sure how I was going to get through the long drive back home. Fortunately, with a Thermos full of strong coffee for the trip, we arrived at the clinic early. Dr. Perses explained that Roger's symptoms were *not* from GVHD of the liver but from the pseudomonas and the high Prednisone dosages. He said his lab numbers looked a tiny bit better, but that it would take time. He then looked at us as if we were supposed to ask questions. I had a pit in my stomach and was so discouraged. One minute we are told it was GVHD, then told it was not GVHD, then told it was the medication, then it was the pseudomonas. At this point, all I was hearing was that it was all a mess. One minute a hint of hope, the next there was no hope or encouragement that things would get better. I didn't even know what questions to ask anymore. The answers were all the same with Perses; "This is the way it goes; it is what it is."

I said, "He just wants to sleep 24/7 and he's so weak again. You put him on high doses of Prednisone, he feels great. Then he crashes. It's the GVHD, it's the medications, it's the pseudomonas." I didn't expect an answer, it was just a statement. He didn't say anything as I looked at him then the tears flowed.

He saw my pain, he saw my open, broken, frustrated heart. He saw me raw and vulnerable. He looked away, took a breath and said, "I will need to see you once a week in the clinic for a while for lab work. I'll have the nurse give you a schedule. Do you have any questions?" Neither of us said anything and he left the room.

We stayed with Roger's mom for the next several days until we were released to go back home. Rog slept most of the time. I brought him food, pills and insulin, and kept him comfortable. When he wasn't sleeping, he enjoyed his time visiting with his mom.

Day +486

We had been back home for a few days and Rog was doing pretty well but still weak. We were in need of groceries so I ran to the store for a fast and furious shopping trip. When I got home, Roger was pale and out of breath. I asked him what happened and he said he'd had a vomiting spell and was barely able to crawl his way back to his chair. He said, "Somehow I was able to pull myself up in the chair." I took his temp and it was in the normal range for Roger, 97.4. I looked at him and saw, for the first time, him giving up. He was so tired and his life was not a life he wanted for himself. I saw the end coming but I couldn't let that thought linger for more than a second. I asked, "What can I do for you?"

He said weakly, "I'm all stoved up."

I asked, "All stoved up?"

He said, "I can't go to the bathroom. Will you help me?"

I said, "Of course," and went into the bathroom, and got the petroleum jelly and a pair of gloves. My heart hurt for him. This was something he would never EVER let me do unless he was in real need. His private time in the bathroom had always been that. Never was the door open when he was doing his sit-down business. I helped him back to the bathroom and explained to him what I was going to do and that he needed to breathe while I did it. I told him it would be painful then realized he was vomiting because he had a stool blockage. I looked at him before I started, asked him when his last bowel movement was, and he said he didn't know. He looked down at the floor, and I could tell he was extremely embarrassed. I had him sit down on the toilet as I knelt in front of him then had him spread his legs. He sat so much taller than me. I leaned my head against his chest and faced the far wall so he couldn't see me and I couldn't see him. I reached between his legs and felt his rectal area, which was swollen beyond belief. Together we were able to disimpact him, and it was a tremendous amount of stool. The bowl was full, and by the time we were done, he was bleeding from all the swelling and manipulation. He had tears in his eyes and I told him I was sorry a billion times.

When I was done, I stepped away, got him a warm washcloth and Anusol for the pain, and left the room so he could have a moment of privacy. When he was ready, he asked for help and I got him to his chair. He had no appetite, but I made him some broth with noodles and started him on stool softeners. He was able to get the warm broth down. A couple hours later, he said he was feeling much better and apologized for me having to do that. He said with tears, "I don't want you to remember me for that."

I knelt in front of him, kissed him gently, and said, "We are a team. Sometimes it takes two of us to get the job done, that's all." He hugged me for a long time as we both cried. It was getting real and scarier by the day.

Todd showed up and asked if I needed any help. Together we got a lot done as we worked until dark. Roger had tried to come out and see us, but he took a fall and, thank goodness, Todd was right there to help him up off the ground. I could tell Rog was embarrassed, but none of us said anything, we just acted like nothing happened. I think it was a wakeup call for Todd.

Before bed, I got Roger into the shower and gave him a nice good scrubbing. He put his hands up on the wall and rested his head on them while I washed him. He was so thin, his legs were like twigs. With over a hundred pound weight loss, his skin just hung. I weighed him and he was at 202. He had lost 114 pounds! I dressed him and propped him up on his pillows so he could breathe better. I tried to get him to do some leg exercises to get a little strength back, asking him to just slide his feet up and down the sheets, bending his knees and letting them back down to rest, back and forth. I had tried to get him to walk more or even just point and flex his toes while in the chair. He listened but never followed through. I felt like I was always nagging him to do something. He knew what he needed to do, and if he chose to get his strength back, he would do it. After I showed him the easy exercise, he said okay but was asleep in seconds.

Day +488

The past few days had all rolled into one and I'd had to disimpact Rog a few more times. I was giving him a mild stool softener three times a day. This was an office visit day at the clinic so I gave Roger his pills with an added Provigil to help him get through the day. Dr. Perses said Roger's numbers had come down a few points which was good since it takes months to get back to normal. He decreased the Prednisone to 25 mg in the morning and 20 mg in the evening, and raised the Tacrolimus to 1 mg to help with the GVHD. Roger asked to have the Prednisone decreased back down to 20 mg, complaining it took all his strength away. It was such a roller coaster ride; increasing the Prednisone initially gave him energy then it zapped his energy. The doctor asked him if he was exercising and Roger said, "Yes, when I have the strength to do it." I didn't say anything.

Dr. Perses asked me how I felt about that. I didn't know what he was referring to, so I took the high road. I said, "I worry about you lowering the Prednisone too much because every time you do, it sets Roger back or he ends up in the hospital, only to increase it again. He gets back on track for a while and then it's downhill again."

He looked at me quizzically and I looked at him. He said, "I agree it's not time to lower it yet, Roger. Right now, your body needs it."

I asked about the constipation and explained what had been going on. He reminded Roger to get in his fluids and continue the stool softener. He then said, "You can now be seen by Dr. Moros for your care. If he needs our support, we will be there for him, but for the most part you're discharged from the BMT clinic." And that was that. So, I guess we were not coming back here ever again.

When we got home, I tried fixing soft vegetables for dinner with his broth to help with his stools, but he gagged and couldn't get any of it down. He said he would just drink more. As the days went on, every other day we were in the bathroom, dealing with his constipation. He got used to me helping him and it didn't bother or embarrass him any longer. His hemorrhoids were so swollen and inflamed. I put Preparation H or a Tucks pad on him when I was done to lessen the pain. At that point, I knew the pain pills were the culprit. He was taking about 6-8 a day because his bones, joints, back, eyes and head hurt all the time. Sometimes he couldn't even get out of bed for an hour after he had taken one. Also, his skin was terribly thin, he was now wearing the cut off socks I had made him all the time, and he had bandages everywhere. I didn't know why he had to take them off all the time; he said he needed to look to see if the wound had healed. When I saw him picking at the sores left behind, I yelled at him to stop, and he told me he didn't even realize he was doing it.

Over the next several days Roger held his own, but then all hell broke loose.

Day +499

Something woke me up. Roger had been having trouble breathing at night so he decided to sleep in his chair which was just outside our bedroom door. He sounded like he was struggling and his breathing was labored. I called out to him and he yelled, "I need help!" I darted out of bed and into the living room about four feet away. He'd had trouble getting the footrest down on his recliner and had somehow climbed halfway out of his chair with the footrest still upright, and was laying halfway into my chair next to his, got stuck and lost his urine. It was all over the floor. He said, "Hurry, get me a cup so I can finish peeing!" His arm was bleeding everywhere and he was so embarrassed. I cleaned up him and the mess then helped him shower, change his clothes and got him into bed. I propped him up to an almost sitting position with his neck pillow. He apologized over and over, saying his legs were too weak to push the footrest down on his recliner now. I needed to have a serious talk with him about a cane, a wheelchair and a lift chair. When I had tried to talk with him in the past about using these tools, he was adamantly against them all. I think he felt if he started, he would never be able to go back. He said they were for old people, not him, but I told him they were tools to help him while he was sick, but he wasn't having it. So, I stressed constantly over the thought of him falling and me not being able to pick him up. I reminded him of this stress and he said he would do better not to stress me out.

I got up early and gave him his pills, adding a Provigil, went back to bed and fell right back to a hard sleep. He got up and made his own coffee, which I was surprised he wanted, and made me a smoothie. When I heard the machine start up, I jumped out of bed and as I rounded the corner, I realized what he was doing and jumped back in bed. He brought it to me, along with his coffee, and got back in bed. I said, "Thank you! Is it my birthday?"

He said, "I don't think so, is it?" I looked at him and realized he was being serious. I thanked him and wondered where he got the strength and balance to do this. I knew the Provigil helped a lot with concentration and gave him a bit of energy, but balance and coordination was outside the pill's miracles. This seemed to be how it was. One day I thought he was dying then the next day he got up and made coffee and a smoothie. I just didn't get it! I asked how he was doing and he said, "Pretty good this morning." The rest of the day, he was a little unsteady on his feet and had to sit a lot, but he did it! By the time evening arrived, he was really weak and his voice was scratchy and without projection. Before he went to sleep, he made a list of things to ask Dr. Moros on Wednesday:

1. Problems breathing and coughing at night
2. Decrease Prednisone
3. High heart rate
4. Weakness and fatigue

Day +501

It was Roger's appointment with Dr. Moros. Roger started the conversation right out of the gate, his voice at a whisper. I gave him some lozenges after a long night of coughing, but they didn't seem to work. Rog asked his four questions and we were both surprised at the answers. The doctor sat down in his chair in front of the computer and turned to face Roger. He was almost on Roger's level. He said, "Roger, one-third of transplant patients die. One-third of the transplant patients wish they hadn't survived, and the last third live a very poor quality of life. You are one of the latter two. First, if I reduce your Prednisone, you will lose your liver, and GVHD is still a huge problem. Your numbers are still off the charts and you have a long way to go. Your voice is very weak, and the last time I heard your voice like this you had an onset of HHV6. These high Prednisone dosages will reactivate it. I'm going to have you seen by the CDC doctor again and schedule you for a lumbar puncture. Roger, do you understand that you are really sick and this is why you feel crappy?"

I just wanted to cry! He was being so blunt and in our faces. It was like he was giving us a wake-up call. I started to ask questions about when he would be able to decrease some of the medications when Dr. Moros interrupted me and said, "You are wanting to know how to get him back to four years ago?"

I said, "NO, I understand the reality of all of this. I want to know how to make his life, his quality of life, better! So, he has cramps at night that hurt him. Can he have some valium? The testosterone gel was never approved by the insurance, and I have been giving him my Provigil. He's more focused and has more energy throughout the day. Can he have a script for that?"

He stopped me and said, "Absolutely to both." I realized at that moment that Dr. Moros knew his prognosis wasn't good. Before, he had refused these medications, yet today, no problem. And his blunt conversation was getting us ready. He had never talked to us like this before. He was matter of fact, almost forceful instead of cordial and sensitive. He gave us the medication scripts and said the CDC doctor would be in touch. We got up and followed him out of the exam room to the appointment counter. He patted Roger's shoulder and disappeared.

In the elevator, I asked Roger how he felt about what Dr. Moros had said. He said, "He was different today." I didn't want to push the point. I really didn't want to know what he was thinking, nor did I want to bring up those stats again. I felt it was best to just forget it was ever said.

We never talked about all the "one thirds."

Day +506

Over the last few days, Roger's breathing was becoming labored. After a heated phone conversation with his brothers, he collapsed into his chair, started coughing, and couldn't catch his breath. I got him some water and his inhaler, and after a minute or two he was okay. As a wife and caregiver, I wanted to protect him from the outside world, but sometimes it creeps in unexpectedly. All I could do was support him and help him through these moments. I left him to his thoughts for a while, just sitting next to him and staying quiet. He was deep in thought for quite a while. I made him tea with honey and a teaspoon of whiskey. He drank it slowly then rested. At bedtime, I helped him dress and noticed his ankles were really swollen. I asked how long that had been going on and he said he didn't know. I said, "It's probably why you're having trouble breathing, you're full of fluids."

He said, "Don't give me a water pill please, I just want to sleep." I explained that going to bed would help since his ankles would be up and level with his heart, but in the morning a water pill was to be expected. We snuggled up and fell asleep. He miserably coughed through most of the night.

Day +507

This was a lab day and Roger was up early. He slowly made his way to the shower, using the chair and wall as a way to balance. I made him a bagel and some fruit then heard a crash. Roger came out of the bathroom bent over, shuffling quickly, looking as though he was going to take a nose dive. He made it to his chair and collapsed, breathing hard and gasping for air, naked and wet. I ran and got a towel and a blanket and put it on him. I knew he was in trouble. I looked down at his legs and they were like balloons. I ran to the bathroom and got 60 mg of Lasix and a potassium pill and gave it to him. After a few minutes, his breathing settled down, but he was wheezing terribly. I asked what happened and he said he'd lost his breath and almost passed out. After four hours and still no urine, I gave him another 20 mg of Lasix. One hour later, he was filling up the urinal fast and furious. It reminded me of the debacle in the ICU with his kidneys. Once they slammed him with high doses of Lasix, he had peed out ten pounds in one night.

I rescheduled the lab work for tomorrow, and by the time the evening arrived, he had filled up the urinal 11 times, his wheezing was gone, and his ankles were visible.

There was still some edema in his calves, but not much. Before bed, I had him get on the scale. His weight was 197.2. We were both shocked.

For dinner, he had his bagel, fruit and two protein drinks. It took all he had in him to get it down.

Day +508

I ran into Dr. Moros at the lab the next day and told him what had happened. He said, "Increase the Lasix to 40 mg twice a day with a potassium pill until I see him next week." He went into the lab and checked Roger's feet and ankles. They looked better, but his breathing was still labored and there was still a little wheezing. Every time we complained about it, we got, "The culprit is the pseudomonas and it is going to take a long time for it to clear." So, Lasix and potassium would be our friend for a while.

When we got home, his B/P was 132/94 and his pulse was 132. He said he felt like he was going a hundred miles an hour but he was just sitting. He was nervous so I gave him his metoprolol and an Ativan and let him rest. He was getting weaker again. He was weak all the time, but then there was the abnormal weakness that set in. It's hard to explain but when you saw him every day, it made sense. His voice got small, his legs trembled, he used the walls and chairs to help balance, and he wouldn't eat. He also fell asleep mid-sentence and just stared at the TV.

I made him chicken noodle soup with small bites of veggies, a bowl of fresh fruit and a protein drink for dinner, and watched him from the kitchen. I just stared at him. He looked so tired, so small and frail. When he breathed, his neck veins protruded. He was using so much energy just to breathe and I was afraid of the day I would lose him. I just kept trying to get through each day, one day at a time.

Day +509

Roger didn't get out of bed. I woke him several times throughout the day to drink broth, protein drinks and Gatorade. It was becoming harder to wake him. I cried off and on all day as I paced the floor after each cup of fluids. He was showing signs of another downhill spiral. I was torn between calling for an ambulance and getting him to the hospital or just letting him rest. Thankfully, his vital signs were all good and he was breathing okay while lying down. I lay next to him off and on, just smelling him and touching him. He slept through it all.

PART NINE

1

Who Dropped the Ball?

By day +511, Roger had continued to get weaker and was relying on the cane 100% of the time. I had finally gotten him to use one after a few close calls. Getting from chair to toilet was a struggle so he was using the urinal in his chair at times. Today he had wanted a shower but was afraid. I told him he needed a haircut and a shave, and I would do both then shower with him. A lot of the time I showered with him so he felt safe. I had him wash the top half while I washed the bottom half. I could see both bones in his legs now, and his stomach was a little bloated compared to the rest of his body. His pelvic bones were protruding and his barrel chest was just rows of ribs. I told him he had to eat, but he said he couldn't, that it would all just come back up.

He looked down at me with such sorrow and pain. I could see him in there, so broken and sad. He was such a beautiful man. He eyes were such a crystal blue and he looked into my eyes with love, a slight smile, and a thank you for helping him. I didn't want to break the moment but we were both shivering from the cold. I said, "You are so handsome with your new haircut and shave." He reached down and kissed me, hugging me for a long time. I didn't want to leave this moment, I wanted to stay there forever! My tears started flowing and my body started softly shaking from quietly crying while he held me closer. I was going to lose my best friend – my husband was going to leave me. I didn't want to let go so I just cried and held on.

I slowly towel dried his body so as not to hurt him or break his skin. I got him to his chair and he rested.

No one understands what is going on inside you. We're all different. I thought about Roger and me. No one really wanted to know how Rog was. It was too hard on them. What do you say each time they ask how he is? The answer is always, *Not so good.* Friends just fade away and stop calling. As their lives continue to be fruitful and happy, and vacations come and go for them, guilt sets in. They no longer have anything in common with you, and for them to call and tell you about their wonderful lives as you sit there watching your loved one die is too uncomfortable for them.

For a long time I heard, "Robin, you need to get away and have some Robin time. You need to get some help, some respite!" Roger didn't want some stranger in his house taking care of him. He would panic if he couldn't see me or hear my voice, and I was afraid, at this point, to leave him. I was afraid he wouldn't be able to get to the toilet or that he might fall. I was afraid he was going to die and if I was out shopping or having respite when it happened, how would I live with myself? Sometimes I just wished one of my friends or family members would stop by for a bit so I could shower, dye my hair, or just visit with us and make us feel like people again. I think if they could have walked a mile in my shoes, their suggestions would have changed. Who leaves their sick spouse to go get a massage or pedicure? But that was what they suggested, along with other ridiculous ideas. Plus, I had no money to do these things. We pinched every penny.

At 4:00 a.m., Rog started having problems breathing again. His lungs were wet, he had to sit up to breathe, and his legs were swollen again. I propped him up and gave him an Ativan. He settled down and slept off and on while I read. His color was good, but he was using a lot of energy to breathe.

At 6:30, I called the exchange to get ahold of Dr. Moros. He called me back and said to give Roger more Lasix and keep him quiet. He said to take him in to see his family doctor.

At 9:00, I called our family doctor. They had an opening at 10:15 a.m. I told Rog he had to get up and make this appointment. He said okay and was barely able to help me dress him, but as he got up and moving, he got a tiny second wind.

At 10:15, I ran into the doctor's office and got a wheelchair for Roger. Our family doctor was surprised to see us at his office. I explained that the oncologist told us to be seen there. He took a chest x-ray and said that there was a hazy area in the right lung. He sent it off to be read and said he would get back to us tomorrow if there was anything to worry about. He told me to stop by the pharmacy to pick up some over-the-counter decongestant, and he would call Dr. Moros then us later in the day.

By 1:00 p.m., we were back home and in bed. His breathing was still labored and he was unable to move in bed without help. Since he couldn't turn over to use the urinal, I placed and emptied it for him. The follow up call couldn't come soon enough!

At 3:00, I called Dr. Moros back and told him Roger wasn't doing well, his breathing was still labored, and he was having trouble getting up. I told him we went to the family doctor and he'd had a chest x-ray that showed a hazy area in his lower right lung. I was told to keep the appointment on the 30th for the repeat follow-up CT scan of his chest and to keep the Lasix in him.

By around 6:00 p.m., breathing was painful, his B/P was 94/54, his pulse was 162, and he was using every bit of energy to breathe. I wanted to call an ambulance, but he said no, just get me to the ER. I don't know how I did it, but I got him to the car, basically dragging him all the way. It was a twenty-minute drive from hell. I was losing him. He was turning blue as I drove to the ER as fast as I could. I ran in and asked for help, and a team came out to the car, put him on a gurney, and took him in. His B/P was 88/40, pulse 168, sats 84%, and he was in and out of consciousness. His neck veins were protruding with each breath. He was in big trouble! The ER doctor drilled me fast and furious. In one minute, I gave him a rundown on Roger's lungs, pseudomonas / Aspergillus and the transplant. I gave him a list of medications and his last dose of each. I told the doctor about the chest x-ray a few hours ago, and that we were sent home on Mucinex. While I talked as fast as I could, he was pulling up the chest x-ray in the system. I continued, "I called Dr. Moros early this morning and he said to go to our family doctor. Please call Dr. Moros, he knows everything!" The ER nurse was pulling up records on the computer as I spoke, and within minutes of our arrival, Roger had a team of people working on him.

At 7:30, I could barely see Roger through the team of nurses and doctors hovering over him. They were starting IVs, getting an oxygen mask placed, and pulling off his clothes. Roger was out and not responding. Everything was happening at once. Nurses and techs were all on phones, clearing the CT scanner, ordering an ICU bed, calling the pulmonary doctor on call, and asking me question after question. I rattled the answers off as if I was a robot. I was shaking, drenched in tears, and my nose was dripping, but I barely noticed. I just took question after question as fast as I could. All I wanted was to not lose sight of Roger. As long as I could see him, I could see him breathing. In a mad rush, he was gone and so was everyone else. I was immediately alone in a trashed room. No Roger, no bed, just paper, EKG tabs, IV paraphernalia, towels, sheets, and his clothes on the floor. One shoe was in the corner and one shoe was in front of the door. He was gone! I sat down crying and started praying and praying that he would come back.

At 8:40, a nurse walked in and asked, "Have you been in here this whole time?"

I said, "Yes. What's happening to him? Where is he?"

She told me he was in radiology in the CT scanner and that he was really sick but in good hands. She said, "The team has shown up and they are trying to figure out what to do. He is coming back here with chest tubes so don't be frightened, but he will be breathing better." She told me to sit tight then got me a glass of water.

At around 10:30, Roger returned and he was awake. He was connected to four IV poles with six bags of saline infusing into him, with B/P cuffs on each bag. He was being slammed with fluids. I ran to him and just hugged him. I was crying so hard I couldn't see him. He reached up, wiped my tears, and said, "I'm okay now. It's going to be okay now." I just laid on his chest and cried.

The ER doctor touched me on my shoulder and said, "Robin, we need to talk." I wiped off my face, stood up and looked at him. He had pulled up the CT scan pictures of Roger's lungs on a TV monitor on the wall. It showed a huge white mass on Roger's lower right lung. He said, "This is an Empyema. It is a large puss pocket between the lining of the lung and the lung. It looks like it has been there for quite a while and is very large. Can you tell me when he started having trouble?"

I explained what had transpired over the past several weeks. He said, "This is pretty serious because it's so big and it has collapsed his lung. This white mass here is full of puss. The chest tube will hopefully drain most of it off, but he'll be here for a while. He's also severely dehydrated. If you hadn't brought him in, tonight would have been his last." I started sobbing so hard I couldn't stand up. He came over to me, pulled me up and said, "The team needs to talk to you. We have a lot of questions. Can you do this for us, answer some questions?" He handed me a box of tissues.

He wanted me in the hallway, but I said, "No, I want to stay in here."

He said, "They're going to be taking blood and putting a urinary catheter in him. He'll be in good hands and you'll be right outside the door."

In the hallway were the CDC doctor, his pulmonologist, Dr. Moros's on-call partner, and a few other doctors I didn't recognize. They had the medication list I had given them, and two screens were pulled up on the computer showing Roger's records from other hospital stays. They started with his medications, concentrating on the steroids, Lasix, antifungals and antibiotics. Then they went down the list, asking when they were started and for what reason they were being used. Afterward, they went on to his symptoms. When they were done asking questions, they all started taking turns on a treatment plan. The CDC doctor seemed to be the one in charge, with the others adding to her plan. It was a very intense conversation. They talked in front of me as if I was part of the team. I listened and heard the word Cefepime.

The CDC doctor then turned to me and asked about his reaction to the medication. She wanted every detail. I told her the story of his reaction that had occurred nine days after the transplant. She said, "I don't think he had a reaction to Cefepime, I think he had an overdose of Cyclosporine. I'm going to start him on a Benadryl drip and at the same time start him on Cefepime. He has to have it! It's the only drug at this point to get him out of this crisis."

I nodded okay. I trusted her and the other doctors did too. They all said thank you, hang in there, and each gave me a hug. They left me with, "This will a long and complicated road ahead considering all his diagnoses." I told them I had heard this many times.

Roger was transferred to the ICU. His breathing was getting better by the hour and his vital signs had calmed down. I found a chair, pulled it next to the bed, and got comfortable. Roger was asleep and it was my turn. I sat next to him and held his hand, leaned my head back, and thought about the last 48 hours and everything that had just happened. I then wondered how both Dr. Moros and our family doctor were going to react when they found out what just happened, knowing they both dropped the ball. How were they going to face me? I was tired, pissed, sad, and disappointed, but most of all, I had lost faith in them. They had given up. I wasn't giving up and neither was Roger, and that was all that mattered. How was I going to rest? I needed to be with him all the time. How could I get help?

I watched him breathe and sleep until I too fell asleep. I moved only when the pain in my shoulder and back woke me from being in an uncomfortable position in the chair.

Day +515

Roger woke up feeling much better. His chest tube had drained off 80cc of bloody puss so far, and it was awful looking! I couldn't believe all that was in the lining of his lungs, and there was more to come. It seemed like this was the pattern. Everyone missed the mark until he was in a crisis. I felt like I had written this over and over again in my journal!

The aides got Roger up to a chair with the Hoyer Lift since he still had no strength to get up on his own. He was able to eat a whole bowl of oatmeal with bananas. I was glad to see him eating; he needed to eat. Roger's team of doctors showed up while he was in the chair and told us everything was moving in the right direction. They explained that a few TPA injections into the lungs would break up any blood clots and bacteria clots that were lingering around in there then all should be good. TPA is given to break up blood clots in the body that could result in a stroke, heart attack or in Roger's case, pulmonary embolism. I asked how long this visit would be but no one had an answer. They said one day at a time then all hell broke loose!

Outside our room, all personnel were running to TVs. Several of the nursing staff came into our room and turned on our TV, totally ignoring us and all the doctors in the room. We watched the news unfold. There was a school shooting nearby and several of the victims were on their way to this hospital. The head ICU doctor was going from room to room telling nurses which patients to transfer out of the ICU, and Roger was one of them. He looked at me and said the same thing he'd said to the people right next door, "There has been a shooting and we need the beds in here. I'm really sorry, but Roger can go to another floor now that he's not critical. All of our nurses here can take care of a chest tube."

I said, "I understand you have trauma patients arriving but these patients are important too! Roger cannot go to just any floor. He has no immune system and a medical floor has a lot of airborne bacteria he can't handle. Please put him on the oncology floor."

He said, "People are sick there too."

I said, "Yes, inside they are sick with tumors and blood cancers, but not sick from respiratory issues, sores and viral infections that nurses are carrying from room to room. Please, I beg you! Put him on oncology!" I put my hands together as if in prayer. Our team just watched as this conversation took place. The ICU doctor looked at them, then at me. There was one bed left and Roger got it.

Everything was moving so fast. People were running and patients connected to tubes were being shuffled around. The nurses tried to get Roger up from the chair and he fell on the floor as if he had no legs. I let out a gasp and ran and grabbed the chest tube canister from the bed as it was being pulled taunt from Roger's chest. Roger let out a scream. It took the Hoyer Lift to get him up. He couldn't help at all, his legs were useless. I was holding Roger's hand while we moved into the elevator and out of all the commotion. When the doors shut, I could hear myself breathing and crying. No one said a word, they just stared up at the numbers changing on the elevator panel. We got settled into the new room, but the staff was sparse.

Through the evening, the chest tube continued to pull puss out of Roger's lung. His breathing, O2 sats and vital signs returned to normal, his oxygen was turned down to 2 liters, and his color returned to normal. If he hadn't been connected to tubes lying in a hospital bed, I would wonder why he was here. The night nurse came in to change, poke and prod Rog as they do. She said, "We got back the lab results from a few hours ago. His liver enzymes are normal again. His phosphate is still elevated but that's most likely from the infection. Everything is looking up!"

I said, "His liver enzymes were 1127 a couple days ago, how could they be normal?"

She said, "Right? I know – crazy! Everyone seems to be all abuzz about it." She started talking to Roger about his comfort while I sat back and contemplated this. His enzymes had been elevated since August. Did that mean he had been growing this infection since August? Did he really have GVHD of the liver? Does liver tissue change if there's an empyema or does this infection make a liver biopsy look like GVHD? It didn't make sense and I couldn't wrap my head around the fact that there had been four office visits with labs, x-rays, blood draws and biopsies, yet this was overlooked. We had been told, *He's sick, it's part of the process. He has GVHD of the liver and elevated enzymes, but we're not too worried about the level. One-third of the people die, one-third of the people wish they had died, and one-third of the people live with a poor quality of life, and Roger you are in the latter two.* Was I to believe that Roger had hit a point where they just didn't want to deal with his diagnoses or his care any longer? Had he hit the point of no return? No more telling me the same thing over and over? No longer having to look me in the eye? I was so disillusioned...

Day +516

The CDC doctor came in early. She started right in saying, "The antibiotics are helping curb the infection and the drainage is making the puss sac smaller in the lower right lung. But in the upper sac where the chest tube is, it's still producing puss. The organism is definitely just pseudomonas causing the puss pockets." She discontinued several of the GVHD medications.

When she stopped talking for a minute to look at her tablet, Roger asked, "Where are my keys to the boat?"

I looked at him and said with a firm voice, "Where are you right now?"

He looked around the room, then back at me and said, "In the hospital."

She continued, "The empyema is curable, but it's going to take a long time. His mental status will return to normal." When I asked about his weakness and deterioration, she explained that he'd had so many things going on and had had a lot of unusual diagnosis. She said his mental capacity should be okay, but his body might not return to the Roger I first knew. I asked for physical therapy and she said, "Yes, of course." She then said, "Oh, and GVHD and empyema are not related. They're two different diagnoses with two different mechanisms, just occurring at the same time, I think." She started to say something, stopped then stood up and found a pen for the white board on the wall. She drew a lung on top, a line, then a liver below the line. "The line represents the abdominal lining. We just don't know how pseudomonas crossed all three barriers to create one problem-causing bacteria, yet this is what we have, though no one has said there is pseudomonas in the liver. It's not in the charts nor in the biopsy reports so I'm not sure where that came from." She touched and squeezed Roger's toe, shook my hand and said, "We're on top of this. You have a great team and we all get along great, so progress is good."

A few minutes later, we heard her talking to a doctor in the hall. It was another lung doctor from the same group. He came in, sat down and explained, "The bacteria isn't being treated by the antibiotics, just the lungs are. Kind of in a way to prophylactically prevent his lungs from being consumed by the pseudomonas. Unfortunately, the sac of puss is on the outside of the lung, and the barrier between the lung prevents the antibiotic from treating the puss in the sac. The drain is there to drain it, yet the bacteria continues to grow even though it's being drained. We're hoping it's draining fast enough to out-speed the growth factor." He sat down and looked at the canister for a second then looked back up. He slowly said, "Usually, drains are the last resort. Surgery is first but Rog is so sick and his body is so frail that drains were the safest choice, and it was somewhat of an emergency when they finally diagnosed it in the ER. I will repeat the CT scan tomorrow and determine if the drain is working and look at the sludge on the wall of the lung cavity to see how thick it is and what it looks like. If the drainage method isn't working, we'll all reconvene and discuss the possibility of surgery to scrape and wash it all out. It's extremely dangerous, but so is doing nothing if the drain isn't working." He had said a lot. He stopped and asked if we had any questions.

Rog said, "I guess we wait until after the CT scan then?" He said yes, shook our hands, and out he went.

Physical therapy came in after breakfast and tried to get him up. His knees buckled and down he went, but it was a controlled fall. The therapist had a belt on him and held him up just enough to make the fall a gentle one to the floor. She wrote orders to always have two therapists when ambulating. While Roger rested after therapy, I decided to run home and check on things.

I sat in the living room in Rog's recliner thinking about an upcoming family visit. I found myself hoping we were still in the hospital when the family came because all the commotion would be really hard on him. He would try to be stoic and participate, but it would do more harm than good. I thought about his fragility. How could I take care of him if he couldn't bear his own weight? How would I get him to the bathroom or shower? How would I dress him? I knew I could do a lot, but I couldn't hold him up. With the family here and Roger in a frail state, how was I going to pull this off?

Day +517

It was the weekend and I hated weekends. We ended up seeing the infamous on-call doctors filling in for our regular doctors. Most of the time they did nothing but come in and say, "Wow, so much is going on. I'll leave the big decisions for Monday." They did quick heart and lung checks with their stethoscopes and say, "Hang in there," then out they'd go. I don't know why they come in to tell us *nothing.*

I looked at them, and in my head, I was saying, *So that was a waste of 325 of my dollars.* It had happened with two other doctors already that morning. I just sat, crossed my legs and stared at them, then smiled and shook their hands when they left. But to my surprise, the lung doctor came in and earned his money. The pulmonary group had it going on.

He pulled out the results of the CT scan and explained that the right lung was now open and producing oxygen like it was supposed to. But a cyst had burst, which had caused a leak in the wall of the lung into the lining sac where the empyema was. He showed us the CT scan, pointing and explaining that there were a few cysts in the lung right now, but in time they should dissolve. He looked at the canister collecting puss and showed us the air bubbles floating to the top every time Roger took a breath. I hadn't noticed the bubbles. He said it had just happened in the last 36 hours, and explained that in two to three days, it should seal itself off and told us not to worry too much about it. He said, "Roger, your IGG level is still really low. I've ordered two doses to be given back-to-back in the next day or two. I'm not restarting the Tacrolimus yet because the pseudomonas feeds on it, but unfortunately your liver needs it." He sat staring at us for a moment, perplexed. He said, "I'm still contemplating this one." Wow, no one had ever told us that before! He told us he was very familiar with transplant patients and their medications and that he had transplanted lungs in his practice. He explained that Rog's lungs were still full of pseudomonas and it had caused a thickening in the lining of the lower right lung. He was going to double up on the antibiotics and said Rog would be in the hospital for a least another seven days and would be going home on IV antibiotics that would need to be administered three times a day for four to six weeks. He then said, "Basically, Roger, you're standing on the edge of a cliff leaning over and we're hoping you don't fall off."

The nurse walked in soon after and boastfully said, "You want to get up and get out of this room?"

Roger stared at me and I said, "He can't. He can't support his own weight."

She smiled, left the room, and soon returned with a toy called a Sara Assist. She said, "Well, I've got a cure for that." She helped Rog sit on the side of the bed. With this machine, the patient puts both feet on a platform with their knees slightly bent, resting against a padded plate. There was a hand bar grip in front of the patient, allowing them to pull themselves up with their arms then a little seat swings around so they can sit against it. The legs are slightly bent in a comfortably seated position. You can then wheel them around, including to the bathroom and shower – you just move the seat and they sit down on the toilet, pull themselves up a few inches then back onto the swivel seat. It only takes one person to situate the patient on the seat. It was remarkable! Whoever invented this machine should win a Nobel Prize. Roger was so happy!

The nurse pushed him around the halls while I pushed the IV poles with the suction canister hanging from the side of the Sara Assist. She said, "Now, kind of shift your weight from the right leg to the left leg like you're rocking a baby in your arms. How do you feel?"

Roger said, "Invigorated!"

She said, "We're moving some blood in that tall body of yours." I was so happy for him and told her I wanted one. She said, "For the low price of $5,000.00, you can have one of your own." We were shocked! Such a great tool, but who can afford it?

After a while, the nurse left us and I wheeled Rog all over. We talked and enjoyed the newfound freedom.

That night I got upset with Rog. He was using the urinal while lying in bed. They had taken his Foley catheter out a couple of days prior and he would just pee in the urinal then hang it on the side of the railing for me to dump. He was getting lazy with all of us doting over him. He had been saying, "I need this. Get me that. Dump this. Move my pillows. Straighten my covers. Close the blind. Cut up my food." His mind was clear, and he was back to eating and drinking and playing with the remote again – and he was getting demanding.

I told him, "You need to try to sit on the side of the bed to pee. Do you hear yourself? You've gotten a little demanding and you're starting to frustrate me."

The next time he peed, he did a great job! No problems at all sitting on the side of the bed to do his business. I was proud of him and gave him a thumbs up.

I stepped out to get some tea and asked the nurse how he did when I wasn't there. She said, "He does everything himself."

I said, "*Really*? So, you don't fluff his pillows, cut up his food and straighten his covers?"

She said, "Nope. You might want to think about being gone a bit more. He's doing pretty good. Take some time for yourself. Go home and get a nice shower. I promise I'll take care of him!" We high-fived.

The x-ray department showed up for a quick chest x-ray. I took a walk around the unit, thinking about what the nurse said. He was in the hospital, pretty stable, ornery to the core, and in good hands. I decided I was going home the next day and was so excited!

Day +518

It was a Sunday, and the only doctor that came in with news was our lung doctor. He sat down and explained that the chest x-ray was showing a bigger pneumothorax from the air leak. He said, "I'm not worried about it yet. I restarted the Tacrolimus, lowered the steroids, and I'm keeping the antibiotics the same." He said he was still on the fence about the medications and the leak still had not sealed itself, so the chest tubes had to stay in place until it did. He explained it was still a waiting game.

I told Roger I needed to go home to get some things done since the kids were arriving soon. I needed to shop and get the house ready. Rog had the same nurse from yesterday, thank goodness. I told her I was taking her up on her offer; I go home and she takes over.

She said, "Fun! I will whip him into shape for ya."

He looked at me and the nurse, clasped his hands together over his chest and said, "Okay, are you coming back tonight?"

I said, "Yes, but it will be late."

The nurse said, "Well, looks like you're stuck with me." I got my things together, kissed him and headed out.

After running errands, I took a long hot shower and got back to the hospital at 11:30 p.m. The night nurse still hadn't shown up with Roger's medications and he was pissed. He said, "I'm glad you're back. Go tell her not to bring the Lasix now, I'm not taking it. I'm not staying up all night peeing!"

I said, "Well, hello, I missed you too." I kissed him and he asked what I did all day. I went over my day and asked about his. He said it was fine. I asked if the nurse had helped him.

He said, "By the time she answered my call light, I had already done it myself, so I really didn't need her." I almost busted up laughing since I understood what she had done.

I asked, "So you were able to take care of your needs by yourself?"

He said, "I had to. She didn't come when I told her to!" I looked at him and he said, "What?" Right then the night nurse came in and started with the evening medication and IV changes.

I said, "Don't bring the Lasix, he won't take it. He doesn't want to pee all night." She was okay with that. It had been a long day for both of us so we snuggled in for a good night's sleep.

Day +521

Roger finally started showing signs of improvement with the new antibiotic, Meropenem, but it was causing his platelets to fall a bit. All his other labs were pretty good. The days seemed to be melding into one. Roger was getting physically stronger and was able to support his own weight better with the help of two therapists. He still used the urinal but wouldn't poop in a bed pan, so he got up for that with the help of the Sara Assist.

At noon our lung doctor came in and said the empyema was pretty much gone. What was left was a few cysts and a very spongy, unhealthy lung which would need to be protected for a while. Unfortunately, the chest tube had moved and was now causing the pneumothorax to increase in size. Rog had been having more discomfort on that side. The doc told us he would have to replace the tube and would do so right there at the bedside.

After loading Roger up with some pain medications and a series of numbing injections into his ribs, he pulled the old chest tube out, put a few stitches in then stabbed him with a scalpel, making a hole for the new tube. He stuck his finger in the hole and carved out a tunnel to place the new tube a few inches higher. His confidence was impressive, but Roger wasn't having as much fun as I was. He, like always, was stoic and dealing with the pain. His face was scrunched up, his teeth were clenched, and his hands were trying to bend the bedrails in two. I hated that he had to go through this. I asked how he was doing, he asked how much longer, and with that, the tube was stitched into place and the doctor said, "Done!"

Roger paid the price all night. He was so sore! I made sure he had two pain pills every three hours around the clock. He had trouble moving in the bed and repositioning himself. I helped him all night so neither of us got any sleep. It seemed whenever he started feeling good, something happened and his joy was gone in a heartbeat. It was a long night.

Day +522

At 5:50 a.m., Roger woke me up, calling my name with a very weak voice. I looked up and he was at the foot of the bed with the bed controls in his hand, doubled over. I jumped up and said, "What are you doing?" There was diarrhea all over him and the floor.

He said, "I need to go potty." He was trying to move toward the bathroom, but the chest tube was preventing him from moving forward.

I said, "Wait, you cannot walk without the walker and you're still connected to the chest tube canister." He showed me what was in his hands – he had thought it was the canister.

Right then he fell onto the bed and started seizing. I yelled for help and leaned against him so he wouldn't fall to the floor, but no one came! I reached over and pulled the light cord. His eyelids were flickering, and his head was arched back. It took everything I had to keep him on the bed. His legs were over the side and only his body from his waist up was on the bed. I yelled for help again and finally someone came. The seizure was slowing down, but lasted about two minutes. The nurse pushed the emergency button on the way in and a team arrived. I was yelling Roger's name, and he finally came to and said groggily, "I have to go to the bathroom." Stool was everywhere. He had no clue that a team of people were working on him. They got him up on the bed and lowered the head of the bed. His B/P was 88/42 but his sats were 100%. Finally, when he was somewhat stable, the ER doctor arrived and did an assessment. Roger kept asking to go to the bathroom as he tried to sit up against all the hands holding him down.

Finally, they sat him on the side of the bed, and he tried to stand up against everyone holding him down. He passed out again and started seizing. It was at this point I noticed the chest tube. I said, "The chest tube is full of blood."

The nurse said, "He had his chest tube replaced this morning. It's residual."

I looked at her and said, "No, it's not. He had it replaced at 1:00 p.m. yesterday for a pneumothorax. No blood, no puss, no fluid. And that was over 16 hours ago. This happened since we've been asleep tonight!" I leaned over the top of him and yelled his name over and over and he woke up again but was disoriented. The ER doctor left the room and was on the phone. Roger tried to get up again, and again he passed out. The male CNAs were trying to hold him down. He finally went limp. His B/P dropped to 70/40 and his pupils had dilated. The ICU doctor ran into the room with a gurney, an 02 tank and a crash cart. Roger was breathing. They got him onto the gurney and rushed him to the CT scanner, along with two male CNAs and the crash cart. I was once again left in the room alone, having a panic attack. My heart was beating out of my chest and I couldn't get my breath. I bent over and put my hands on the bed until I calmed down. A CNA came into the room, put her hand on my back, and handed me a cup of ice water, asking if I was okay.

I said, "Help me clean this up before he comes back. He should be back in a minute."

She said, "I'm not sure he's coming back here."

I said, "HELP ME clean this up before he gets back please." She let go of me and started helping me clean up. Together we cleaned up the stool, changed the bed and got it ready for him.

At 8:00 a.m., Roger returned with his pulmonologist. He had been sedated and was out. The doctor told me that the CT showed more damage to the right lung and now there was a large blood pocket where the tip of the chest tube was. The blood pocket actually sealed off the air leak, so that was gone now. He explained that the area where the tip of the chest tube was, was close to one of the cysts and it looked like it caused it to burst. He said the area around the cyst was necrotic, dead, and was possibly why it burst. He said that Roger was to rest; no getting up and they would just monitor him over the next few days.

At 11:00 a.m., Roger woke up. I was outside the room when Roger decided to get up to go to the bathroom. I heard him, went into the room, and he was on the floor seizing. I dropped the phone, yelled for help, and started yelling his name again. The nurse was in the room in seconds and helped me with his head until his seizure passed, which was about 30 seconds. The team was back, and everyone lifted him into bed. They lowered the head of the bed and he laid there until he came to a few minutes later. His B/P had dropped again but all other vital signs were good. The doctor arrived and asked Roger what he was doing.

Roger said in a confused voice, "I have to go to the bathroom."

The doctor said, "Have you gone since the last time you got me in here?"

Everyone said, "No."

He said, "Get the man a damn bed pan – now!" All that came out was a lot of gas. Roger had seven people watching him pass gas, and I was a mess.

Roger said, "I'm done, did I go?" Everyone said, "Yes!" at the same time. I wanted to strangle him and hug him. He settled down and went to sleep. The doctor was pissed. They put a Posey jacket on Rog and tied him to the bed. I was beside myself, but Roger didn't fight it. I don't think he even knew he was tied to the bed. He slept for hours.

Day +524

After a few hours of sleep, I finally got an update on the chest tube. At the time of the insertion, the doctor punctured the lung so the chest tube was draining blood from the lung, hence the blood in the canister. Roger's blood levels dropped to 19, which should be 42. He was pale, short of breath, and had no energy to move. He was given two units of blood which sent him into an energy frenzy. He wanted pen and paper, and he was bound and determined to figure out his mom's estate. I wasn't sure why he needed to do this and where the energy was coming from, but I supplied the pen and paper. When he took a break from it, I glanced at his progress, and although his writing wasn't legible, he seemed to know what it said. He rattled off all kinds of ways to fix the problems. After a while, I just sat back on my bed and watched him talk to himself. There was no therapy.

I spent the day trying to figure out how to get through the upcoming visit with all the kids in three days. I called Todd and asked again for the favor of spending the night with Dad. He said sure and would be there tomorrow.

As Roger wrote on and on, I watched him and reminisced about our lives together. When we first met, he wore pressed Carhart pants and long-sleeved dress shirts. He meticulously ironed his pants each day and rolled up the shirt sleeves each morning to make a nice, crisp, five-fold pattern so the sleeve rested mid-forearm. He wore leather shoes and a tight belt to finish off the look. He reminded me of a man used to a dress code, a uniform. Even though he was retired, he had still worn this very clean, proper look in his new job.

He went from that to seizing, pooping himself, and being put in a straightjacket tied to the bed, then to sitting up in bed, frantically writing with not a care in the world. It was unbelievable. I looked at him and just couldn't seem to wrap my head around all of this. The man was an enigma, to say the least.

Day +525

The CDC doctor came in and said, "The chest tube and the blood leak have sealed off the infection and it's now growing again. Roger's white blood cell count is rising either because the infection is growing, from the blood transfusion, or simply because of the trauma from the chest tube insertion, we're not sure yet. The liver is no longer an issue, but the pseudomonas has become really problematic and is serous. We'll be keeping a close watch on it, but for now, we wait. All we can do is wait." She left with a half-smile and a pat on Roger's toe.

Todd showed up, and Roger was so happy. I kissed Rog goodnight, told them to call if they needed me then left the boys alone to catch up.

I called the kids and told them that most likely Roger would be in the hospital when they arrived. I explained the infection, the chest tubes, and how frail he was. I questioned them on how long they were staying. They would stay with me a few nights, with Todd for a week, with their mom for a week then back to us for a few nights. I was happy they decided not to stay the whole three weeks with us. I just didn't know how I would have been able to handle it. At the last minute, they called and decided to stay with their mom first.

Day +526

I didn't return to the hospital until 2:00 p.m. I had slept in and took another long, hot shower. When I arrived, both boys were glad to see me. Todd hadn't told me that he had to work night shift that night. On the outside I was sorry, on the inside I was, *You're young, you can handle it!* Before he left, he told me Rog had had an uneventful night and morning.

Roger's chest tube was still draining blood, but very little. He ate well and was ornery and joking. Sometimes he made sense and sometimes he didn't. There was no rhyme or reason for it. I just had to pay attention a little more closely now. It was an uneventful night.

Day +527

In the morning, Roger wanted to shower, shave and put on his own clean clothes so I helped him with that. I was so thankful for the Sara Assist! I was able to take care of his hygiene needs without help.

After breakfast I headed home, and the kids had already arrived. The nurses had Roger taken care of so I decided to stay home and hang with the grandkids while the adults went to visit with Rog.

At midnight I called the kids at the hospital. They were all hunkered down, watching late night TV with Dad. He'd had a great day of reminiscing. They had a few questions regarding Roger's care because Rog had confused them a bit on the sequence of events and what was going on now with his infection. I cleared up the confusion. The adults had decided to stay with him overnight. They found chairs to sleep in and made out my little couch bed. I was beside myself with joy and exhaustion since I'd been up since 4:00 a.m.

Day +528

I could tell when the kids left the hospital that they were a little uncomfortable at how much their dad had deteriorated since the last time they had seen him. Craig asked how long he had been confused like this. I asked Craig what had happened, and he explained that Dad's time and day was off and he talked about things that never happened. He said Rog was looking for Todd on his phone for 20 minutes before they could get him to understand that he was in the room with them. I tried to explain that this had been going on for a while, and more so since the pseudomonas outbreak. I explained this was the reason I stayed with him as much as possible.

I asked Roger how his visit was, and he said it was great! He said he wished he could have seen Todd though. I reminded him that Todd was here and spent the night with him too. He just looked at me. He was tired from all the conversation and the excitement of all the kids so I climbed up in bed with him and let him fall asleep.

Day +529

This morning the hospital had a fantastic surprise for me – Home Health. They interviewed us and said they would be coming to the house two times a week to give Roger physical therapy, blood draws and do his dressing changes. I wouldn't have to drive him into the clinic twice a week now. I was so thankful! This would be the first time I had gotten help. I was especially thankful for the physical therapy. He was able to stand on his feet and support his weight, but his ability to walk further than a yard or two was out of the question. His legs buckled and down he went. He had gained a few pounds back since he'd been eating four times a day here at the hospital. They were also supplementing him with in-between meal snacks of yogurt, cottage cheese, fruit and protein drinks. At home he wouldn't eat like this, which was so strange. I fed him all the same things and even gave him things to choose from. All he would say is, "I'm not hungry."

I thought about Roger's slow decline and I wondered how much longer I would have with him. As time went by and with each doctor's visit, I could hear in their voices and see in the physician's eyes that it was getting harder and harder on Roger to continue to keep up with these heroic measures. I was beginning to realize each hospital stay was not a victory, just an extension. I was realizing that I needed to be honest with myself – I didn't have a lot of time left with him. I was losing my will to fight for him, and started feeling the need to let go for Roger's sake. I didn't want to continue to fight to keep him alive if he only recovered long enough to get even sicker the next time, which was what had been happening. Sometimes I fell into a depression about everything, feeling sorry for myself.

2

Trying To Stay One Step Ahead

It was Day +535, and Roger had come home a few days earlier. Home Health was out twice. The first time it was for signing the agreement papers and a million and one questions about health history and a medication review. No therapy. The second time, the nurse spent so much time catching up on how Roger "feels" and taking blood, she didn't have time to do a dressing change. I explained to her that I had been doing it for a while and would take care of it. She called her boss who told her to do the dressing change and not leave it for me. After she hung up, she looked at me and I said, "I have your back, go. Don't make the next person wait. I got this." She was grateful and left. No therapy.

Day +537

This morning our family doctor's office called to tell us that Roger's potassium levels were low and that we needed to increase his potassium to two tablets a day. It struck me funny and pissed me off at the same time that this doctor called wanting to regulate his medications. He had seen Rog once in a year and at that office visit he sent him home on a decongestant. I said yes, he just got out of the hospital, thank you.

I was now giving Rog an IV antibiotic medication push three times a day. I had bags and bags of IV flushes, boxes of vials of antibiotics and dressing change materials that I was now responsible for doing. I bought a plastic three-drawer unit to put everything into. Roger just sat and watched TV while I injected him. He had gotten so used to it that most of the time I don't think he even realized I was giving him IV medications.

Day +538

Rog was finally getting stronger. Up until now he needed help getting out of his chair, but at one point I came into the living room and couldn't find him. How did he get out of his chair? I found him on the toilet. I was shocked and said, "How did you get in here?"

He replied, "I walked in here. I used my walker." I had bought him a walker and it had sat in the corner for weeks now. I was just amazed!

That afternoon, I realized Rog was doing things he didn't remember doing. I found the bottle of Ativan in his chair and I couldn't find any of the phone charges. I had one plugged in every room; bathroom, kitchen, bedroom and family room. Where did they all go? I had spent about 45 minutes in the office paying bills and while I was doing that, Roger became the little green monster, scurrying around the house, collecting his trinkets; Ativan, phone chargers and candy. I found them under his tablet, all curled up as if he were packing them to take on a trip. I asked, "What are you doing? Is there a reason you collected all the phone chargers and wrapped them up and stored them here?" He looked at me as if I was asking him a strange question. He didn't know how they got there. I unrolled them and plugged them all back in.

It was a long evening and night. All night he tinkered with his water and urinal. He was moving them to different places as if he was hiding them then re-hiding them, especially if he saw me watching him. I couldn't get him to go to bed. He was having an OCD moment that lasted three hours. There was nothing I could do to get him to stop. He finally got tired, lie down and fell asleep.

3

Organization Is a Talent

It was now day +539, and so far the IV antibiotics and the insulin injections, along with getting a handful of medications down three times a day, was going well. Just keeping everything straight was a chore for me. I set my alarm to go off six times during the day to help me stay on schedule.

Roger's back was killing him. I knew it was his posture. He was hunched over while he walked, with his upper body two steps in front of the rest of his body. I got out the electric massager I had gotten from my chiropractor and put it on his back. He just moaned with pleasure and said thank you a dozen times. It helped for a few hours then the pain came back. I massaged him again and again until he'd had enough. I wasn't sure if it was a good idea to do a deep massage over the top of his lungs, but he said it felt so much better after each session.

We had our first real fight today. Roger demanded ALL his medications so he could organize them. I asked how he was going to organize them and he said, "I want all my medications in one bottle, all together. There are a lot of medications in the cabinet and in that bag. I want to go through them and put them in one jar so there aren't so many bottles."

I said, "They're all different medications. We can't put them in one bottle."

He said, "I want to organize them in case of an emergency we can have them all in one place. Give them to me!"

I lost it! I said, "NO, I am not giving you all the medications in this house to put into one bottle! I have them very organized, and a lot of these meds you don't even take anymore. The blue bag is the emergency bag. If we need to leave immediately, I grab that one. The red bag is all the excess that you don't take right now. The daily pill box has the medications you're taking throughout the day."

He was livid! He got up abruptly and headed toward me. When he did, four bottles fell out of his chair; his Ativan, OxyContin, Oxycodone and Valium. I wasn't sure what he was going to do coming toward me like he was, but the bottles falling startled him. As he looked down, I dodged around him and got the bottles. Needless to say, it wasn't pretty. He slammed his arms to his sides and made fists. He wanted them back and I wouldn't give them to him. I asked why he needed these in his chair, but he just stared at me. He finally turned around and sat back down.

Five minutes later he said, "I'm hungry," then he said, "I want to shower."

I said, "Which do you want first – dinner or shower?" He said he wanted to eat so I made him some chicken, rice and veggies. He played with the food, ate a little and asked for a shower. After the shower he ate the rest of his dinner.

At 9:00 p.m., his back began to hurt again. I gave him a massage and put him to bed. I decided to read a bit. Fifteen minutes after we got in bed, he turned over and used his urinal then dumped it all over his side of the bed. Thank goodness I had put a pad under him. It caught the liquid without getting on the mattress. I wanted to yell at him for not getting up, but I just went through the motions of helping him out of bed, cleaning him up and helping him redress. I changed the linens and we got back in bed.

Day +540

It started all over again this morning with Rog wanting to organize things. He took the computer bags and went around the house and put everything he thought he needed in the bags; flashlights, phone chargers, pens, pencils, glasses, batteries, and a bunch of other things. He spent a few hours doing this and then hid them. I waited until he was engrossed in his shows before I got the bags, unloaded them and put everything back.

I had been looking for a lift recliner chair and a hospital bed for the house. Off and on he'd had trouble with his chair so I thought the lift chair would be nice for him. He wouldn't have to work so hard to get the footrest down. He was still having problems getting out of our bed too. I found both a hospital bed and a chair for $400.00, which was a great deal. The chair alone retailed for over $2,000. I told him I had found them and was waiting for the lady to call me back. He said, "I am not buying them!"

I asked, "Why are you fighting this? It will allow you to get up and out of bed and your chair easier. It raises up and down, and the head of the bed goes up and down. It will be easier to watch TV and breathe." Why the refusal? He had been falling into bed, and I had to manually spin him around then raise each leg and place it over the waterbed frame. If he ended up too low in the bed, that was another 30 minutes to help him move up.

He said, "Because you won't be next to me, for one—"

I interrupted, "That's not fair."

He said, "And second, it's like giving up."

I said, "No, it's a tool that's going to make life easier on both of us, like using a hammer drill instead of a regular drill. The hammer drill makes it easier to set the screw. The bed will make it easier on both of us to get you in and out of bed. If your lungs get sick again, the head of the bed goes up to help you breathe instead of me constantly propping you up on pillows all night. It's a tool, period!"

He said, "We'll see." I was beside myself.

The physical therapist came today, staying for about 20 minutes. She said Roger's walker was too low and he needed an extension that I could buy at the medical supply house, and this was probably why his back was hurting so much. I had no idea there were extensions available for the walkers. I don't think I had ever seen someone this tall using a walker that had extensions on it. I wished someone would have told me this sooner! She watched him walk nine laps around the kitchen island, get exhausted, and sit down. I told her with just a shower and me doing all the work, this kind of exhaustion happened. She said, "It will for a long time. Just take everything slow. But I want you to go get the extensions tomorrow."

Day +541

This was an outing day. I needed to go grocery shopping and run a few errands. I asked Rog if he wanted to go. He did so we went to the medical supply store first to get the extensions for his walker. When I got to the grocery store, he decided he wanted to stay in the truck. He said, "I'm not using a walker in the store, only at home. I don't feel up to walking right now." When I returned 35 minutes later, he had cleaned out the jockey box and the glove box. He had everything he didn't want in a small trash bag and everything else was wrapped up in rubber bands and any string he'd found. Everything was in a wad and a mess. Rog held up the trash bag and wanted me to throw it away now. I took it and walked to the trashcan outside the grocery store where Roger couldn't see me. He had thrown away two full magazines to his Glock pistol, my sunglasses, pens, two pocket knives, the little manual booklet for the truck, and a bunch of change. I flattened the bag the best I could and shoved it in the back of my pants under my shirt. Thankfully, I wear baggy shirts so he never knew. I put all the stuff back later.

When we got home, Roger got his two computer bags, sat down, and started pulling everything out of the bags. He had done this twice before. When I wasn't paying attention, he opened one of the laptops and fussed with it, then told me it was broken and to throw it away. It was my computer! I said, "What do you mean it's broken?" It had everything on it; our life and pictures, videos, my doctorate thesis, banking, all our correspondence. Somehow, he had crashed my computer! Roger, who built the new Sheriff's Department computer system and computer room had just crashed my computer within 45 seconds of opening it. I was freaking out inside. He started to open the second laptop, his laptop, and I took it from him, grabbing it right out of his hands and said, "Oh no, Rog. I need this computer. You cannot use it right now." He said it was his and he wanted it. I looked him right in the eye and said, "NO, YOU CANNOT HAVE THE COMPUTER!" He got mad and started to get up so I said it again. This time I added, "You crashed my computer, Roger, in 45 seconds, and told me to throw it away, our important computer with everything on it. ROGER, you crashed the computer. You don't crash computers, you fix them. NO!" It sank in. He looked at me and said he was sorry then started taking everything out of his bag to organize it. I took the computers upstairs and hid them.

After Roger had wound everything into a ball and taped it all up with electrical tape as well as throwing away a bunch of stuff in the trash next to him, I had dinner ready. He wasn't eating much again. His mind seemed to be somewhere else, and his behavior was neurotic. He wanted to organize everything, unfortunately, his organization didn't make since. It was like he was obsessed so I waited for him to fall asleep then snuck out of bed, checked all the trash cans and put everything back in its place. He wasn't even aware of what he was doing.

I laid there in bed, awake, staring at the ceiling just wanting to cry. He was losing his mind. It was the one thing that we had both expressed as the worst possible ending to life – losing your mind and making everyone around you want to put you in a home. We told each other that we would never let that happen, and talked about different ways to help each other out. I laid there and realized it was easier said than done. There was no way I could ever follow through on any of the ideas we had talked about. I loved him so much and never wanted him to leave me!

Day +542

We saw the pulmonologist for a follow-up chest x-ray. Roger got up early and took his own shower while I sat in the bathroom and waited for him to get out. When he did, he was out of breath. I asked him to just stand still while I dried him off and helped him dress. He ate scrambled eggs, yogurt and a protein drink.

Our lung doctor said the x-ray looked better than the one from discharge, but the damage had been done. He said Roger had had this infection for a while. This infection had taken over his immune system and became the "King of the Systems." He explained that this infection would be what took him down in the end. He told Roger he needed to build up his strength and muscle mass. Only then would his body have a fighting chance. He said he would ask Dr. Moros to order Roger testosterone shots to help with muscle growth. He also told Roger that his intake of food needed to be increased whether he wanted food or not. He asked, "Roger, does your body need food to survive?" Roger nodded. He said, "Then eat, no matter what, just do it!" This upset me because Roger knew what he needed to do; but when he got home, he didn't do the work to keep his body strong. I didn't get it!

Day +547

Roger had been walking around the house and doing more for himself over the last few days, slowly building up a little stamina and not getting winded as much.

This day we saw the CDC doctor. Roger liked her and so did I. I was interested in finding out how many more days of IV medications he had. She came in and said her pleasantries then got to the point. "I saw your chest x-ray; it's not better but it's not worse. You need to stay on the IV meds for at least two more months. After you have your CT scan on the 12th, I'll know better about future plans." She asked Roger how he had been feeling, and he told her he was having really bad back pain. She said, "It's not back pain, its transference pain from that right lung. Like when you have gallbladder or liver problems, you have right shoulder pain. The back pain is not going to get better, but I will prescribe you lidocaine patches." Unbelievable! His back pain was so bad I had been giving him Valium and pain pills all day it seemed, and it was getting worse by the day. No one told us that this pain was coming from the lung. I learned something new every single day!

By 7:00 p.m. the lidocaine patch seemed to be working. He said it cut the ache down to being tolerable, and he was moving more and with ease. It would be great if they worked, not only with the pain but also with the constipation that the pain pills caused. Those damn pain pills were causing a lot of other problems as well, most likely the cause of a lot of his confusion.

Day +548

I dragged myself up at 6:45 a.m. Rog had IVIG and an office visit with Dr. Moros. It would be an all-day'er in the clinic. I had packed most of our stuff to take with us last night. I made Rog a nice breakfast and we headed out.

Dr. Moros didn't do much. He went over the potassium regimen, telling Rog he needed to take in as much potassium and protein in his food as possible. I had tried making him smoothies with bananas, kale, spinach, carrot juice and honey for lunches along with his protein drinks. It seemed to be easier to drink his food versus chewing it. His potassium, with all that intake, was 3.2, and normal is 4.0. His problem was that the Lasix and Fludrocortisone were robbing his body of potassium. I explained that Roger's leg and feet had been swelling and he had no feeling in them. He added his Metoprolol back, saying his heart rate and blood pressure was up again. It had been up since he was put on the extra steroid. Dr. Moros explained that after the CT scan on the 12th, all the doctors would reconvene and decide on what was next for the lungs. It could be to continue antibiotics or decortication of the lungs, a procedure to remove the outer lining of the lung or peripheral sack. They were also considering debridement of the lung or more drains. I knew there was no way he could go through the decortication surgery.

He asked Rog how he was doing. Roger said, "I'm pretty tired." I explained his confusion and his need to organize and hide things. Dr. Moros explained the "Brain Fog Syndrome" and that time was the only cure for some.

When we got home, I asked Rog how he was feeling and he said he was feeling better each day, but he seemed more confused, doing the same things over and over, becoming obsessed with this pattern. Maybe he was just bored. It was driving me crazy but as long as I could find what was missing, what he'd hid, for the most part I just let him be.

Day +554

Over the next few days Rog seemed to be getting a little stronger. He was leaving his walker and taking his own dishes to the kitchen, slowly rocking side to side but maintained his balance. He seemed more motivated and kept asking me to look at his legs all the time. "Look, they're getting bigger and stronger!" Stronger, yes. Bigger, no. He was carrying more water weight in his feet, but his legs were skinny and scaly. For some reason, he was getting big red spots, like bruises, all over his body, and getting more confused as the days went by. It was getting harder for me to be happy for him. I watched him suffer with back pain, no sleep and confusion. His everyday activities were so hard for him.

I got a letter from our insurance company saying they would no longer pay the full amount for the Tacrolimus medication next year, they would only pay 30%. Our insurance premium was also doubling in price. I was going to have to sit down and really study this insurance problem and look into finding another company. I had a feeling his illness would prevent us from being eligible elsewhere, and I might have to drop my health insurance to be able to afford his. If I couldn't figure something out, his doctors would drop him if we couldn't pay. This really scared me the most. By the time Rog left this earth, I would be left with nothing. I had to figure something out. The problem was, every direction I turned, the doors keep shutting on me. It was getting so frustrating and exhausting!

Day +556

The day didn't start out well. Every time Rog tried to eat, within minutes he would throw up. I asked when he'd had his last bowel movement and he couldn't remember. He wouldn't drink any fluids, saying they wouldn't stay down. Most of the day I tried to help him go to the bathroom, trying warm prune juice and stool softeners. He didn't have a bulging anus like he did when he was constipated, but he was uncomfortable. I tried to feel for an impaction, but wasn't able to feel one. He had active bowel sounds so I put a heating pad on his stomach, trying anything to get it to settle down. He was having a lot of pain in his belly and upper GI area. At 8:00 p.m., he went to bed with two pain pills. He was up all night trying to have a bowel movement. It was a long night with back and upper right abdominal pain. He kept belching long, loud belches and the only thing he wanted to do was have a bowel movement, but the straining only caused dizziness then back to bed with no results. Neither of us slept.

4

No More Heroics

The morning of day +557, Roger tried to get out of bed but got so dizzy he started falling over. Whenever he tried to get out of bed, the dizziness returned and his lack of equilibrium caused him to fall back onto the bed as if he had passed out. No body control, just a hard fall onto the mattress. When this first happened, I ran over to him and noticed his body was red from the waist up and he was hotter than a firecracker. His temperature was 102.4, his breathing was becoming shallow, and he was unable to help me help him get out of bed. I told him I was calling 9-1-1 and he didn't argue.

When the ambulance arrived, Roger was severely nauseated and confused. I had told the 9-1-1 officer that he was 6'7" and 200 pounds and was unable to help with his movements, and please send strong men. And they did. Four men and one woman showed up and they somehow got him out of our low bed onto a gurney. I was so thankful!

In the ER, they diagnosed him with another pulmonary embolism and bloods clots throughout both of his legs. His confusion had gotten worse also. He thought it was 2003. His breathing was labored and it required a lot of effort to get air. Our team of doctors once again arrived in the ER and started working on Rog, but this time they weren't talking about heroic measures, they were just trying to stabilize him and help him breathe. The sentiment in the ER was one of complete respect for this man trying so hard to live and wanting to just help him get comfortable. I felt it and was overwhelmed with compassion and grief at the same time.

The ER was packed and people were being sent to other hospitals. There was a flu outbreak and the hospital was full. After a very long ER stay, IVs going, and blood thinners on board, we were told he was going to need to be admitted to ICU but there was only one bed left and the ER had five people who needed that bed. I could see those five patients, and my heart and soul prayed Roger got it.

Roger was slowly going downhill. I was getting really scared and started praying out loud to get that ICU bed. I called Todd and told him to come to the hospital now. A series of medication changes were happening and his breathing was getting worse. I was being asked if they could intubate him if they needed to and what his advanced directive was. The nurses were scrambling for it in his chart. Rog wasn't awake, he had passed out. I started feeling sick and could feel the blood rushing from my head. I was going to pass out. The doctor ran around the bed and sat me down as I started crying and couldn't stop.

I fumbled with my words saying, "If he needs a ventilator because his lungs need a rest while you get them well then do it, but if that's not the case then no ventilator."

The doctors started working on Roger. A ventilator machine was brought in just in case and crash cart medications were being pumped into him. Was this it? Was this how I was going to lose him? After 30 minutes, Rog opened his eyes but wasn't present. The doctor said, "He's finally holding his own now, but this isn't going to go well. We'll monitor him through the night." A nurse fixed a station inside the room and stayed at the bedside working on the IVs, oxygen mask, and all his vitals while continuously typing on the computer between each body check. Rog was breathing better and his sats were at 91%.

At 3:00 p.m., Rog was still holding his own. His vital signs were low but still within a good range for Roger. His breathing was poor but sats were still ranging from 89-91% and the 02 mask was at 7 liters. I asked the nurse how she saw Roger's health right now. She said, "If he makes it through the night, that will be the determining factor. Right now, he's just barely hanging on."

The doctor came in and said, "His lungs are just not perfusing well. They are really sick, but we are monitoring him closely. Just pray."

Day +558

Roger made it through the night. The ICU doctor and the pulmonologist came in early and said the infection in his lungs and the PE were under control, but his pancreas had taken a hit this time. They said when he was more awake and alert they planned on doing a nuclear scan on his abdomen and pancreas then would have more answers on what to do next. In the meantime, he stayed in the ICU under observation. Our pulmonologist sat down and said, "Robin, he can't go through much more. His body is shutting down and slowly dying off. He'll probably beat this one too, but the next time he most likely won't. It's just a matter of time. I want you to consider just keeping him comfortable from here on out. No more heroics. After the scan, I'll know more but it won't change what I just said."

I just looked at him, not knowing what to say. I felt numb and had no thoughts. I just wanted to go to sleep. I was tired. I looked at Roger and he was sleeping so I told the doctor, "I want to go to sleep now." He said okay then left.

Day +560

I had lost track of time, but it was dark outside and Roger was awake. The nurses were repositioning him onto his side. One of the nurses said, "They put a catheter in Rog. They will be giving him high doses of Lasix and he won't be able to get out of bed. Other than that, he's doing better and asking about you." I asked what he needed. They said, "He wanted to know why you were sleeping and told us to wake you up. We told you needed to rest right now. He was okay with that."

I sat back against the wall and just stared at Rog. I didn't know how long I sat there, but he woke up and started pulling on his catheter. He was saying, "Hey, hey, hey." He had it in his hands and wanted me to get it out of him. I quickly got up, went to him, and told him what it was and to stop pulling on it. He said he needed to go to the bathroom. For the next hour I battled with him over it. I explained and showed him the bag of urine and that he was going to the bathroom through the tube. He understood for about five minutes then it started all over again. I started crying and told him to put it down. He looked at me and put it down. I explained, "It feels like you have to go because a little ball on the end of it is pushing against the area that makes you feel like you have to go, but you don't. If you pull it out, it will be the worst pain you've ever experienced." He just looked at me and asked me why I was crying. I said, "Rog, who am I?"

He said, "You're my nurse."

I turned around until I got my composure then said, "I'm just having a bad day, that's all." He tried to get up. I showed him that he couldn't leave his bed because of all the tubes and wires connected to him. He didn't care; he was bound and determined to get up. I yelled at him and said "Stop!" He ignored me and was on the side of his bed, about ready to fall. His nurse came in and put her hand on his chest to hold him in bed. He wasn't making any sense and didn't seem to know where he was. The nurse asked him who the President was, he didn't know, and he didn't know the year. He wanted to know why we were holding him hostage. He was becoming combative, pushing the nurses away. The doctor came in and gave him some Ativan via IV and a muscle relaxer for his bladder. They had a male CNA stay in the room until the meds took effect. After about 30 minutes, he was okay and went back to sleep. I went back to my cot and fell asleep.

After waking, I went to the waiting room and got a big cup of coffee, then went to the bathroom to wash up. I had been wearing the same underwear for a few days. I couldn't remember when I last ate, but I wasn't hungry. I sat on the toilet and tried to figure out what I needed to do first and then do next. I wished I'd had a piece of paper and pencil with me.

Someone knocked on the bathroom door and I woke up. I guess I had fallen asleep! I said, "Just a minute!" and got my coffee and took a drink, but it was cold. When I opened the door, the ICU nurses were there to take me back to Roger's room. They didn't say anything, just took my hand and walked me back. There was food and more coffee waiting for me. I cried and said, "Thank you!"

Roger was awake and alert. He looked at me and asked me to come to his bed. He asked, "What's wrong?"

I started crying harder, grabbed ahold of him and said, "Are you okay? He said yes and asked me again what was wrong. He just pulled me in tighter and held me as I cried. We laid there for a while together before the tech came in to get Rog for his CT scan.

The CDC doctor came in and said, "The scan shows that Roger's gallbladder is working at only 10%, and the pancreas is enlarged. It took the biggest hit this time. There's nothing we can do for the pancreas." I asked if GVHD was a cause. She said she didn't know and they weren't planning on testing for it either. I asked about the pulmonary embolism and the lungs, and she said they looked just as bad today as they had on the last scan, but the PE was resolving itself. She said, "I also did an HHV6 culture on his spinal fluid right after the scan and it was negative." A nurse walked in and handed her his latest lab results. She looked at me with raised eyebrows and a little laugh and said, "His numbers are almost back to normal. This man is an enigma, to say the least. Okay then, the plan is to have him rest a couple more days, go home on a higher dose of Prednisone, and an antacid and blood thinners again." I asked if I could just give him Enoxaparin injections so we didn't have to deal with running to the lab every other day for bloodwork. She said, "Absolutely!"

The pulmonologist came in shortly after the CDC doctor left. He was much more blunt with me. He asked me out into the hallway. He said, "Roger is just going to progressively go downhill, a small rollercoaster ride down. We all feel it's best to just give comfort care from now on. No more heroic measures. His body has taken so many hits that it's a miracle he's survived this long."

I started crying, and he just stood and looked at me. I said, "It's not fair! They all doted over him, telling him this transplant was the cure, he was going to get better and that everything was going to be just fine. They told us if he made it 30 days, then 45 days, then 100 days, all these mile markers were hope for a healthy future. Well, it was all a lie! I read the studies, all the studies they didn't tell us about when they gave him that pen and told him it was the only cure, to just sign the papers. It was all for the next generation of leukemia patients, not for Roger. They're making the mistakes on Roger so the next group receives better treatment. They use him like a guinea pig! Like a lab rat, watching him falter at all the tests, giving him crap that just made him worse. Why? There's nothing that shows the Philadelphia Positive ALL men over the age of 50 make it. Why didn't they just tell us that and if we chose to participate in the study, it was only for the benefit of all the men in the future? What does comfort care mean anyway? Just keep him home and fill him with narcotics until he dies? Is that what you are asking me to do?"

The doctor was backtracking with his words, but I wasn't listening. I sat on the floor and just cried. He sat down with me and didn't say a thing, he just sat there and handed me tissues.

Dr. Moros came in a few minutes later with a nurse. He started telling me the same thing the pulmonary doctor did. I just stared at him. He said he was sorry and asked me if there was anything he could do.

I said, "I don't know how you do what you do, knowing what you know, and live with yourself." He said it didn't always turn out like this. I said, "It does if you have Philadelphia Positive Acute Lymphoblastic Leukemia, and you knew that."

He said, "I'm glad it's rare. One only sees a patient or two in my practice in a lifetime.

5

Trying To Keep My Sanity

By day +566, Roger's lab numbers had returned to normal pretty quickly, normal for Roger that is. As soon as they did, he was out the door. We were back home now, and he was doing pretty well except for the water retention in his legs and feet. The last two nights they had swelled up to one-inch and were pitting when I pressed on them. They were freezing cold and he pretty much couldn't feel them. I'd been having him keep them up and covered with warm blankets all day. He gained seven pounds in the hospital but, as usual, we came home and he didn't want to eat. I could only get him to eat about half a cup of food three times a day. I just didn't get it! I asked him why this was since I fed him exactly what they gave him. He said he didn't know. I asked him if he understood that he had to eat, and he said yes. I had been giving him protein drinks all day long with whatever I could put into a blender for him to drink instead of chew. He was back to TV and sitting all day so it was good that he was on a strong blood thinner.

Day +572

Roger was holding his own. He could walk short distances to the bathroom, but that was all. His weight had dropped to 194. He was taking in food but not enough to maintain his weight. I had to balance his water pills and his potassium pills carefully so as not to dehydrate him since it was so easy to do. I was giving him a water pill every third day per the doctor's orders, and a potassium pill every day. Even if his lungs became wet and he started to become short of breath, I waited, and on the third day he peed all day. I finally got him a wheelchair although he wasn't too thrilled about it. Since we got it, he started grocery shopping with me; I pushed him and he pushed the grocery cart. He had fun! I cracked up watching him maneuver the cart around people and down the aisles. He said, "I can handle you pushing me faster." So I did. It was a new game, and it was so nice not having to power shop and forget things all the time. Now we could take our time.

I had a long talk with Roger and told him I thought it would a good idea if we moved to Mom's house since she had passed away. He agreed. He was doing so well that I asked him if he wanted to go to the movies. He said he couldn't sit in one of the chairs, it would be too hard on his back. I said, "You'll sit in the wheelchair. There are wheelchair spaces."

He said, "What if I have to pee?"

I said, "We'll bring a jar with a lid on it for you to pee in."

He said, "People will see me doing that, no way!"

I said, "I'll bring a lap blanket for you. You can hide it!"

He laughed and said, "We're going to the movies, aren't we?"

I said, "Yes!" We went and really enjoyed it. Sure enough, Rog had to pee. It was hilarious, but he was so cool about it! He peed with great success without spilling a drop. He handed me the jar, I put the lid on it and no one was the wiser.

Day +574

Over the last two days, Roger had started tinkering with his computer bags again. He spent every waking moment writing lists; what he needed to fix on his guns, his computers and in his garage. When I asked him what he was writing, he explained it to me in great length, but when I looked at the paper, it was just a jumbled mess of letters and numbers with no rhyme or reason. His writing was squiggly and undecipherable, but he read it back to me, knowing exactly what it said. He had become obsessed with writing lists.

He was unstable on his feet again, and his legs weren't holding him well. I had been helping him stand up, use the walker for one or two steps to the wheelchair then I pushed him to the bathroom or the bedroom and back again. Getting in and out of bed and his chair was the same, and my shoulder was taking it hard. It started swelling up again and hurting all day. A few times I had to take one of Roger's pain pills just to sleep. I was putting ice on it whenever he got into his list writing since he didn't seem to know I was alive when he was in that world. This gave me time to just rest with the ice pack.

While I was resting and he was list writing, he abruptly asked me how I liked the movie. I said, "What movie?"

He said, "The one we just finished watching."

I looked at him and said, "It was great! Did you like it?"

He said, "I liked the other one better, but it was good," then went back to writing. Abruptly he said, "We need to go get everything on this list today." He handed it to me and it was just a bunch of squiggly lines. I asked what the list was for. He started explaining that we needed to get these things for the space shuttle and the cargo ship. Neither would run without the parts. People were waiting so we needed to get going. He reminded me to get the bag of money by the desk, but only take half of it. He would use the pockets in the boat to hold all the parts. I helped him up to the walker then over to the wheelchair and asked him to use the bathroom before we left. After he used the bathroom and I transferred him back to the wheelchair, he wanted to return to his recliner. He then said, "It was great that we were able to get that big job done. Everyone was really happy with me for all my really good ideas. They're going to use all of them."

I said, "That's why I married you! You are so smart!" He just smiled and went back to writing more ideas for them. Who were *they*? I didn't know…

This was the beginning of another downhill slide. What was I going to do? No one wanted to help us anymore. No more heroics, and I was scared.

Day +576

We went to see our family doctor for a follow-up from the hospital stay. The other doctors had pretty much gone into hiding. I needed some medication refills but was told Roger needed to be seen first. Basically, he went over Roger's hospital discharge notes and care since we last saw him. I kept my mouth and thoughts to myself on the decongestant debacle. He asked Roger a bunch of questions about his hospital stay, his breathing, his medications and how he was feeling. After the barrage of questions, Roger looked at me to answer. The doctor said, "So you are his memory and his caregiver." The appointment was short and sweet.

When we got home, I made him lunch and told him I needed to get some work done outside. I checked on him every 30 minutes. One time I found him walking with his walker in the bedroom. Shocked, I asked him what he was doing. He said he was taking care of some things. I was surprised he could even get up, but he did this all the time!

Day +577

Shockingly, I found Roger's passport and birth certificate in a box on the table next to his chair. Whenever I was out of his sight, he had been going through cabinets and drawers, rearranging them and throwing away most of the contents. This was getting serious and I realized I couldn't leave him alone anymore. Most nights I spent undoing or searching for lost items. I was beginning to feel animosity toward all this even though I knew it wasn't his fault. It was so hard to deal with. How could I be a wife when all I did was take care of him like a child has to be taken care of, and watch him like a child so he didn't throw things away or hurt himself? He couldn't even remember to take his medications or eat. When there was nothing to take care of, I sat with him, but all he wanted to do was make lists and watch TV. He didn't want to talk, share his thoughts, worries or concerns; he just wanted to watch TV with me sitting next to him 24/7.

Yesterday while he was alone, he found my nail polish and permanent markers of every color, and decided to label everything in the house. There was nail polish and permanent marker scribbles everywhere! His mind seemed to be somewhere else most of the time so I kept the office locked. I had found him trying to break in a few times when I came down to check on him. I asked why he needed to be in there and he said he wanted to get to his guns. I reminded him that they were firearms and were very unforgiving. He argued with me and said he would kick the door down. When he tried, he usually lost his balance and had fallen a few times then got really mad at me when he had to ask for help getting up. I wasn't giving in on this one. I was exhausted. I called a girlfriend to vent but all she said was, "You need to hire someone or have home health come over and stay with Roger so you can go and do something for yourself." I would like to see that person try to stop Roger from kicking the doors down or drawing on everything, let alone deal with his bad behavior. I *wanted* to hire someone to help me but there was no way I could! I said this to EVERYONE yet they kept throwing it at me. I felt like saying, "Can you please come over and sit with Roger for free while I go do these fun things?" They gave the advice but never offered to help. I didn't get it!

Although I didn't know it, Roger was listening to my call. He said, "I feel like I'm in your way. I feel like I'm making your life harder to enjoy, harder to live."

I said, "Is your life hard to live right now? Is it hard to enjoy?"

He said, "Yes, it is."

I said, "Okay, we have something in common. Life is hard right now and it's hard to enjoy, but it isn't hard all the time, is it?"

He said, "No." I took his hand and went to the couch, sat in his lap, and watched TV with him for the rest of the night. That is what made Roger happy.

Day +585

Today we got up and I made him a nice breakfast with fried potatoes in coconut oil with two over-easy organic eggs on top. He ate it all! I said, "Right on there, big boy. That filled up one leg." He smiled and slapped me on the behind when I walked away.

He watched TV for a bit and watched me clean up the kitchen. Then he said, "Why are you cleaning up? I didn't get breakfast."

I turned and said, "What did you just eat for breakfast? You filled up one leg."

He stared at me for a minute then said, "Oh yeah, that's right. I'm really full!"

Roger had been getting around with just his cane. He was still wobbly but as long as he was on flat ground, he was doing well. Before bed, I gave Roger a shower. I noticed his right testicle was hard as a rock and swollen. I asked him if he had noticed it. He said no and reached down to examine it. He said, "Oh wow, it doesn't hurt." I told him we need to call Dr. Moros first thing in the morning.

PART TEN

1

A Surprise in the Shower

Dr. Moros had us come in right away. He said Roger needed an ultrasound "stat" and called over to the hospital. They had an opening right away. After the test, we were told to wait for a call later that afternoon.

When we got home, there was a message waiting for us. Roger had leukemia in his right testicle, it needed to come out right away, and the surgeon would be calling sometime today. It wasn't long after, the urologist called and said we needed to come in tomorrow for an examination and to see if Rog was a surgical candidate. He explained it was a simple in-and-out surgery to remove the testicle. Rog had never been an in-and-out kind of guy. Everything was always a 7-14 day stay. I asked if it was normal for a patient in remission to have the cancer come back in the testes. He said, "Yes, it is. Chemotherapy doesn't cross over into the testes. Cells can hide there, and over a period of time, they multiply then a teste needs to be removed."

I said, "I didn't notice it three days ago. That was fast! Does this mean it will spread throughout his body too? What does this mean?"

He said, "We can talk more tomorrow after I examine him." Once again, I was scared. I got on the computer and looked up Ph+ALL in the testes, but the only cases were male children. I couldn't find one case study on adult males so, once again, Rog was falling into that .1% group. I noticed that Roger had been getting slower over the past few days, more tired and was really not looking forward to Christmas. It made me wonder if being out of remission meant his whole body could be infected, not just the right testicle.

Day +587

We got up early and headed to the urology appointment. We were told that the right testicle had advanced leukemia in it and needed to be removed. I asked how it came on so fast and was told, "That's the golden question, isn't it?" I asked why they didn't take out both; if it happened to one, wouldn't it happen to the other? It was explained to us that insurance wouldn't pay to remove a healthy testicle so Roger's surgery was scheduled for December 24th. Rog was silent on the way home. I asked if he wanted to talk about it and he said, "Not now," so I let him be. He stayed quiet, deep in thought, over the weekend.

Day +601

When the alarm went off, Roger literally jumped out of bed and headed to the shower. I was in disbelief! This morning was surreal, to say the least. I couldn't believe, first of all, that he'd gotten up without my help. Second, when I heard the shower running, I was wondering how he planned on washing himself since he hadn't been able to in almost 18 months. The shower was the one place that always seemed to zap him of his energy.

We needed to get some shopping done and we did our usual; I pushed him and he pushed the cart. Rog was tired after we went shopping and unfortunately took a bad fall when we got home. He was trying to pick up a piece of paper from the floor, but the cane slid out from under him and he crashed to the floor onto his elbow. I came running when I heard the thunderous impact of his body hitting the floor. His left elbow was torn open and blood was gushing out of it. His skin was so thin from the blood thinners, it tore the top couple layers back, revealing a wet, open wound. Canes and hardwood floors don't mix well!

Day +603

We were up and headed to the hospital at 5:30 a.m. Roger was the first case. They took him back as soon as we got there. I kissed his cheek and said sweet dreams. He said, "Goodnight, see you in a bit."

I found the coffee counter, filled a large cup, and found a seat away from everyone else in the waiting room. I put my head back, closed my eyes, and thought about our previous night's conversation. Roger was sitting on the bed crying. I went to him, knelt in front of him, and waited for him to talk. He said, "I'm going to be less of a man tomorrow."

I said, "Am I less of a woman because I have no uterus?"

He said. "No."

I said, "So you don't need it. It's just a source of more problems in the future with your leukemia, so good riddance!"

He said, "I guess you're right." We sat together and just held hands for a while until he felt better.

I laid my head back and fell asleep. I woke up with my name being called over and over again. I thought I was dreaming but when I realized I wasn't, I jumped up, raised my hand and yelled, "HERE, I'M HERE!" I fumbled half-awake to the desk.

The woman told me they were ready for me. I asked what time it was, and she said it was 9:30. Rog was awake and he was fine! The surgery went perfectly.

The doctor said, "I'll send the testicle for biopsy. Afterward, we'll decide what to do next; chemotherapy, radiation therapy or both. The sutures will dissolve on their own and I'll see you in the office in seven days."

We were back home by 2:00 p.m. Of course, I made the famous pharmacy run before we left. Rog had no complaints except for back pain, which the nurses kindly gave him a pain pill to go home on.

It was perfect! No complications and no weird .1% disaster! Roger didn't want to watch TV, he just wanted to talk. He started with, "I'm not afraid to die. I just want to know that you're going to be okay, that you're going to be taken care of. I just want you to be able to do the things you like to do, like play in the garden and enjoy the ranch. I don't want to worry that you don't have a home or money to live on. My pension will be gone when I'm gone; there won't be any money for you to draw. I wish I would have set it up better, but I didn't know then what I know now. I don't want you to worry about me either." For the first time he said, "I'm living as long as it takes to get this property taken care of or I can figure out how to get you the money you need to pay it off. I just love you so much!"

I started to get choked up and said, "The universe will figure it out for us. I just need you to heal from this surgery and let this be our year!" I asked him if he was going to have chemotherapy or radiation if the doctors suggested it.

He said, "I'm not going to roll over, but it depends."

I said, "I feel if they give you aggressive treatment, you won't be able to handle it and it will take away your quality of life. It's tough enough as it is. I just want you to enjoy every minute now." It was such a hard decision but also an easy one for me to make. I didn't want him to suffer.

He said, "I won't take my own life." I was shocked he would say this. He said, "I don't want to suffer, but I won't take my own life." We held each other, and as the words that were just spoken out loud really sank in, we sat together in silence with sniffles.

Day +606

Rog decided to take a shower. I carefully put his scrotum in a little plastic bag and he sat on the shower chair while looking at the handicapped toilet seat. With his head down he said, "You have no idea what great gifts these two things are. I am so happy! My life is going to be so much easier!" You would have thought I had bought him a new car! I knelt down in front of him, raised his chin up to look at me, and he had tears in his eyes. I had also put bars up on all the walls so he could pull himself up and have balance no matter where he was. He held his little plastic bag in place while I scrubbed his back, legs and bottom.

We ate leftovers and rested while Rog watch TV and I tinkered around the house.

Day +607

Rog turned the channel to Super Soul Sunday and asked me to sit with him. I crawled onto his lap and we watched. The message tonight was, *We are exactly where we are supposed to be right now, in this place. This place* was teaching us what we had to learn, but it didn't mean it was where we were supposed to stay. We should listen and follow the breadcrumbs because tomorrow was a different day with new potential or a new path, and today is where you were supposed to be.

We sat in silence for a bit when the show ended. I thought that if this was where we were supposed to be, then Roger must have chosen to be here and I chose to go through this with him. Was this a contract we had made together when we came back to this earth? Did he choose me because he knew I would take care of him? And did I accept because I could handle it? Was this my lot in life, to always have difficulty surrounding me because I could handle it? God never gives you more than you can handle, right? Well, I was about tapped out!

I asked, "Do you ever regret marrying me?"

He said, "You made me the happiest man on earth! You're my angel. I was looking for you."

I said, "And I you. Thank you for picking me!"

He hugged me and said, "Thank you for accepting the invitation."

Day +608

Most days I looked in the mirror then looked away quickly. I hadn't worn makeup in months and my hair was always in a bun. My eyes just drooped and I look about 20 years older from worry and lack of sleep. Most days I wore jeans and T-shirts, although some days I slept in my clothes and wore the same ones the next day. It was sad to think that not long ago I would have never left the house without makeup on, my hair all dolled up, and attractive clothes on. I always wanted to make Roger proud of me. But now, most days it was just too much of an effort.

We received a call from the oncologist stating that we would be getting a call from the BMT clinic in regards to the testicular leukemia and what to expect next. It would be interesting to see what they had in mind, if anything. At this point, I really doubted they would do anything.

2

Tests, Tests and More Tests

The morning of Day +612 I got a call from the CDC doctor. She told me to stop the IV antibiotics and gave me a schedule of upcoming tests that she and the other doctors had agreed upon. The schedule included a lumbar puncture, a bone marrow biopsy, a series of bloodwork, and a whole-body CT scan. When they were completed, we were to follow up at the hospital. I asked her why they were putting him through these tests and what would happen after they were done. She said, "It all depends on the results."

I said, "I understood that comfort care was all you all wanted from now on. Why all the fuss now?"

She explained, "The leukemia is back, and maybe that was one of the big problems all along – it was hiding. Now we know. We'll cross that bridge when the tests are done."

I said, "He's still having quite a bit of back pain, his biggest complaint right now. With the antibiotics discontinued, does that mean his lungs are better? Will his back pain get better?"

She answered, "His lungs will always be a concern, but the infection is under control now. His back pain will most likely always be a problem, but considering everything else he has been through, that's not bad." I didn't know what to think about all this. Was she saying that maybe there was more that could be done now that they had a finger on the leukemia, that maybe there was something new or something else that would help Roger out of this mess? My heart was so light and I hung up with a smile on my face. I could actually feel the blood running through my veins with excitement! It was a good day for me and hopefully a wonderful day for Rog!

My day continued with lightness in my heart. I shared what she said, and Rog smiled and said, "I'm not leaving yet!" As the day progressed, Rog's back pain got the best of him and he went through a lot of pain medications. That scared me because at that dosage he was going to have constipation. I let the pain meds have about two hours to get settled in before I followed up with warm prune juice. Thank goodness he liked it, but it filled him up. He ate very little.

Day +617

This morning was Roger's bone marrow biopsy. Unfortunately, this hospital used the old manual method. With a corkscrew-shaped device, the tech literally screwed it in manually through the hip's flesh, into the hip bone, and then pulled out a plug of marrow tissue. The BMT clinic uses a power drill which takes about 20 seconds and it's done. With this method, they push and screw, push and screw slowly, around and around until they push through the dense bone. Roger's hands were tightened into a fist and he was profusely sweating and wincing with pain. It was 20 minutes of torture while I held him on the bed. He couldn't lie on his stomach due to back pain, so on his side on a 24" table, my 6'7" man laid in a C position with his left hip exposed to the torture.

I said, "This is horrible! You need to learn how to use the drill method. This is so not necessary!"

The tech looked at me and said, "I'm sorry, they never taught us how to do that."

I said, "If this was your child on this table, what would you want for them? Don't accept this to be 'okay.' Demand to be taught what the rest of the hospitals are doing. This is barbaric!"

For the most part, Rog had been doing pretty well. He was pooping plus eating a least 1000 calories a day with his protein drinks and the carbs in his noodles. He was maintaining his weight at 190 pounds. His balance and strength were poor, but as long as I was near him, I could help him with that too. I tried countless times to help him with exercises to build up his leg muscles since he wouldn't walk, but he wouldn't do them so I stopped nagging him about it.

Day +616

I received a call explaining there were 100 patients waiting for a lumbar puncture and they were short staffed. The CT scan was scheduled.

The days were again melding into each other. I spent my days trying to keep up with Roger's strange behaviors. He was back to cleaning and organizing. When I wasn't looking, he was collecting things and throwing them away again. He found my rolling drawers with everything a person might need in them; scissors, tape, pens, pencils, tacks, reading glasses, batteries, cords of all kinds, paper, staples, etc. It was a tower of drawers in the washroom and he found it and emptied it into the kitchen trash can. While he was cleaning it out, I was down getting the mail. When I left him, he was in his chair staring at five computer cords, trying to make heads or tails of them and watching TV. I just let him be when he started with the computer stuff. It kept him busy and he seemed to be happy and not in pain.

When I got back from the mailbox and found him in the washroom, it startled him. I asked, "What's up?" He asked me how the shopping was so I told him I went to the mailbox. He just stood staring at me then asked me how the movie was. I ignored the questions and asked what he was doing. He looked down at what he had done, looked at me and said, "This is in the way so I took care of it."

I said, "Okay, thank you," and he went back to the computer cables.

When he went to sit down, the chair swiveled and down he went. He bruised his knee and the palms of his hands. It took about 30 minutes to get him up off the floor. I just didn't have the strength in my shoulders to pull him up. Finally, we inched him up to the footstool by using a smaller footstool first, then up to the bigger footstool, then up to his chair. When he made it up to his chair he said, "That was the biggest fish I ever caught! It was heavy!"

I busted up laughing then realized he was being serious. He asked me to cook it for dinner. What I didn't understand was how he walked around the house when I wasn't there, but when I was present he had no strength. That had been weighing on my mind for weeks. I felt like he was playing me sometimes!

I put all the items back in the drawers in the washroom and cleaned out all the trash cans he had put things into. This behavior continued for days.

Day +623

Rog fell again. It was a controlled fall so no skin tears, just some bruised ribs. He said he was okay, and once again it took a while to get him up off the floor.

Rog's conversations were confusing and hard to keep up with. He talked about and believed he was in other worlds and had conversations with imaginary people. I wasn't sure if he was talking to his angels or spirit guides or just imaginary people. Sometimes I found myself asking him for advice like I used to do. I would forget that he was only really present in body. When he gave me a jumbled answer that didn't make sense, I sighed, realizing I'd forgotten and had to figure it out myself. I hated those moments! There were times even he caught it saying, "That didn't make sense, did it?" I told him no, and for a few short minutes he would become completely lucid, and cry and apologize, explaining that he didn't know what was happening to him.

It was so hard! In those moments I cried and he saw it. I was just so happy to have my Roger back that it was overwhelming, and the tears just came from nowhere. I hated it when he saw me like that. He didn't understand. I wished I could have held it together better.

The call came, saying the bone marrow biopsy was negative. I was so happy! I told Rog, but he didn't remember he'd had one and wanted to know why I was jumping up and down. I said, "It's one step closer to getting better!"

Over the next two weeks Roger had two doses of IVIG and continued his lab follow ups. But as time continued he became weaker and more confused.

Day +639

It was Rog's whole-body CT scan and we were both exhausted. Yesterday, beginning at 4:00 p.m., Roger thought he needed to be on a train and was petrified he was going to miss it. All afternoon and through the evening he was getting ready to get on a plane. I wasn't sure whether it was a plane or a train, he just needed to get on one and it was very important to him. He wanted his bags packed and to change his clothes and leave. The more I resisted, the more scared he got that he was going to be late. He had physical strength like I hadn't seen in months. He got the suitcases out and was packing them with anything within his reach as I watched in disbelief. There was nothing I could do to calm him down so I sat down in the room and watched, slowly becoming overwhelmed with sorrow. He didn't see me and was unaware of anything but the train. I didn't know what to do when he started for the door so I locked the deadbolt. He pushed me away from the door, trying to get out but he couldn't figure out how to unlock it. I told him to look at me, and when he did I made up a story, telling him to look at the clock, and when the little hand got on the 11, it was time to get on the train. I showed him the left-over ticket on the suitcase from our last trip and told him I had already paid for the tickets and the bags were tagged to go. He settled down and stared at the clock. I crushed two Ativans, put them in some juice, and asked him to drink it because the drinks on the train were too expensive. He drank it and finally, after half an hour, he lost the thoughts.

When the Ativan wore off, he was back to wanting to get on the train. I did everything I could think of to divert his attention. His sense of time and place were slowly disappearing, and I was so tired inside. I was beginning to realize there wasn't going to be a cure. The more I went over in my mind exactly what the doctors said, I think I'd heard what I wanted to hear and not what they were saying. Actually, they really didn't say anything. The longer I sat and helped Rog work through his hallucinations, the more I realized his mind was leaving. His body was losing weight, and his belt was now seven holes tighter and I needed to make another one. His strength was appearing stronger because he was in another world, like he was being transformed into something else while he was getting sicker and disappearing before my eyes. I didn't understand what was happening; sometimes he looked at me but wasn't looking at me, and his face was stern as if concentrating on something that was going on inside his head. I asked him questions and he just readjusted his eyes to me and said, "What? What are you saying?"

Today he had his suitcase near him and when it was time to go to the hospital for his scan, he took it with him. When we got there I said, "You need to have the whole-body CT scan first."

He looked at me and said, "Where's my Ativan?" The CT scan went well, and Roger became lucid during the test and communicated with the staff that his back and ribs were hurting. I had given him two pain pills before we left to help out with having to lie still on his back. The pills didn't seem to be working very well, even though they were recently increased in dosage. The pain in his back was getting more uncomfortable. No matter how much I massaged or put ice or heat on it, he was in pain. The next day was our appointment at the hospital, so hopefully we would get some answers.

Day +640

We left for the BMT clinic with Roger's suitcase. Dr. Perses said we had three options regarding the testicular leukemia:

1. Start back on the Dasatinib, take it forever, and hopefully it would prevent the leukemia from returning or metastasizing to other parts of his body;
2. Whole body radiation with IV chemotherapy *and* the Disatinib; or
3. A one-time targeted radiation to his left testicle.

I asked if there was anything else and he said, "No."

I took a deep breath and once again the tears started. I said, "You need to explain something to me. Why didn't they just take out the left testicle when they had him in surgery to take the right one? We were told the insurance wouldn't pay to take out a healthy testicle, but the insurance would pay for all these tests that Roger just took plus radiation, chemo and medication that costs $10,000 a month. This was to prevent a possible reoccurrence of leukemia in the remaining testicle that they could have removed for a small additional fee of $1,000.00 while he was already in surgery. Why? Can you tell me why this is? This treatment you just explained will kill him. He's too fragile! Just removing it would have saved him from all of this. I don't understand, so you have to explain this to me."

He put his head down, took a breath and said, "No, I can't explain this to you. He can have the target radiation near you. It won't be necessary for him to come back here. I know it's a long trip for him."

I interrupted him, asking about Roger's mental confusion. He asked Roger some questions like who I am, time and place, and if he was feeling confused.

Roger said, "I wake up at night and look at her and wonder who is sleeping with me." All the other questions Roger got wrong; 1976, President Reagan, and he was living with his ex-wife, Sandy. Roger explained that I wouldn't let him on the train and he'd missed it. He said he was mad at me for that. After he was done, I wanted to run out of the room. My husband didn't know me! He had just been tolerating me because he knew I was helping him and getting him his food.

I couldn't hold it in. I started crying so hard that I didn't have any concerns about who was in the room. I had gotten it all wrong! There was no more help out there for him. This was it! How did I get it so wrong? Roger was fading away from me. I cried and cried. I felt a hand on my back and a tissue was put in my hand. When I looked up, Roger was staring at me and the nurse was trying to console me. No one else was in the room. I sat for a while until it all sank in. I had been fighting for nothing. I was so alone. Why did this all happen? Someone tell me why!

The drive home was surreal. We didn't talk. I just drove, my mind blank, my thoughts still. I don't even remember driving.

I woke up at 2:00 a.m. and went into the living room and sat in the dark. I thought about when things were different, remembering when I was Roger's everything. I wanted him to fix this! What was going to happen to me? How was I going to get through this? My tears were so heavy I couldn't even see anymore. I sat sobbing in the dark.

Day +645

We got a call from our family doctor saying Rog needed to be seen. He informed us that Roger had a few compression fractures in his back. He explained that it was most likely the reason he was having so much back pain. He said the lungs looked good, for Roger, and he believed the pain was no longer coming from the right lung. He told us about a procedure called Kyphoplasty that could be done to relieve the pain. They put cement in the fractures, immobilizing the spine and reducing or possibly eliminating the pain. I told him we would be seeing Dr. Moros in a few days and would talk to him about it and get back to him.

We saw Dr. Moros two days later and told him what we were told. He lowered his head and said, "Yes, we knew they were there and they have been for quite some time. It's not unusual to see these types of fractures in people who have been on steroid therapy like Roger has. But Roger isn't a candidate for Kyphoplasty." He explained that insurance wouldn't cover it due to Roger's other diagnoses and that it would be too dangerous. He said his spine had so much osteoporosis that it would be a disaster. He increased Roger's pain medication and told me to give him meds every four hours to help keep the pain under control. He scheduled Roger for a spinal MRI to get a closer look at the fractures.

The previous day I had noticed six large, dark red nodules on the backside of Roger's right forearm. They were hard and about the size of a silver dollar. I asked him if they hurt and he said no. I asked how long they had been there and he said he'd just noticed them too. Dr. Moros looked at them and said, "These are most likely leukemia nodules. We can biopsy them if you want, but it's pretty textbook. Usually we would radiate them and do a round of chemotherapy, but with Roger, I'm inclined to just ignore them. He won't survive chemotherapy." We left without any further treatment.

I had become numb to all of this. Before, the doctors jumped right into healing mode. At this point, they just acknowledged the symptoms and bypassed any further treatment. Roger seemed to be going along for the ride now. He got in the car and showed up with me. We answered questions and got back in the car. We didn't talk about it, just showed up then left. I thought about just not showing up anymore, but deep down, I didn't want to give up.

Day +647

The radiation clinic called, asking Rog to come in. I wasn't sure what was going on but I got Rog bundled up and made the trip. The radiation doctor wanted to discuss target radiation to Roger's left testicle. For thirty minutes he explained all the risks then said quickly, "It will require you to come here every day for two weeks. Each visit we will radiate the entire scrotum for 15 minutes." He examined the scrotum and said, "Right now the teste and scrotum are perfectly normal. This is not an emergency. Go home and think about it. If you decide to do it, just talk to the scheduler and she will get you set up with the appointments."

When we got home, I sat down on the footstool in front of him and told him to look at me. I took his hands and said firmly, "Roger, do you want to have radiation on your scrotum for the next two weeks to insure you don't get leukemia in your left testicle? We will go to the same office we were just at every day for only 15 minutes to do this. Do you want this?"

He was listening. I saw him in there. He said, "I want to think about it. I think I will have them take it out if it comes back. I don't want radiation."

I said, "Do you want to have the MRI scans for the fractures in your back? You'll be put in the tube like you have done so many other times and they will take more pictures to get a better view of the fractures. Do you want to do this?"

He said, "No, they aren't going to do the surgery, so why do it? The pills are helping the way you're giving them to me." The tears were rolling down my face. He was with me. He knew what he was saying, and he told me to cancel the surgery.

PART ELEVEN

1

Shhhh, Breathe

By day +649, Roger was showing signs of extreme weakness all over and at night he was having problems breathing. During the day he seemed to be okay, just weak everywhere else. I called Dr. Moros who called the lung doctor, who called me. I was told to start Roger back on the IV antibiotic, Mucinex and Day-Quil, and have him use the inhaler at night. I wasn't too worried during the day, it was the nighttime that was tough. When his breathing got bad, he was unable to help me do anything. I hoped the meds worked.

Day +650

Roger's breathing was getting worse and he was using a lot of energy to breathe. The previous night he was gurgling in his sleep like his lungs had water in them. I took him to the ER where they did a chest x-ray, some bloodwork and an EKG. The bloodwork showed he had a tremendous amount of inflammation somewhere and his white blood cell count was up, but not bad for Roger. The rest of the bloodwork was normal for him. The chest x-ray showed diffusion in both lungs. Normally it was only the right lung that looked bad, but this time both were showing signs of infection or fluid buildup.

I asked the ER doctor where the inflammation was. He said, "I'm not sure. It could be from his lungs, those enlarged nodules on his arm, or somewhere else in the body." He said he had called Dr. Moros with the results and he wanted me to call him in the morning. I asked about tonight. He said, "Just keep doing what you're doing and have him sleep in his chair tonight."

When we got home, I got his chair ready to sleep in. He said he was feeling better and would sleep with me, propped up on pillows. I gave him a double dose of Prednisone which seemed to help. I made him some hot soup and we talked. He was very lucid and talking about his health, going over all the other times he was in the hospital and comparing notes. He said, "It just feels like allergies this time. It's not a deep pain like I've had before. It'll get better." He slept sitting up and did pretty well.

Day +651

Roger's breathing was becoming more labored and difficult. After a quick trip to the ER and a chest x-ray, I called Dr. Moros's office. His nurse returned my call saying, "Dr. Moros wants you to get set up with hospice."

I said, "Hospice? What does that mean, hospice? Did he look at the test results from the ER? Can't he give him something for his lungs?"

She said, "No, the ER doctor said to stop the Meropenem antibiotic, it was the wrong medication for this anyway. It's not doing any good."

I said, "If they know it's not the right one then which one is the right one? I can go and pick it up right now!"

She said, "No, there's nothing more. It's time for hospice. They will help you keep him comfortable."

I said, "I can do that, keep him comfortable! He's able to get up and help me help him. All he needs is something to help him breathe!"

She said, "I will give them a call for you and have them get in touch with you."

I said, "What? That's it? Nothing? I could increase the Prednisone. It seemed to help last night. Can you ask if that's alright to do?"

She said, "You have an appointment on March 21. We will see you then," and she hung up. Hospice… hospice…what did that mean? I could take him back to the ER if he got worse. What was in his lungs? Why did Dr. Moros not talk to me about this? One of his nurses calls and tells me to call hospice? What's going on?

Day +658

I hadn't gotten much sleep the previous week, and Rog's breathing had been up and down. Some days were good, some days not so good. He was getting around okay with my help. He leaned on me for balance and support, and needed full help getting up and down from the chair. Some days he ate well and had even eaten a few tuna sandwiches, which was new. Some days it was just noodles and dry toast.

He talked to me all the time now, from the time he got up until the time we went to bed. He had never been a talker, now he didn't stop. He was in a different world, but he talked like it was his world and he was fully present in it. He was like a two-year-old that finally found its voice. I gave him my full attention and found myself watching his expression and lips move. His smiles and voice changes were interesting, and he talked like he was entertaining me – with animated expressions, arms and hands. His lanky arms with his huge, heavy hands would flail around as he talked like a man in front of an audience.

His clothes were hanging on him and his body was ailing. His weight had dropped into the 180s, his skin was full of leukemia lumps, and his face was so thin that it looked taunt and uncomfortable. His gums even looked stretched, with the bone around his teeth so receded that I could almost see the beginning of the roots. He didn't complain about pain as much anymore, but when he moved, he did so with slow, shuffling movements, and I could sometimes see him jerk as if hit with a stabbing pain. His feet had swollen so large that I ordered a pair of size 15 shoes so he didn't slip. He usually wore a 14. I could barely get the 15s on him so I took out the shoelaces to make it easier.

I was feeling dead inside. The thoughts that were going through my mind were making me feel so bad about myself. I found myself praying that he died soon so I didn't have to watch this any longer, then as soon as I caught myself, I prayed for forgiveness and the strength to go on. I also didn't want him to leave me. I was afraid for him to leave me. Every day was consumed with him and his care and needs. I couldn't imagine waking up without him. What would I do with myself? Hospice was supposed to be here, and I wasn't sure I was okay with that.

A hospice equipment person showed up with a 5-foot oxygen tank, a bedside commode, and a hospital bed. Months ago he fought me over this; today he was excited. When they put the bed in, he told them to push it up next to our bed so he could still hold my hand while he slept. He said, "It will be nice to raise the head of the bed so I can breathe better."

After the doctors stopped taking my calls a few weeks ago, I decided to start him on a higher dose of Prednisone so he could breathe better. I stopped some of the other meds that caused breathing side effects and he seemed to be doing better. Since he started talking non-stop, each morning he woke me, asking to get up. He wanted to get ready for the day as if he was getting better, but I knew this phenomenon since I had seen it many times. It was the calm before the storm, the body preparing us for the final moment, for us to come to terms with the inevitable. I spent my days listening to him, touching him, and breathing his exhales into my body. If only one cell took hold in me, I would be happy. He would live inside me forever!

I found the tears were endless. They seemed to just be a part of me, like breathing. I didn't ask him questions anymore. I wished we would have talked more about this; this time, the end time, what was coming, but he wouldn't have it. He was never going to die. I felt so alone in his presence yet so blessed that I could still hear him breathe and hear his voice.

At 10:20 p.m., Roger was in bed, snoring. I decided to have a small piece of banana bread then head to bed. I was starting to get scared, and felt mad and sad at the same time. I was trying so hard to keep this up, trying to keep it all in and just be strong for him.

Day +662

Roger slept really late, and I had a hard time waking him up. He acknowledged me but didn't open his eyes. When I finally got him to the side of the bed, he started having coughing fits and difficulty breathing. I gave him an Ativan, but that didn't seem to work. At 11:30 the hospice nurse showed up for his first evaluation and I quickly told her that he was having problems with coughing and breathing. She opened her pack and filled a syringe with morphine, gave it to me, and told me to give it to him. Within seconds, he was breathing and feeling better. We both thanked her. She introduced herself, sat down, and got comfortable. She went over his medications and asked him several questions about time, place and how he was feeling. He answered the questions correctly and said he was tired and wanted to know if he could keep the morphine. She told him that the bag she came in with was ours to keep. She explained how the meds were to be given then turned to me and said, "You'll be giving them to him as you see fit. It will be up to you to make the decision when you see him in distress. Roger, are you okay with that?" He said yes then she asked me the same question. I too replied with yes. She handed me each drug; liquid morphine, liquid Ativan and liquid Haldol, as well as a small bottle of atropine to dry up secretions if he started producing too much saliva. She explained the dosages for each and that the times were up to us. "If he's doing better after the first dose, then don't give another dose until he's in need again. If the first dose doesn't work, give him another," she explained.

She helped me get Rog up to his chair and we talked for a bit about the oxygen and his blood pressure. She went over his regular medications and while she did, he fell asleep. She told me it was time to stop all the medications and only give him the meds she brought when he needed them. My breath caught when she said this. It was happening. I was stopping *all* his medications. She said, "Soon, he won't be able to take them, and he could choke on them and that would be horrible for you to go through." I told her I understood. I asked her about the need to get on a plane or a train. I explained that it was all he talked about. She said, "This is *Symbolism*. It happens with 99.9% of all hospice patients. It's a time when they are internally coming to terms with death, even though they aren't focusing on it. When he does this you need to say, 'Go to the train and I'll meet you there with our bags.' This gives him an, *I'm okay with you going. You're okay to go to the other side.*" When she left, she hugged me and told me to call anytime day or night, someone would always answer. I asked how long I had with him. She said, "No one knows, but it will be soon. He's really sick inside, Robin. He will be at peace."

I let Roger sleep in the chair. I put a blanket on him and propped his head up with a pillow. I called Roger's mom and told her what was happening. She cried and said, "A mother never wants her child to go before she does. I thought I would go before him." Todd said he would be coming as soon as possible and that he would take care of calling his brother and sister.

Roger woke up and wanted to go to the bathroom. He tried to get up but couldn't. I helped him, but it took several tries before he got to his feet. With the wheelchair I was able to get him to the bathroom, but had trouble getting him out of the chair. He was limp, expecting me to just lift him up, but I couldn't. I gave him the urinal and asked him to use it. He wasn't happy because he wanted to have a bowel moment. He demanded I get him up to the toilet. Instead, I got the bedside commode and put it as close to the wheelchair as possible. I had him put his arms over my shoulders and I pulled him in and hugged him hard, counted to three, and pulled him up. With one hand I fumbled with his pants and finally got them down and leaned him over to the commode. He flopped down, but he made it. I couldn't believe I'd done that! He urinated about 200cc of dark amber urine and wanted to try to have a bowel movement. I waited next to him as he tried. He couldn't, and asked me to check him for an impaction. If there was one, I couldn't feel it. He got angry and said he wanted to stay on the chair until he went. I got his night pants and a clean T-shirt and dressed him while he sat there.

After 30 minutes, I told him it was time to get to bed. He was falling asleep and I knew my window of time for him helping me was being shut. I couldn't get him up and he started getting mad at me. I moved everything out of the way and pulled the bedside commode close to the hospital bed. With all my might, I repeated the same motion as I did before and got him to his feet. I leaned him to the side and he fell onto the bed. He almost fell to the floor, but I rammed my body against him and caught him. Slowly, I put each leg then the rails up and asked him to help me raise him in the bed. I bent his legs so his feet were flat on the bed and put both of his hands on the rails. I pushed the bed away from the wall, got behind the head of the bed, and grabbed him under his arms and said, "On three, Rog, push with your feet." On three I pulled but he did nothing. Somehow that pull got him to the top of the bed.

Day +664

Roger had tossed and turned and asked for the morphine a couple of times through the night. I gave him his OxyContin with it and he finally settled down. I woke up with a phone call from Todd. He said he would be there that night and that Craig would be arriving in a few days.

Roger didn't get up the entire day so I stayed with him. I held his hand and reminisced out loud about our lives together. Sometimes he would squeeze my hand or smile a bit, but he didn't talk. When he moaned, I asked if he needed meds and he nodded enough for me to know the answer was yes.

That afternoon, he started sweating profusely. His clothes and the bed were wet. I called my son for help. When he showed up he helped me change him, wash him, and change the bed. I could tell this was really bothering him, but he helped me. He had tears in his eyes when Rog mumbled thank you. He left and came back with his smart TV and put it up in our room so Rog could listen to his favorite shows. While he did this, I went to the bookshelf and looked through all of the books and picked one to read to Roger. I began reading the book to him and never left the room. I had a bathroom and that was all I needed. I held his hand as I read, and told him I loved him a thousand times. He mumbled it back to me and squeezed my hand, never opening his eyes.

I slept next to him, I prayed next to him, and I cried next to him as I listened to every breath.

Day +665

The hospice doctor came the next morning and told me Rog was in a semi-coma state and talked about the final moments. I was so uncomfortable with Roger hearing this. He didn't respond to pain but did have some facial movements while the doctor talked. I felt bad that he was talking in front of Rog. He said that I was doing well and to remember to reposition him a lot. He checked the medications, left more, and went on his way.

I stayed with Rog and read all day. He never woke up.

I spent the next day reading and crying all day. I kissed his hands, face and chest, and ran my fingers through his hair. I touched him, caressed him, and crawled as close to him as possible as he slept.

Day +666

My best friend was now comatose, with no response to my voice, and his hands were limp. He was no longer squeezing me back, and his breathing was shallow but rhythmic. He looked peaceful while he slept.

Laurel came by and talked to me about the end. I can't remember what she said, but I remember her holding both my hands and looking me in the eye while she talked. She handed me a card from the same mortuary that my mom went to then she left. I had the card in my hand for a long time before I realized it was there. I put in on the fridge and went back to Rog.

When Craig and Todd both arrived, they talked and sat with Rog for a while then went to Stefan's house. When the sun set, I called the boys to come and help me reposition and wash Rog. They did, and when they rolled him onto his side so I could wash his back, I found a bedsore starting on his tailbone. I put some cream on it and took the egg crate off his living room chair and put it under him for more padding. When I took his shirt off, I noticed his right arm was completely swollen and red. The leukemia nodules looked really bad and I knew by the looks of it he had a blood clot in that arm. I finished his bath and let the boys stay with him for a while. When they left, I crawled back into bed with him and began reading again. When I turned over, I noticed the oxygen tubing had been removed from the tank. One of the boys had to have done that. My first thought was to get it plugged back in immediately then I realized why they did this. I turned the tank off.

Day +667

It was two years, two months and ten days from diagnosis day. I sat in our room on the bed, just thinking about my life with Rog. I knew that at any moment he would be gone. I just watched him sleep. His breathing was getting wet, a sound that time was near. I had heard this sound at work many times.

The tears just kept coming. It seemed like our whole lives together were scattered and in disarray. So many things I would have done differently. How was I going to do this? I asked Rog for help, to be my angel, my spirit guide, to help me get through life when he was gone. I didn't know how I was going to be able to stay afloat. His pension would go away and there was no money left, just enough left in the retirement fund to get through about a year and a half. I wanted him to wake up and tell me what to do, but his hand just laid limp in mine. The room – the entire house – was so quiet. No TV, no sound, just his breathing.

Through my muffled cries, I gave him his last rites and told him to go to the train or the plane, whichever one he saw. I told him to save me a seat for when I saw him next. I kissed his face and lips and combed his hair with my fingers. He was so peaceful.

I read all day and through the evening then finally fell asleep. At 2:30 a.m., I woke up, checked on him, went to the bathroom, and came back to his bedside. I looked down at him resting. He took two deep but quick breaths and died. I put my head on his chest and sobbed when I couldn't hear his heart anymore. He was gone. Roger left me at 2:38 a.m. on March 2, 2016.

Prologue

The first three months after Roger passed, I spent most of my days and nights in bed crying. My family and friends worried about me, tried to say all the right things, and invited me to all the social gatherings that came their way. I lost interest in food and lost 32 pounds. I walked around the house, sat in his chair, smelled his clothes, looked at his picture, and held his ashes. One night while I was going back over all his pictures on my phone, I stumbled upon a video I had taken of him in the hospital that I had forgotten I took. It was seven minutes long. His wonderful chuckle is on that video. I have watched it a million times and I still watch it just to hear his chuckle. I wish I would have taken more.

Hospice sent me flyers to attend group therapy, but knowing I would just cry, I didn't attend. When I look back now I wish I would have. I think talking with others that understood, that walked that mile in my shoes would have helped me heal faster.

Unfortunately I had to put the ranch up for sale. It sold in two weeks. So saddened, I walked away and headed to the coast. At night I lay alone, listening to the crashing waves, and I'm thankful for my life. I've spent many hours reliving the events of the past two years in my mind, and the emotions that consumed me. I believe Roger and his story were brought into my life to teach me what is important, and to rein in the bull and quiet my brain. I believe I was brought into his life to help and comfort him through this terrible illness. When I think about it, we helped each other in so many ways. You can look at it from a lot of different angles, but at some point you must come to terms with it.

This chapter of my life was packed with *every* emotion in just two years! Most of us have to go through a whole lifetime to feel each of the emotions at the intensity a caregiver does. Before this happened, my mind was racing with hopes and dreams of a fantastic life. I was a fighter and had the world by the horns! Now my brain is quiet, void of the drama I once inflicted on myself, as we all do. I feel as though I understand so much more. I don't need to fight for answers or fix things or people anymore. I lived it and it was exhausting!

I will never forget those crystal blue eyes looking into me as if he knew my soul. No words, just a look that let me know I was his and we were one. I miss Roger terribly. My memories are all I have now, and I'm glad I have them.

For anyone who has read my story, I hope it doesn't become yours. But it's a story that happened; the good, the bad and the ugly. Through this journey of trial and error, I realized that I wasn't alone. Many families, spouses and caregivers are going through the same scenarios I did. Many are asking the same questions and looking for the same answers I was. I decided the back of this book would contain a list of items and tools that I discovered to be very helpful throughout my journey as a caregiver. I wish I'd had this chapter available to me. I hope you too find it helpful.

My heart and love goes out to you! Be good to yourself, trust yourself, and don't be afraid to fight like a bull if you need to. Your journey, your story, is one you want to be proud of. From my heart to yours, I send you much strength and an abundance of energy! Remember in times of great despair, Shhhhhhhh, Breathe.

Caregivers' Responsibilities

1. Getting the patient to each and every appointment, beginning at 7:00 a.m. Sometimes this is seven days a week.
2. Preparing and giving all medications on time.
3. Making all phone calls regarding appointments and schedule changes.
4. Preparing and finding meals the patient will agree to eat and encouraging them to eat when they don't want to.
5. Preparing and giving insulin injections.
6. Encouraging the patient to swallow a cup full of medication three times a day when their mouth is sore and painful and every swallow causes gagging.
7. Getting the patient to the bathroom multiple times a day and night to vomit or potty. Keeping a clean bedside bucket nearby.
8. Encouraging the patient to walk to keep their strength up when they refuse to get out of bed because of debilitating fatigue and pain.
9. Help with bathing, toileting, eating, changing clothes and putting on shoes.
10. Shopping for food and making pharmacy runs without being gone too long.
11. Having and setting an alarm to wake up to give the patient medications and fluids around the clock.

The caregiver will become an unwanted cheerleader, especially every morning at 6:00 a.m. when he or she is pushing a cup of pills, a bottle of fluid, a meal, a stab in the finger and then in the arm with insulin, along with a 7:00 a.m. car ride to the BMT clinic. The caregiver will eventually become the patient's memory, making all decisions for them.

I encourage the caregiver to pack a bag for an all-day stay at the clinic before you go to bed. The caregiver will be given a small plastic chair to sit on next to the patient while they're receiving the weekly transfusions post-transplant in the clinic. Find a hobby. I saw caregivers knitting, crocheting, beading, reading, painting, drawing, using their tablets for games, research, work, paying bills and making to-do lists. Carry a phone charger and a healthy lunch for the day for both of you. The clinic provides juices, sodas, coffee and tea but no food. Bring a journal, pen, writing paper and address book with everyone's phone numbers, a reading book for both of you, lip balm, hair clips, etc.

The caregiver's job is added to the job they already have at home and/or work. Home and all its dynamics don't stop when the new job of being a caregiver begins. It will be double duty. I encourage you, right from the get go, to immediately find help and figure out a schedule to allow for rest and respite. Don't think you can do this on your own unless you're a superhero!

The caregiver will be exhausted most of the time and in turn will need to remember to take care of themselves. He or she is not allowed to get sick, discouraged or slack at his or her duties, no matter what. The patient will become 100% dependent on you.

The caregiver will need to find time to vent, cry, call friends for moral support and have friends to depend on. Make those arrangements early.

This is not meant to scare you – it's a wake-up call. The caregiver's job after transplant is the hardest job they will ever have. It doesn't end until the end.

Tools

During this journey I learned many things through trial and error. One is that, had I been given a list of tools and ideas that would become a go-to manual, a PH+ALL Bible, per se, it would have made our journey a whole lot easier. The caregiver class explained in great detail the do's and don'ts and the ugly side effects of Prednisone, but it didn't explain the many valuable tools the caregiver and patient would need on a daily basis. I encourage you to have these items in place before the transplant or very soon after.

First and foremost, install safety grab bars around the toilet, and outside and inside the shower. The patient has strength in their arms to pull up but little strength in their legs. The bars allow them to get up from the commode and get in and out of the shower without falling, especially if you have a tub shower.

Install a raised toilet seat with safety bars. This allows them to get up easier and have an armrest if they need to stay on the commode a while. A hand-held shower head is a big plus as well. He held it so I didn't get drenched while I soaped him up. A bathroom heater is nice for them as well during shower time. They just shiver in the cold while being bathed and this is energy they can't afford to lose.

A shower chair is a must! I found the double seated chairs handy. If you have a tub shower, place half the chair in the tub and the other half outside the tub. The half outside the tub or shower is great for holding washcloths, soap, shampoo, etc. It's also easier for them to slide into the shower versus trying to get over the edge of the tub.

As the patient becomes weaker, it will be harder for them to make it to the toilet, especially at night or if you're out and about. Accidents will happen. Have a bedside commode available to them for nighttime use. For daytime, use incontinence pads and incontinence briefs. They make them for men and women. Keep a supply next to the toilet for them to use as needed. Dignity is sacred!

For the bed, have a few large pillows available if you don't have a hospital bed or a bed that allows you to raise and lower the head of the bed. Many nights they will need to sleep sitting up to breathe. A neck pillow like the airplane pillow was necessary as well. This pillow comes in handy when they sleep in their recliner or at the clinic. They will sleep a lot in the BMT clinic.

A small bedside rail helps the caregiver's back. It allows the patient to help himself to the side of the bed easier, and this exercise will keep their arms strong. Also, the caregiver doesn't have to bend and pull the patient up to the side of the bed. Always save your back!

Have a large bedside table next to the bed for juice, water, protein drinks, snacks, thermometer, remote control, medications, tissues and any other needed items. Everything is in reach of the patient if they're unable to get out of bed.

To prevent falls, remove all throw rugs from around the house. Railing around the house, like the ones you see going up stairs is a plus, or situate the furniture, couch and chairs so the patient has something to use for balance as they walk through the house.

Eventually a cane and a size appropriate walker will be necessary. Roger was 6'7" so we needed to buy extensions for both so he wasn't walking slumped over and causing increased back pain.

Plan to purchase or borrow a wheelchair at some point. It will become a godsend, especially when the walk into the clinic becomes too much for them. Also, it's great for getting out of the house and enjoying the outdoors or going on walks together to feel the sun and breathe the fresh air.

Roger liked to spend a lot of time in his recliner. There came a time when he didn't have enough strength to push the footrest down to get out of the chair and many times he had accidents trying to get out. I recommend getting a lift chair as soon as possible, before the induction period of the transplant.

When Roger started losing weight, I had to buy him new clothes. I knew he was going to continue to lose, so instead of buying brand new clothes that wouldn't fit for long, I started buying clothes at the secondhand stores. It saved a lot of money.

The secondhand stores are also full of used medical equipment, i.e. shower chairs, canes, walkers, handrails, bedside commodes, etc. for pennies on the dollar. Hospice is also a great resource for used equipment. Many families donate big-ticket items like wheelchairs, lift chairs, walkers and hospital beds to others in need.

For your car, always carry a bag with surgical masks, gloves for both of you, bacterial wipes, hand sanitizer, adhesive bandages, water bottles, Gatorade and snacks. At the front door, I had a pre-packed suitcase, just in case. In it I had a phone charger and laptop charger, as well as five days worth of clothes, toiletries and supplies. I put a note on the wall above it that read: Get journal, laptop, phone, book, food, hobby bag, and medication bag. When the situation is intense and the emergency room is inevitable, you forget what you need to take with you. Having a reminder is very valuable, to say the least. Many times ER visits become overnight stays so always take your pre-packed bag with you. Having what you need with you will decrease a lot of stress from having to go back home and pack.

Purchase a bead box from the local hobby and craft store for all the large pills that don't fit into the small medication boxes from the drugstores. They are perfect and easy to transport.

Buy a few pairs of thick tube socks. When blood thinners are added to the medication list, the skin on the patient's arms become thin and tear easily. Roger was always bleeding from a skin tear and covered in bandages. Cut the foot out then cut a small hole for the thumb to fit into, freeing the fingers. We pulled them up to the elbows to protect the arms. It worked great! Roger was never without them. Plus they helped keep him warm, a win-win.

The most important items of all is to ALWAYS have a few copies of the patient's entire medication list, along with the times they are given, with you at all times. It will be the first thing the medical staff will ask for when you are seen, whether it's in the clinic, hospital or ER. You won't get that list back so having copies is a must!

Always have a bottle of the patient's pain and anxiety medications with you at all times.

Items I encourage the patient to have in place before the induction phase of the transplant: A Will, a Power of Attorney and a Health Care Directive. Make an appointment with your financial planner and bank for potential concerns that might arise. Talk to your boss about time off work and any financial help the company can provide. Have a strong understanding of what your insurance company will and will not pay for during treatment. Also very important, have a "What if" talk with all family members. Everyone should have an understanding of the patient's last wishes, how they want to be taken care of during treatment, and where and how they want to be buried.

I wish I had known about these tools and the necessary items in the beginning. It would have made many moments a lot less stressful.

Chemotherapy, Radiation and Mucositis

As we sat day after day in the clinic, watching the other patients come and go, we realized that the post-chemotherapy and radiation patients were experiencing the same side effects; sore mouths, problems eating, irritated and painful skin, stomach bloating and intestinal discomfort, vomiting, severe diarrhea and malnutrition. We were warned, "All hell will break loose soon after chemotherapy is started" by one of the patients, but we were never warned by the doctors or nurses prior to induction.

We came to understand these side effects as Mucositis. Chemotherapy and radiation destroys cancer cells, but it also destroys normal cells in the process. These include the cells that protect and line the gastrointestinal track. Mucositis is an inflammation of the mucous membranes lining the digestive tract from the mouth to the anus.

Not knowing this was normal was very scary for us, but it wasn't long before we realized it was normal. Due to the mouth sores, eating becomes very difficult and even harder when the patient can't taste the food they're eating. Weight loss begins quickly, which leads to deficiency in nutrition, energy and a further weakening of the immune system.

While Roger was in the hospital, I noticed each meal was high in carbohydrates; creamy sauces, creamy mashed potatoes, milkshakes, puddings and breads. He was encouraged to eat everything to keep his weight up. Later we learned these creamy, high carb, sugary staples only increased the inflammation process, increasing malabsorption. The intestinal tract, for a long time after the induction process, is unable to absorb food due to this damage. Roger lost 107 pounds in the first year. Some of the suggestions to help with mucositis I wish I'd been given in the mandatory caregiver class include:

1. Drink 2 liters of fluids a day WITHOUT caffeine and sugar. Water, G2 Gatorade and clear organic broths are best. Drink between meals, leaving room for food.
2. Eat small, frequent meals instead of three large meals. Avoid broccoli, corn, peas, cabbage, milk and milk products, fruits and vegetables with seeds, and fermented foods. This will help prevent gas, bloating and irritation to the bowels.
3. Cook all foods to soften them for easy digestion. Avoid foods hard to digest like dense meats, fried foods or foods high in fat, including heavy sauces and rich sweets.
4. Refrain from spicy and acidic foods that will irritate the mucosal lining.
5. When the rectal area becomes irritated, use petroleum jelly as a barrier between bouts of diarrhea. Sitz baths relieve discomfort as well.
6. Eat foods cold or at room temperature to avoid nausea. Sugar-free popsicles can relieve mouth pain.
7. If nausea occurs after you eat, lay down on your right side, head elevated on a pillow. This will settle the feeling of the need to vomit. It also helps with indigestion.
8. Brush teeth with a soft tooth sponge or a small piece of gauze with fingers. Don't use a bristle toothbrush. This will prevent irritation and possible open sores of the

gums. Simply use mild, warm salt water to brush and rinse. A baking soda rinse – 1 teaspoon in 8 ounces of water – will help cleanse the mouth if vomiting occurs.

9. Try not to eat right before bed; if you do, make the meal light. Broths or soups with crackers are best.
10. Getting protein in is very important. Eat proteins easy to digest like bland fish, finely cut up organic poultry, scrambled eggs, hard boiled eggs, tofu, creamy nut butters and drinks high in protein. There are many organic broths in the grocery that are high in proteins if you're unable to make your own.
11. If you suffer from dry mouth, rinse your mouth with warm water prior to eating. Sucking on ice chips, sugar free gum and sugar free candies is also helpful. Dip bread/toast or crackers in broths to moisten prior to chewing.
12. Drink fluid or broths through a straw to make swallowing easier.

Do the best you can to get nutrition and fluids in. Small amounts at a time and choose the right foods to feed the body to help it heal.

Other side effects that accompany mucositis caused by the induction process include skin irritation and hair loss. Both are devastating and very uncomfortable. Ideas and suggestions include:

1. Don't use harsh bacterial soaps that dry the skin. Use mild, gentle soaps to bathe with and use hands to wash tender skin instead of a rough washcloth.
2. Pat skin to dry. Your skin may turn pink or darken and be itchy and peel like a bad sunburn after induction. It will also be sensitive to the sun. Be gentle with it, rub the areas for relief. Don't scratch.
3. Don't use perfumes, shaving creams or apply any ointments to the irritated areas.
4. Don't use heating pads, ice packs or balms to irritated areas.
5. Wear loose fitting clothes made with cotton or flannel.
6. Cover up while in the sun to prevent sunburn.
7. Avoid excessive combing of the hair and frequent shampooing. Use mild baby shampoos or just warm water.
8. Avoid scratching the scalp, pat to dry to avoid over rubbing.
9. Don't use adhesive bandages or tape on skin if you can avoid it during times of high sensitivity.
10. Put soft sheets on the bed to prevent chafing.

Fatigue is going to be your worst enemy! Just when you think it's gone, it will creep back up on you. You'll feel particularly tired for 6 to 12 weeks after induction and this could and most likely will become severe for the first couple of weeks.

1. PACE YOURSELF! Never push yourself to exhaustion. It's simply not worth it. This will only cause a day or more in bed.
2. Walk a little each day. If you only get in one walk a day, that's okay. There will be days that it will be impossible to even try.
3. Try not to spend too much time in bed. Get up and shower and be mobile in your surroundings. This will help with blood circulation and oxygen throughout your system.

4. Sit outside and enjoy breathing the fresh air. Meditate by just listening to the sounds outside and concentrating on your breath whenever you can. This will help quiet your mind.
5. Wear comfortable, easy-to-walk-in shoes. Don't wear sandals, flip flops or slippers.
6. Always use a cane for support if walking outside or on uneven ground, just in case.
7. Manage your stress to help prevent mental fatigue. Remove yourself from stresses if you can. If this is impossible, ask your doctor for an anti-anxiety medication.
8. Take naps in the clinic during IV fluid replacement appointments and travel time. These small windows of rest are great!

Simple Chemistry to Food and a Few Great Recipes

When we eat, foods are metabolized then leave waste in our bodies to be filtered out or excreted. This waste is either acidic or alkaline in nature, depending on the food. Foods with an alkaline composition are quickly excreted from our bodies with little effort or energy. Foods that are acidic are very hard for the body to eliminate and are stored in our organs and tissue as solids that create blockages and disease. The more you take in acidic foods, the more the body becomes acidic. For example, processed foods and foods that have a long shelf life due to chemical manipulation are especially hard on our bodies. Most acidic foods don't offer much nutritional value and are not alive, nor do they offer healing properties. They just store trash in our tissues and organs like a junkyard. Pesticides are acidic-based chemicals that are consumed in great quantities by humans, contributing to a weakened immune system

When we become too acidic internally, our microbes start the destruction or decomposition process and disease starts. Eventually, this will cause death to one or more organs, if not the entire body. Cancer feeds off this kind of environment, along with a high sugar intake. Cancer is in heaven!

Only in these past few years has nutrition been taken seriously regarding disease. More and more cancer programs around the world, more so outside of the United States than inside, are providing educational classes on organic diets and nutritional alkaline-based diets to their patients undergoing cancer treatment. What we eat and its relationship to disease is simple common sense. Those who don't get it, do after they get sick, unfortunately.

When I met Roger, he was a steak and potatoes man. After his transplant, he became a soup man. It's easy on the stomach and if he couldn't eat it, I blended it and he drank it.

There are so many recipe books available offering organic, healthy meals. I encourage you to find a few and have them available to refer to when mealtime becomes difficult. Always remember to cook with organic foods and stay away from processed, sugary, creamy sauces and acidic foods. And remember, if they can't chew it, blend it.

I hope these tools have helped you prepare for life after being diagnosed with Ph+ALL. I send you all my love, strength and encouragement throughout your journey! My prayers are with you!

Robin Clark

Following are a few recipes that became a staple in our kitchen. Each is full of nutrition, easy to digest and hydrating.

Recipes: Use only organic ingredients and wash well!

Pot of Life (as I like to call it!)

Combine 2 carrots, 1 yucca root, 1 medium yam, a finely diced small onion, 5 finely chopped celery stalks, 1 small grated turmeric root, 1 tablespoon of chopped fresh ginger, 2 cups of finely chopped spinach, 2 cups of firm tofu, 3 tablespoons of ground flax, and 1/2 cup of rice in a large soup pot. Pour in 64 ounces of organic chicken bone broth and cook over medium heat until rice and all vegetables are soft.

Serve warm, not hot.

If the patient cannot eat the vegetables or meat, scoop off the broth only and drink. Roger drank this broth for weeks until he could handle food. It provides nutrition and fluids replacement.

All-In-One Soup

This soup is wonderful when the patient is feeling better and is ready for flavor.

Combine all the ingredients from the Pot of Life soup and add a cup of shredded zucchini, finely chopped sweet organic apple sausage, 1 small leek, 2 finely chopped chicken breasts, a tablespoon of Italian seasoning, and garlic and salt to taste.

Cook until all ingredients are soft and serve warm, not hot.

Garden Beef Stir Fry

When Roger was ready to chew again, he asked for this dish and ate it a lot!

1 cup of finely chopped kale, 2 cups of baby spinach, 10 sprigs of half inch cut asparagus, 1 cup cauliflower cut into small pieces, 1/4 cup of chopped red onion, organic steak chopped into small pieces, 1 garlic clove, 1/4 teaspoon of mint leaves.

Sauté lightly in 2 tablespoons of grape seed oil and add pink salt to taste. Pour over sautéed rice and/or Thai noodles and add a sprinkle of parmesan cheese if you want.

Breakfast (I use the Bullet machine for smoothies)

Smoothie

I mixed a combination of fruits without seeds, yogurt, cilantro, spinach, protein powders, peanut butter or fresh almond butter with organic apple juice. I asked Roger before each meal what he wanted in the blend. Many times, Rog just wanted something he could drink and not use the energy to chew. He liked smoothies best if they were cold.

Scrambled Eggs

Scrambled eggs with garlic, cilantro, sautéed onions, red pepper and cherry tomatoes were a favorite. The spices helped him taste flavor yet not so much that it irritated the intestines. I found fresh cilantro was a spice he could taste. Just a little bit goes a long way.

Protein Drinks

When his protein levels became alarmingly low, I searched for drinks high in protein that he would drink. Ensure and Boost did nothing but nauseate him. I found one called Premier and it contains 30 grams of protein per drink. It comes in several flavors without the thick medicine taste. He loved them! I kept all flavors in the refrigerator for him at all times. Sometimes, for weeks at a time, it was all he had in his stomach.

What I did find interesting is that he really liked V8 juices. I thought they would be too hard on his mouth and stomach, but they weren't. Another patient recommended them to him and he became a fan.

Drinks for Hydration

Dehydration was a constant battle. His favorite drink was G2 Gatorade. It's low in sugar and tastes refreshing when cold. I had cases of all flavors in the house and car. I kept gallons of filtered water on hand and installed a whole house filtration system with an added UV light for possible bacteria outbreaks since we had a well and actually lived through a contaminated water ordeal for a week.

When I couldn't get Roger to eat at all, he would usually turn to Top Ramen. I think it was because of the salt and the heavy flavor. I hated the noodles in the packages, so I would use egg noodles for added protein a lot of the time and used the flavor packet.

When we first started this journey, I was frantic about the food I put in him. Organic, clean and fresh was my motto, but there comes a time when the fear of food is gone and just getting something in them is more important. Just do the best you can.

About the Author

Robin Clark is a retired, accomplished Cardiac Nurse with published clinical studies in Circulation; Volume 96 #8 Oct 21 1997 – Direct Current Cardioversion and in Coronary Artery Disease & Hypertension – Hong Kong Oct 28 1993 – Re-Entry Post Aortic Valve Replacement Stenosis. She self-patented a female supplement, Fem-Ease, for the disorder and symptoms of Interstitial Cystitis, patent # US6143300A – September 2000.

In 2003 she owned and operated two successful restaurants in Oregon and owned a 216 acre waterfront parcel, which she rezoned to be developed into a high-end multi-unit RV resort on the mouth of the Coos River. In 2009, she received her PhD in Metaphysics and Master's in Divinity. She is the mother of two wonderful children, one the recipient of two Purple Hearts from Iraq, the other a practicing Esthetician, as well as two beautiful grandchildren. She currently lives in Bandon, Oregon and continues to write.

Battling Adult Philadelphia Positive Acute Lymphoblastic Leukemia, The Real Fight for Those with Ph+ALL chronicles her and her husband's lives during a clinical study for a rare leukemia and bone marrow transplant. It covers the humor, the challenges, the fear, the pain, the strength and the unbelievable miracles that come with this diagnosis. It's also an instructional guide for caregivers of this particular cancer, as well as other cancers. Robin shares the many tools and ideas she learned throughout this process that will help others going through this terminal illness. It's a story of unconditional love, the pure love that asks for nothing in return.

Made in the USA
Coppell, TX
14 July 2021